WHY WE BEHAVE
LIKE HUMAN BEINGS

BY

GEORGE A. DORSEY, PH.D., LL.D

Formerly Associate Professor of Anthropology
University of Chicago, and
Curator of Anthropology
Field Museum of Natural History

BLUE RIBBON BOOKS
NEW YORK

PRINTED BY THE CORNWALL PRESS, INC.
CORNWALL, N. Y.

TO

FATHER AND MOTHER

CONTENTS

CONTENTS

CONTENTS

CONTENTS

PREFACE

HUMAN beings are the most interesting objects on earth, and to know themselves and get along with one another is their most important business. That business drags because they do not know where they come from, how they get here, what they bring with them, what they do with it, and what they could do if they stopped quarreling among themselves and used their brains to solve their common problems. It will speed up when the raw materials of human nature and the possibilities of intelligent behavior are more generally understood. The facts for such an understanding are known, but they belong to several sciences and are scattered through many libraries. To pick them out, put them in order, and make them tell a complete and up-to-date story that can be held in one hand and read without a dictionary is the object of *Why We Behave Like Human Beings*.

"Complete" is a large word and must be taken with a grain of salt. Nothing is really complete in this world of ceaseless change and expanding horizon. The earth itself is not the earth it used to be when I first went to school. Man's story will be *complete* when there is no human being left to tell the tale. Keibel and Mall's *Human Embryology*, with 1,600 pages, is more complete than Minot's, with only 800. Quain's *Human Anatomy*, with 2,000 pages, is more complete than the average textbook of anatomy, with only 1,000. This is not a textbook; the changing human body, from a rejuvenated ovum to senile decay, and its origin from primordial protoplasm, are part of this story.

Nor is "up-to-date" to be taken too literally. Science moves fast these days. I may state that the hormone of a certain gland is "not yet known"; Professor John Abel may have isolated it yesterday and announce the fact next year. When I studied anatomy under Thomas Dwight—to whom I owe much—I was told nothing about a certain little gland in our throat without which we cannot live. The activating principle of that gland has been discovered, and the secretion of another vital gland has been isolated, since I wrote the first word of this book. No one had heard of a vitamin a few years ago, nor had any vitamin been isolated when I began this book; one, and possibly two, has since been isolated.

By "complete" I mean comprehensive. This is the most comprehensive account of human beings that I know of. It is as up-to-date as I can make it. It moves as fast as I can make it, and avoids blind alleys which lead nowhere. It does touch many problems not yet solved or only partially guessed at; its handling of such problems is as sound and sane as I can make it with the help of many friends. This does not commit them for my errors of omission and commission, nor lessen my responsibility for statements of fact or inferences from facts and hypotheses—nor signify that they approve an anthropologist's use of their materials for his story.

The paleontologist, for example, claims fossils. But when he finds a skull which he says belonged to an ape-man or to a man-ape, that skull belongs to me also; when he finds a set of dinosaur eggs, I am not interested: there are no dinosaurs in our family album. The bacteriologist and a dozen other 'ologists, as well as the family doctor and dentist, deal in bacteria; as do I also, in setting forth the rôle these amazing little imps have played in organic evolution and in the life and death of human beings. The physiologist—and presumably every scientist—is interested in the news about the endocrine glands. The news is startling; but much that is not yet known or is known to be false has been so capitalized by quacks and marvelmongers that I have tried to separate the glands from the grafters. Different scientists specialize in psychic behavior. Psychics and pseudo-psychologists exploit it; they too belong to the story of why we're human. In short, my attitude is that any science which holds itself aloof from life and nowhere comes in contact with human beings is as barren as a Vestal Virgin and as dry as a prayer for rain for the purpose of this book; but that the scandalmongers of science who would fill their lamps at the expense of the gullible, and who illumine no path of life nor sustain any living germ, should be illuminated.

This book does not presume to offer a Philosophy of Life or suggest Science as a substitute for Religion. But as philosophy was moonshine until it began to investigate the elementary properties of matter and energy, so, I suspect, religion will be subject to quackery and hypocrisy until humanity itself becomes more humane than human nature and religion itself ceases worrying about heaven and hell and devotes its energies to making this earth a paradise.

Nor, in ascribing "mind" to a specific irritability of protoplasm and human actions to definite forms of energy, does this book pretend to "resolve life." Life is more easily destroyed than resolved, or even defined. Nobody knows what life is. Much is known of living processes. Of the electric change accompanying irritability, of the action of X-rays on living protoplasm and of heat, light, and sound waves on sensitive human bodies, not much is yet known. But those energies and the living mechanisms which react to their stimuli can be investigated. The few crumbs that science can offer are more nourishing than the no-bread of speculation which works without oxygen, ignores carbon-compounds, and defies the lightning.

Parts of the chapter on the "Processes of Living" will be difficult for those unfamiliar with H_2O and CO_2. Some may even sympathize with the French Republic of 1794 for having beheaded the man who said that life is a chemical function. But Lavoisier was right: life is a chemical function—and living actions are largely concerned with conjugating the verb *to eat*. Without some idea of oxidation processes, of the chemical structure of food, and of the chemical reactions in digestion, *visceral* behavior is a blank. And without some understanding of visceral behavior, *psychic* behavior is up in the air. Life became a science when interest shifted from the dissection of dead bodies to the study of action in living beings and the nature of the environment they live in.

To those scientists who have given me of their time and learning I am profoundly indebted and here offer my grateful thanks: to Dr. W. I. Thomas, who read the entire MS.; to Dr. Adolph H. Schultz, of the Carnegie Institution of Washington, Department of Embryology, Johns Hopkins University, who read Chapter I; to Professor Franz Boas, of Columbia University, who read parts of Chapter I; to Professor George Grant MacCurdy, of Yale University, who read parts of Chapters I and II; to Professor W. E. Castle, of Harvard University, who read Chapter II; to Professor Richard Swan Lull, of Yale University, who read Chapter II and parts of Chapter I; to Professor Walter B. Cannon, of Harvard University, who read part of Chapter III; to Dr. McKeen Cattell, of the Cornell University Medical School, who read Chapter III; to Professor A. J. Carlson, of the University of Chicago, who read Chapter IV; to Professor C. Judson Herrick, of the University of Chicago, who read Chapter V; and to Dr. John B. Watson, who read Chapters VI and VII.

I am also indebted to Professor Carlson for the privilege of examining, while in proof, his chapter on Organotherapeutics in the Blumer edition of Billings-Forchheimer's *Therapeusis of Internal Diseases*; and to Professor John J. Abel of Johns Hopkins University, Professor R. G. Hoskins of the Ohio State University, Dr. C. R. Moore of the University of Chicago, and Dr. John B. Watson, for reprints of articles and for valued suggestions.

PREFACE

Two names I wish especially to mention: Professor Franz Boas, unfailing source of inspiration to all American anthropologists; my wife Sue, untiring and indispensable ally in all that has gone into the writing of this book.

George A. Dorsey.

New York City, June 1, 1925.

WHY WE BEHAVE
LIKE HUMAN BEINGS

"So eine Arbeit wird eigentlich nie fertig"

GOETHE

CHAPTER I

THE INDIVIDUAL LIFE CYCLE AND THE HUMAN RACE

1

WE know of only three kinds of living beings: bacteria, plants, animals. All living beings have a physical body or structure made up of a few of the more common chemical elements. This body is called *protoplasm*, the stuff of all living things. Living protoplasm occurs only in units called cells. Every living being is or has been a cell. Cells are always small and generally cannot be seen except under the microscope.

Many animals consist of just one cell, and hence are called unicellular organisms. Yet that cell suffices for them to live; they eat, they excrete, they grow, they multiply; they obey all the laws of living organisms. For living purposes they are complete. Higher animals have bodies of many cells, and are called Metazoa to distinguish them from the Protozoa, or unicellular animals.

We are animals and belong to the Metazoa group. Our body consists of about twenty-six thousand billion cells. Each cell is alive and must be nourished or it dies.

The cells which make up our body are of different forms and shapes and, except the free floating cells carried by the

1

blood, are united into different kinds of tissue to form the organs and systems of our body. But a section cut anywhere from the body—from bone, muscle, eye, tongue, skin, heart— would under the microscope be seen to consist of tiny cells, each a complete unit of protoplasm.

Our body begins its individual growth and development as one cell, the germ-cell or fertilized ovum (egg). By fertilization, the ovum, an old cell, is stimulated to begin a new life; it is made young again. Being rejuvenated, it can grow, and grow old.

The germ-cells (female, or ova; male, or spermia) are readily distinguishable under the microscope. Ova are much larger and less active than spermia. The latter are very active, and propel themselves by a whip-lash tail. Both are complete living organisms and in their combined bodies carry immortality. In general features, size, structure, etc., human germ-cells closely resemble those of other mammals.

The human ovum was first discovered in 1827. Although it is the largest of the cells in the body, fifty thousand could be mailed across the continent for a two-cent stamp; one hundred could ride on an inch-long spider web.

In both sexes, the germ-cells mature normally only from the beginning of puberty. The ova develop in little pockets or follicles of the ovaries. There are about 70,000 follicles at birth. By the eighth year there are less than 40,000; of these only about 200 develop into true *Graafian follicles*. One of these, containing a single ovum, matures each lunar month of life between puberty and the menopause. It escapes through the ruptured wall of the ovary and enters the Fallopian tube, presumably two weeks before the onset of menstruation. For each mature ovum thus released each lunar month, the male develops about 850,000,000,000 spermia.

One spermium only enters into the body of the matured ovum, leaving its tail outside. The ovum is now *fertilized.* It divides into two cells; these two divide and become four,

2

etc. In nine months, one fertilized ovum has grown five million per cent and increased in volume one billion times; by maturity it will have increased in volume fifteen billion times.

After the fertilized ovum has by division become many thousands, certain cells under the microscope may be distinguished from the others. These are to become the *germ-cells* of new individuals, tiny sparks of immortality, endowed with the capacity to hand life on to the next generation.

The other cells of the tiny embryo are called *soma*, or body cells. They also grow and multiply by division, and assume special shapes to fit them to form the tissues and organs of the body—nerves, eyes, bone, teeth, heart, muscle, blood, etc. Having specialized or become differentiated, they cannot unite with other cells to start new lives—they are not germ-cells.

2

We hear much of *adaptations*. Every living animal is adapted" or it could not live. What it is adapted to and what it adapts itself with depend on the animal and the stage of its development. The tiny germ-cell in the hen's egg is adapted to an environment of yolk and albumin. It draws on these for its nourishment. The human ovum has no such store of food to draw upon. It is adapted to a different environment. For 280 days it is to live the life of a true parasite. It must therefore attach itself to a living wall, from which it can derive its supplies for living and for growth. These early adaptations of the human ovum are of great interest.

But the interest will be increased if we have before us a law of biology which says that *individual* development rehearses or recapitulates the life history of the *species*. This means that our individual prenatal and postnatal growth up to the time of adolescence is a *résumé* of the evolution of the

3

human race. It does not mean that at one stage of development the fetus is a fish, or a reptile; it does say that the ovum develops along the road our ancestors traveled in becoming human.

We begin our individual existence as a protozoon or single-celled animal; not until the end of the third month has the fetus the essential parts of a fairly complete human being. During the last six months the fetus grows more human; the parts begin to mature, and for years after birth keep on maturing.

The embryo begins at once to develop from its own body the two *fetal membranes* or envelopes. The inner one, or amnion (lamb), fills with a pint or more of water. In this the embryo floats, and consequently any pressure to which it is subjected becomes more evenly distributed. By a special growth called *placenta* (cake, because of its shape) of the outer membrane or chorion (skin), the embryo attaches itself to the wall of the uterus.

Through this placenta the parasite embryo derives food and oxygen. But it develops its own blood and its own circulatory and digestive systems: they are at all times quite distinct from its host's. She supplies what the chick embryo receives from the hen egg: support, protection, water, food, fuel, oxygen.

Both fetal membranes and placenta follow the child at birth. The child is freed from the placenta by severing its umbilical cord; our navel is the scar.

In other mammals these membranes are not formed so early, but the upright gait of man seems to put more strain on the abdominal viscera and presumably subjects the embryo to greater pressure. It needs all the protection it can get, hence this marvelous intrauterine adaptation to the upright posture. Anthropoid apes have the human type of uterus and a near-upright gait; their fetal membranes are also formed earlier than in other mammals.

To return to the embryo proper. The ovum divides, the

4

two daughter-cells divide. Four, eight, sixteen, thirty-two, etc. As a result of this rapid division, multiplication, and growth, the embryo passes through certain definite *stages* of development. Much is still conjecture. For this reason: The earliest stages of embryonic development of fishes, amphibians, birds, and of such domesticated mammals as the guinea-pig, rabbit, sheep, and pig are known, and much may be inferred as to the course of development of the human embryo from what is known to take place in these animals. But no one has yet seen a fertilized human ovum, nor has anyone yet seen a human embryo that had not already had ten days' growth—and it measured about one one-hundredth of an inch in length. Even of the second week of human development almost nothing is definitely known, and of embryos of the third week the Carnegie Laboratory of Embryology has been able to assemble only fourteen specimens. What actually goes on, then, during the first eighteen days of man's intrauterine existence can as yet only be inferred from known facts of lower mammalian embryonic development.

First of the hypothetical stages is the *morula* (little mulberry): the embryo is a minute cluster of cells. Next is the *blastula* stage, or blastoderm (germ-skin); the embryo is supposed to form a hollow sphere. This caves in on one side, forming a U-shaped affair, and represents the *gastrula* (stomach) stage. By this infolding, certain cells which were on the outside now lie inside the body; the embryo consists of two layers. By further infoldings, there is an additional layer between these two. Thus we have the famous and important *germ-layers:* the outer or *ectoderm;* the inner or *endoderm;* the middle or *mesoderm.*

Each germ-layer gives rise to certain organs and systems, a fact of far-reaching consequence in medicine and hygiene and in an understanding of our body. The three layers and their derived structures are:

I. Ectoderm: skin and skin accessories; entire nervous

system; special sense organs; pineal gland and part of the pituitary and adrenal glands.

II. Endoderm: alimentary canal and appendages; thyroid and thymus glands; larynx, trachea, and lungs.

III. Mesoderm: voluntary or skeletal muscles; urogenital system and sex glands; part of the adrenal glands.

In addition to these three layers, a particular type of tissue develops, chiefly from the mesoderm. Its cells are branched and form a network of *connective tissue*. From it are derived the heart, blood, blood vessels, and lymphatic system; skeleton; and visceral or involuntary muscles.

All one-cell animals consist of an outside and "insides." Through their outside membrane or cell wall they keep in touch with the world. Our keep-in-touch-with-the-world mechanisms (skin, hair, nails, all skin-glands and organs, lining of mouth, enamel of teeth, special sense organs, and entire nervous system) are all derived from the outside cells of the original hollow body when it caved in to bury certain cells inside the body. From those inside cells we develop "insides"—food and air canals. Muscles and skeleton, blood, sex organs, etc., did not appear until animal life had made much progress in evolution.

During our early prenatal days we live fast; we can be certain of that. In a few days we have developed structures that were evolved only after tens of millions of years.

3

Within two weeks the embryo has become a minute plate-like structure with a streak across it. By the third week this streak opens into the plate at both ends. One opening becomes the mouth. The cavity within the embryo will divide and become the thoracic and abdominal cavities.

Meanwhile, a series of lines appear, dividing the plate-like embryo into segments. *Segmented* animals, such as worms and insects, retain these segments; as do fishes in muscles, ribs, and vertebræ; as do we in our ribs, vertebræ, and the muscles between the ribs. Our floating ribs are simply incomplete ribs, but we have vestiges of ribs all the way down our spine. Those below the chest fuse with outgrowths from the vertebræ and are called lateral processes.

The vast majority of animals have no backbone, and are called Invertebrates. One of the greatest steps in evolution was a backbone or vertebral column. Three types were tried out before Vertebrates developed a true backbone. All three types or stages appear in the developing human embryo. The *notochord* or permanent body axis of the lowest fishes appears early; later it is obliterated by the bodies of the vertebræ, but traces of the notochord may persist and lead to tumors in adult life. Our bony vertebræ proper are preceded by cartilage, the only backbone sharks have. This is replaced by bone.

Our skull and limb bones also begin as cartilage—and in some fishes the skull remains cartilage. Much of our long bones and skull is still cartilage at birth; hence the pliancy of the new born's head.

Shark embryos have five gill-arches with openings, or gill-clefts, between, and two branchial arches from which the shark forms its poorly developed lower jaw.

Most of these arches and the branchial clefts between appear at the third week in the human fetus. The way the clefts disappear and the arches develop into the extraordinarily complicated human throat is possibly the most interesting and confused chapter in human embryology.

From one of the two arches which develop into jaws in sharks, the human fetus develops its lower jaw and two of the three tiny bones of the inner ear; from the other arch, the third bone of the inner ear, the styloid process at the base of the skull, and the cartilage of the external ear. The hyoid apparatus which supports our tongue develops also from this and from the first gill-arch. The second and third gill-arches become the thyroid cartilages, or Adam's apple; the fourth, the epiglottis; the fifth, the windpipe cartilages.

As the human embryo will develop into a lung-breather and will have no need of gills, the gill-clefts do not break through; after the sixth week no outward trace of them remains. But around one end of the first cleft the fetal ear develops; the remainder becomes the Eustachian tube, or passage from the mouth to the tympanic cavity of the ear.

The second branchial arch, from which fish embryos develop gill-cover and gill muscles, is supplied by the seventh cranial nerve. This arch in the human fetus is also supplied by that nerve; it grows upward and becomes the great nerve of our face, supplying ears, mouth, nose, and eyes. An amazing story, this. The nerves of our face moved the gill-covers of our respiratory system when we were fishes.

Six branches of the aorta—the great artery from the heart—supply these fish-like arches of the human fetus. The third pair become part of the two internal carotid arteries. The left branch of the fourth pair forms the bend of the aorta. Of the sixth pair, one part becomes the stem of the pulmonary artery; the other, during fetal life, carries blood from the pulmonary artery to the aorta, thus permitting the right ventricle of the heart to pump impure blood into the aorta and so to the placenta. At birth it closes; blood from the pulmonary artery must now pass to the lungs.

Marvelous adaptation! Part of a gill-arch artery used for placental circulation closed suddenly to meet the infant's cry for air! Henceforth the infant gets oxygen from its own lungs and not from its mother's blood.

During fetal life, the third and fourth clefts become covered by a fold from the second arch. A fistula may develop here—remnant of an enclosed gill chamber. The middle ear, site of the first fetal gill-cleft, is more prone to serious trouble. Tags of skin which may persist on the side or front of our neck are less serious, but none the less echoes of our gill-clefts, reminders of our kinship with the finny tribes.

8

At the time the gill-clefts are present the human fetus has a freely projecting tail and four tiny paddle-like limbs.

4

The ovum only grows and develops if it can come in contact with food; the cells remain alive only as long as they are nourished. This gives us a clue to some of the mechanisms or organ-systems which the human embryo must develop and which we must keep in repair during life. Whether we are a one-cell embryo or a new-born or an adult, we must be able to get food and oxygen and distribute food and oxygen where needed. We have such organ-systems: digestive, circulatory, respiratory, etc.; and a motor mechanism of bones and muscles.

A fundamental criterion of living protoplasm is its capacity to get excited. Because of this irritable nature it does something—it reacts like a living thing. The "organ-system," or mechanism of reactions, is the nervous system in man and in all animals with a nervous system. But just as we must infer that the ovum can "breathe," although it has no lungs, we must infer that it can react, although it has no nervous system.

It is vitally important that at every stage of pre- or postnatal life the organism have all the structure or mechanism required for living purposes; it only needs to make living response to living environment. The nervous system comes to be the visible mechanism by action in which the organism makes such vital responses to vital situations.

Our nervous system is the most complex mechanism in the universe; certainly no other system in our body is to be compared with it in intricacy or in its unique capacity to learn. Because of this capacity, the evolution of man became possible and we are what we are. In fact, the goal of evolution, as we shall see, was always in the direction of a broader outlook, a greater capacity to anticipate change and weather storm. The nervous system is the only key evolved to unlock the future. We shall pay due respect to it; at this point we can only glance at its structural development.

Before the embryo is a month old, a depression or trough appears on the upper surface of the outer germ-layer. It deepens. The upper edges come together, forming the neural tube, so called because from it will develop the nervous system. In the third month the tube expands at one end into three sacs or vesicles; the first and third of these divide and there result five vesicles in all. *The walls of these hollow sacs will develop into the brain;* the sacs themselves will form the *ventricles* (little belly) of the brain.

The remainder of the neural tube will become the spinal cord. This, in the four-months' embryo, is as long as the vertebral column; thereafter the column grows faster than the cord. At birth, the cord proper reaches only to the third lumbar vertebræ; but from that vertebræ to the end of the column the cord is represented by the long *terminal filament.* This atavistic ending of the spinal cord is found in mammals generally, and points back to a time in man's ancestry when the cord extended the entire length of the column.

The cells of the neural tube send out two processes: one connects with a process from another cell of the central system; the other grows out toward the surface of the body. By birth, all parts of the body are connected by these proc-esses with *central*—spinal cord and brain—and by the other processes, all parts of central are connected with one another. At birth, all the cells of the nervous system are present. The new-born will develop no new brain cells, but structural changes will take place in the nerves which are in control of the motor mechanism; otherwise the infant would remain as helpless as when born.

Sometimes the bones of the skull grow together prema-turely; this prevents further growth of the brain. Such a brain is called *microcephalous* and vaguely resembles the brain of monkeys.

10

Monsters are sometimes delivered in which the brain has never developed beyond the first month of fetal life—the original nerve plate remains spread out on the surface at the back of the head.

An English shepherd who died at the age of sixty was normal except for his very small head. He had a human countenance, but a vacant stare. He could count his fingers, but not his sheep or the days of the week. He could talk simple sentences. His brain was one-third normal size and its fissures were like a fetal brain of seven months, but lower in type than that of a chimpanzee. The parts associated with speech were of the size and form found in anthropoid apes. It was the type of brain our ancestors had millions of years ago.

Man's brain is from two to three times larger than that of the gorilla, but, apart from mere size, man and ape brains are more alike than are their big toes.

Brain weights vary enormously. The average for adult male Europeans is about 1,375 grams, for females about 1,235. The brain of Turgueneff, the Russian novelist, weighed 2,012 grams. It is exceeded by that of only two others; one was an imbecile. Next in weight come a laborer (1,925 grams) and a bricklayer (1,900 grams). Gambetta's brain weighed only 1,294 grams. The largest woman's brain recorded is 1,742 grams; she was insane and died of consumption. The third largest woman's brain recorded weighed 1,580 grams; she also was insane.

There is no evidence that size of brain (or of head) is necessarily connected with actual or potential intelligence. Usually, large individuals have large brains; men are larger than women. Large brains have no more units than small brains: the units are large. A small brain is no more necessarily handicapped than a small hand or a small foot.

We do not use the brains we have. Presumably, we no more get the maximum service out of our brains than we do out of our motor-mechanism. For every book on how

11

to train the brain there are a dozen on how to train the muscles. But not one man in fifty who goes in for muscle-training expects to put his muscles to work; he sees physical culture as physical beauty.

5

We no longer tell friends from enemies by smell; but we often pick them by the shape of their nose. Man's nose is not so striking as the elephant's, or even the long-nosed monkey's, but it features his face and is one of his most human and superfluous elements. As it is a new acquisition —it began with mammals—it appears late in fetal life and develops fully only after birth. Its shape and size are hereditary and are distinguishing traits of race. But it has no more to do with brain power than the handkerchief that wipes it.

As the olfactory nerves alone are connected with the hemispheres of the human brain, it is inferred that the brain itself arose in connection with the sense of smell; the original brain was a smelling organ.

In mammals generally, the smell sense is the most highly developed of all senses. In monkeys, it has already begun to diminish. Some mammals have five pairs of ridges supporting the olfactory organs; some hoofed animals have eight; apes usually have three. Man has from two to five pairs.

The nose in the human embryo is at first a pair of pits or pockets in the skin—the condition in fishes. The external nose appears much later.

Man's reptilian ancestors had a supplementary smell organ between roof of mouth and floor of nose. With this they could sample odors while eating without having to sniff. We—in common with other mammals—have its vestige in our *Jacobson's organ.*

The ear also begins as a pocket, in the first gill-cleft. This sinks into the head until its outer opening is closed by the tympanum or eardrum. A rare anomaly is an individual with two, or even three, external ear openings; these represent the second and third gill-clefts. In some fishes the opening remains; their ear is primarily a balancing organ. Our equilibrium sense organ is also located in the inner ear; if our semilunar canals are destroyed, we cannot balance ourselves.

We turn our head toward sounds or cup our hands behind our ears; our ancestors turned their ears. We have vestiges of ear muscles, as do apes. Our external ears are also degenerate, as are those of the orang and gorilla. Some ears are small and lie tight against the head, as in the orang; some are large and stand out, as do those of the chimpanzee.

At the eighth month the rim or helix of the fetal ear begins to fold in—an additional sign of degeneracy. But the tip persists and generally may be felt, often may be seen, near the middle of the infolded helix. It is called Darwin's point; Darwin pointed out its vestigial character.

The lobe, or soft lower part, of the ear generally appears at the sixth month of fetal life, is found in no animals below apes, and in man has no known use other than support for ornament. It is said to be larger in women than in men; it may be absent in either sex.

Our eyes are compound and are made up of the same three parts that are found in fishes' eyes. First, a cluster of skin-cells dig in to form the lens; skin grows over this, becomes transparent, and forms the cornea. Next, a growth from the neural tube reaches out and ends in a cup around the lens. This cup becomes the retina; the stalk which joins cup with tube, the optic nerve. Cells from the middle germ-layer now enter the cup and form the transparent matter of the eyeball. The middle layer also supplies the protecting coat of the retina. As the lens is modified skin structure, it is subject to the horny change of old age. Hence "cataract" of the eye; the lens has become covered with a scale.

13

The Asiatic's eye is not oblique. The "slit" appearance is due to the low nasal bridge supporting the upper lid; the lid thus folds and appears "Mongolian." This "oblique" eye is not uncommon in white children at birth; when the bridge develops slowly it may persist for months, even into adult life.

In the inner angle of our eye is a little fold of skin of varying size called the *plica semilunaris*. It is a rudiment of the third eyelid or nictitating membrane that cleans the eyeballs of birds and frogs; their upper eyelid is immovable.

The tears which wash our eyes—otherwise as dirty as our faces—come from lachrymal glands in the upper outer corner of each eye. Some have additional tear glands at the sides of the eyes, as have reptiles.

Our skin is a double structure. The outside, or epidermis, is ectoderm; the inside, or dermis, is derived from the mesoderm. The fetal skin at first is translucent and not unlike that of fishes. During the third month, the epidermis begins to become horny, as it is in adult life. It is significant that if we lose a third of our skin—by fire, acid, boiling liquid, or flaying—we lose our life.

Color of skin is an inherited trait and is due to grains of brown or yellow-red pigment in the dermis. Entire absence of pigment in skin, hair, and eyes is a developmental defect and results in *albinos*. Albinism is an inherited trait and is found in many animals. White blackbirds are as common as white black men. Pigment is probably due to secretion of an endocrine gland.

To form a better grasping surface, the skin of man's, monkeys', and many other mammals' hands and feet is thrown into minute ridges, especially prominent on the finger tips. These ridges form loops, spirals, and arches. In no two individuals on earth do they make exactly the same pattern. Hence their unique importance as marks of identification.

At the fourth month, the embryo begins to show a fine silky hair coat or *lanugo* (down). This begins to be replaced, even before birth, by a second coat of different character. The lanugo may persist as "down" on the face of girls and women, or even all over the body, as on the so-called dog-faced people of the menageries. The lanugo probably represents our adult ancestral condition. But no satisfactory theory has yet been advanced to account for the fact that man is the least hairy of the primates.

Hair does not grow on our bodies in haphazard fashion, but in lines and sets of three, four, or five, each set being the hairs that grew beneath one scale of our reptilian ancestors. On certain parts, especially on males in the region of the navel, may be detected a vortex pattern like that at the end of the spine where the tail once projected.

Cats "feel" in the dark with whiskers or vibrissæ. Man's eyebrows and mouth and ear hairs seem to be the modified descendants of such feelers. Actual vibrissæ—long, coarse, stiff hairs—often appear in men, especially after middle life, generally in the eyebrows, less often on the end of the nose.

Man's hairy coat varies individually and in races. Because of their hairy bodies, the aborigines of Japan are called the Hairy Ainu. The amount of hair on the face and the parts of the body covered by hair also vary in different races.

We inherit finger and toe nails, almost without change, from our animal ancestors. The nails of our big toe, thumb, and first and second fingers tend to be flat—as they are in apes; the arched nails of our other fingers suggest the rounded claws of certain mammals and are like the long curved nails of monkeys.

Our skin is rich in glands. These begin to develop during the fifth month. The sweat glands reduce temperature and eliminate waste. Sebaceous or fat glands lubricate the skin and hair, and in certain regions (armpits, for example) secrete an odor. Such odoriferous glands are generally sexual in character and are highly developed in hoofed animals. In the male musk deer of Central Asia the gland is as big as a hen's egg. Its secretion is the base of certain man-made perfumes. Consequently, the musk deer is almost extinct.

Mammals take their name from their *mammae*—sweat glands peculiarly modified to secrete milk. On the one-month human embryo appear two mammary ridges extending from armpits to groin. A milk gland develops at the upper end of each ridge. The ridge then atrophies and disappears. But one individual in every 500 has supernumerary glands—three, four, even seven pairs are not unknown. These are clearly a reversion to an earlier mammalian condition. In one case a large gland developed in the middle of the back.

At first a depression appears in the center of the gland—and so remains in the lowest order of mammals. From the bottom of the depression many little bases rise; these, in both sexes, come to form the nipple just before or shortly after birth. The mammæ develop no further until puberty, when, in the female, they are stimulated to further growth by the sex glands. As their function is food, and as they have been known to function in otherwise normal males, they are not primary sexual characters.

6

Now and then a child is born with a common opening for the intestine and the urogenital tract. This common vent is called a *cloaca* (sewer); it is the normal condition in fishes, amphibians, reptiles, birds, and the lowest order of mammals. In man it represents a reversion to an ancestral type which did not disappear until marsupials evolved, millions of years ago, as the second order of mammals.

The cloacal condition is normal in the human embryo during the second month; at that time the intestine and urogenital ducts end in a common chamber. Not until the tenth week is

16

it possible to distinguish a male from a female fetus. Until this time the external and internal anatomy is identical for both sexes.

With the eighth week the cloacal condition ceases and the embryo develops into a male or a female. Whether it is to become male or female is probably determined when the ovum is fertilized. The decisive factor is not known, nor is it likely that we shall discover means by which the ovum will develop into male or female according to our desire for son or daughter. As we shall see later, the sex glands themselves presumably secrete a hormone which, carried by the blood, causes the marvelous changes whereby the neutral rudimentary organs develop in one or the other direction.

The anatomical structure on which these hormones may act consists of four parallel tubes at the hind end of the body, opening into the cloaca. The outer tubes, or Wolffian ducts, will carry the male glands; the inner pair, or Muellerian ducts, will become the oviducts, or Fallopian tubes.

If the embryo is to become a male the inner tubes atrophy; the Wolffian ducts become the *vas deferens;* the cloaca opening closes to form the scrotum. If female, the cloaca remains open; the oviducts grow together in the lower part to become the uterus, the upper becoming the Fallopian tubes; the Wolffian ducts persist as vestiges in the broad ligament. In the male the sex glands descend; in the female they remain within the pelvic cavity. The migration of the glands in the male is common to most mammals, but only in man, due to his upright gait, do the inguinal canals through which they pass remain weak spots which may permit the escape of a loop of the intestine, causing hernia.

The significant fact is that the human embryo of eight weeks has the makings of a male or a female. It follows that neither sex possesses any anatomical parts which are not found in homologous parts in the other sex. The beginnings of all the parts are present from the start; later they come to differ. By change, by shift in position, and by growth or atrophy, the original neutral mechanism becomes male or female.

Most plants and many lower animals are *hermaphrodites* (Hermes-Aphrodite): the organs of both sexes are combined in one individual. Higher in the scale of animal life true hermaphrodites disappear. But sometimes in an otherwise normal human embryo certain parts fail to complete their normal development. The result is an individual anatomically neither a fully formed male nor a female; such are called hermaphrodites. But no human being functions both as male and as female.

While the sex glands or gonads appear at the sixth week, they show no structural difference as to their future sex; yet the cells within under the microscope are already definitely of one or the other sex. If female, the cells are of the ovum type, large and rounded; if male, the cells are of the spermium type, very small, very long, and ending in a fine process, or tail.

The function of the renal organs or kidneys is to preserve a certain constancy in the blood stream and to eliminate certain noxious elements from the body. To perform this double function, three types of kidneys have been evolved. The developing human embryo, as well as embryos of other mammals, rehearses this story, all three types appearing in prenatal life.

The first renal organ to appear, the *head kidney*, becomes an appendage of the sex glands. The second, or *Wolffian body*, becomes part of the seminiferous duct in the male; in the female it remains as the parovarium, a vestige in the broad ligament between uterus and pelvic wall—it is often prone to disease. Finally, true kidneys develop. These are at first furrowed, as they remain in some mammals; later they become smooth. Sometimes the furrows persist, reminders of earlier days.

18

The alimentary canal appears first as a closed tube within the body. It opens later at each end, the upper opening becoming part of the mouth cavity. Below this opening four crevices appear which represent the internal arrangement of the fish-like gill-clefts. Below these crevices a single sac-like structure appears; this divides, and by further subdivisions becomes the right and left lung. From the region of the crevices outgrowths of the alimentary canal develop into thyroid, epithyroid, and thymus glands. From the extreme upper end of the embryonic canal develops a portion of another important gland, the pituitary. The stomach at first is merely an enlargement of the canal. Just below the stomach two outgrowths of the canal develop into the important glands of digestion, pancreas and liver.

Without further details of fetal development it will be worth while to recall certain variations in the systems of digestion, respiration, and circulation, which are significant in light of our animal ancestors.

Our dentition is as well adapted for spinach as for beefsteak, specialized for neither. Our front, or incisor, teeth are only fair cutters; our bicuspids, or premolars, are not strong enough to crunch bones; our grinders, or molars, are not very good millstones. Our snarling muscle discloses no such canines as the flesh-eaters stab and tear their prey with. Our teeth are on the go. A perfect "civilized" set is rare. In hundreds of skulls I collected in New Guinea there was not one imperfect set—all strong, sound, beautifully aligned.

Man, apes, and Old World monkeys have thirty-two teeth, eight on each side of each jaw: two incisors, one canine, two bicuspids, three molars. Man's mammalian ancestor had forty-four teeth: three incisors, one canine, three bicuspids, four molars.

Variation rules. Often there is only one incisor, an inherited condition; there may be three incisors. The canine is rarely absent, but it may be a tiny stump; more often it is over-developed, disfiguring the face. A third bicuspid is not rare. A fourth molar is more rare, but frequent enough to be suggestive. The third molar, or wisdom tooth, is a bad lot among whites—jaws too short; it comes in at any angle, varies in its cusps, often is a mere stump, often never erupts at all.

Most fishes have teeth in the roof of the mouth as well as in the jaws proper. They do not occur in "sets," but are endlessly shed and reproduced. In the fish embryo the dental germs appear before the jawbones; in the human embryo also. In the infant's mouth is a ridge with from five to seven pairs of cross ridges; they are even more pronounced in the fetus. They disappear with age. Apes have ten pairs of these ridges. In pigs, they are strong enough to crush food. Their presence in man, with an occasional more or less complete third set of teeth, points to fish and reptile days: teeth in the roof of the mouth, endlessly replaced.

Tonsils appear in fetal life as pockets. They shift position and develop into prominent bodies. With adult life they begin to disappear, leaving pockets prone to disease. They are not understood and are never alike.

The cricket's chirp was the first music on earth, but it was instrumental. The first voice was the amphibian's. Frog, bird, cat, dog, and man would be silent without a larynx; without the human larynx there could have been no human speech or Tower of Babel. Ours is a wonderful larynx; let us get such joy as we can from it. Our developing respiratory system suggests fish; in our youth it is a hotbed of infection. Our vocal cords are human only in their high development. But we all have the blind pocket between true and false cords which served as a resonator and so strengthened the roar by which our ancestors frightened their foes and called their mates. In man it varies, but is never so deep as in the gorilla.

The vermiform appendix is the worm its name implies. It

is a feeble, narrow, tapering blind alley, opening by a small mouth into the large intestine. At birth, in size and form it is like an ape's. At puberty it begins to shorten; it is about closed in every fourth adult; in every thirtieth adult it is closed throughout. It shrivels up with old age. It may be ten times longer in one brother than in another. It is a true vestige. It is predisposed to disease; appendicitis is a fashionable operation. Only apes in captivity develop appendicitis. For an appendix that functions we must go to the lowest monkeys.

The liver usually has two lobes—it may have none, it may have twelve; it may have two gall-bladders—it may have none.

The abdominal viscera in the human embryo are not human in their arrangement. Only later does the mesentery, or sheet of membrane connecting the bowel, become attached to the back wall of the abdomen and so hold it in place and in perpendicular position. Sometimes the mesentery is found arranged as in monkeys. The loosely attached bowel easily twists and becomes obstructed.

There are more than mere structural variations in our food canal; there are signs of degeneracy—in teeth, in jaws and throat, and in the large intestine. Changed diet does it. To digest raw food our ancestors had to chew it. They had strong jaws, heavy muscles, sound teeth properly aligned, big throats, and a colon that could digest husks of grain and skins of fruits and vegetables.

The lobes of the lungs vary in number and position. Due to man's upright gait, the heart has come to rest on the diaphragm. In monkeys the azygos lobe of the lung lies between. In man there is always a remnant, of varying size, of this lobe.

The chief business of the fish heart is to pump blood to the gills; of ours, to the body. The human embryo at the branchial-cleft stage has a tubular heart of four chambers. When lungs begin to develop the first chamber becomes part of the auricle, the fourth chamber part of the ventricle. These then divide into right and left; the right passes venous blood to the placenta, the left receives this blood and sends it to the body. The fourth chamber may fail to develop normally; the blood passes imperfectly into the pulmonary artery and so is not properly oxidized. Sometimes a heart is found with the vestige of a valve which functions in animals no higher than frogs and salamanders. Variations in the blood vessels are endless. Even the great artery leading from the heart is subject to astonishing variations—all harking back to great changes in the circulatory system since man evolved from a water-breathing animal.

When we recall the branchial-clefts in the neckbend of the human fetus—and their fate; also that for ages man's ancestors derived their oxygen from water through gills and not from air through lungs; also that man only recently left the trees—we must expect to find great variation in human mouths and throats, in the food and air canals below, and in the marvelously intricate system which delivers blood to every cell in the complex body.

8

Suppose it's twins! One in every hundred births is. Ireland averages higher—one pair for every seventy-two births.

Twins run in families. A mother who has twins is likely to bear more twins. She is called a "repeater." She probably inherits twin capacity—and transmits it. Her anatomy is such that twins are possible. That she bears twins only one-fifth of the time is probably due to her own internal weakness. Twins occur also in other mammals that ordinarily bear but one individual at a time. Triplets occur once in every 7,000 births; quadruplets, only once in every 370,000 births.

There are two kinds of twins: *twins; identical twins*. The first type develops independently from two ova that happen to mature at the same time. Each ovum develops its own chorion and placenta—though the two placentas may partially fuse. They are not true or "identical" twins, merely accidents as to time of birth. Both may be boys or girls, or they may be brother and sister. They vary as brothers and sisters of a family normally vary.

Identical twins are always of the same sex: either both boys or both girls. They develop from a single ovum, in the same chorion, and receive food and oxygen through the same placenta, to which each is attached by its own umbilicus.

There need be no doubt as to whether twins are just twins or identical: if identical, they are always of the same sex and there is only one placenta; if there are two placentas, or if they are of different sex, they cannot be true twins.

Sometimes identical twins are so alike that only a string around the thumb, or some such device, will enable the mother to distinguish one from the other.

It was formerly held that identical twins, triplets, quadruplets, etc., resulted from multiple fertilization of one ovum. But twins and monsters can be produced artifically in biologic laboratories. Fish monsters can be grown from eggs deprived of enough oxygen. Monsters of all sorts have been grown by separating the young embryo into two or more parts. Perfect twins have been grown from the two cells of the dividing ovum shaken apart.

Human twins, triplets, etc., presumably arise from early separation of the cells into which the original ovum divided. If the division is not complete, the result is twin, triplet, or even quadruplet monsters. These may take any conceivable form, from twins bound together only at one spot, to a twin inside the body of the other. An autopsy recently revealed a tiny parasitic twin in an abdominal tumor, carried within its twin brother's body for half a century. He had never known of its existence.

Double monsters may have one head, two bodies; two heads, one body; one head, two necks, one chest, two bodies below the diaphragm. One twin may be fully developed; attached to its body is an arm or a leg of the other. One twin may develop no heart, receiving its blood through its umbilicus; it perishes at birth.

In "Siamese" twins, the embryo divides into two at both ends but not in the middle; if they share vital organs, they cannot be separated by the knife. The Two-headed Nightingale, Millie and Christina, had two heads, one body, four legs; she (or they) could sing by each head and each head could control two or four legs. The famous Scottish Brothers —clever musicians and linguists—were one individual below the waist, above quite distinct except at the back.

Single monsters may have no arms or legs; no abdominal wall; a brain outside the skull or other malformation of brain, skull, or face; a Janus face; a Cyclopean eye. There is no end to the range of malformation.

Other abnormalities are only to be understood in the light of man's ancestry. Part or parts stop growth before normal human condition is reached. They point the road man traveled. Some are not easy to classify: vestiges of ancient days, part of our normal heritage; faulty cell division, unfavorable environment, faulty implantation, or defective germ-plasm? In one unique case the ovum had become implanted clear outside the abdominal cavity, just under the skin over the abdomen. It had begun to develop and was diagnosed as a tumor.

The lower jaw may be deformed; no sharp line between face and neck, ears almost meeting in front. Reversion to a fish condition? No doubt as to what happened—the first gill-arch of the embryo failed to develop. It hardly develops at all in lowest fishes.

There may be an extra finger or toe, always outside thumb or little finger. Is this an ancestral echo, or did a finger-bud divide? The tenth-of-an-inch-long four-weeks-old fetus' limbs begin as tiny buds and soon look like paddles. Before the buds appear, the fetus is limbless. Sometimes the paddles never develop into arms or legs; they remain mere flaps. Or, the fingers and toes may remain hidden in the flaps. Or, some or all of the fingers or toes may be webbed—as they are in the embryo.

Rabbits are not "hare-lipped"; their upper lip is cleft in the *middle*. Our lip begins as three pieces; if they fail to join, the cleft is between one or both nostrils and the mouth —never in the middle of the lip. A double "hare-lipped" man is shark-lipped.

We can eat and breathe at the same time because our mouth is shut off from our nose by the palate or roof of our mouth. Our palate begins as two bones; they join in the ninth week of fetal life. Sometimes they do not; result: *cleft palate*, as have frogs, snakes, and birds.

Cysts or hollow tumors may be found in any part of the body. When lined with skin, they are called *dermoid*. They are thought to arise from germ-cells which strayed away from the sex-glands.

Generally, abnormal development is due to disease in the uterus or to such faulty attachment of embryo that its nourishment is impaired. But ova may develop normally in abnormal positions, even outside the uterus. Mothers cannot influence their intrauterine growth by "scares," etc. Possibly her blood altered by fever might upset normal development. It is known that tetanus, diphtheria, and typhoid toxins and antitoxins can pass from the host into fetal circulation. It also seems that the germs of typhoid, and possibly tuberculosis, may similarly pass from host to fetus. But it must be understood that there is no interchange of blood between the two, nor any commingling of body fluids or nerve tissue. The fetus is a true parasite.

9

In upright gait, balanced skull, and arms free at the sides of the body, we differ most from the only animals that ape us. This upright gait is maintained by action of muscle on bone. We hang on a bony skeleton, largely levers. We move by setting those levers in motion. To put us across a hundred yards in ten seconds, the skeleton must be mature. If our bones were cartilage we would be wonderful contortionists, but our upright gait would collapse.

Our ancestors went on all-fours. In acquiring the upright gait, the axis of the body changed from horizontal to perpendicular. This necessitated changes in every bone and muscle in the body and a complete overhauling of everything inside—lungs, circulation, abdominal viscera—everything.

Our pelvic girdle is a broad, shallow basin; it supports viscera. The keystone of the girdle is the sacrum. It supports the backbone and locks the arch behind. The dog's sacrum is long and narrow; ours, broader than it is long. The sacrum at birth varies from four to seven vertebræ. These unite into one bone; but the first, and sometimes the second, never unites with the others.

Above the sacrum is the vertebral column proper: seven neck or cervical, twelve thoracic, and five lumbar vertebræ —twenty-four in all. But there may be six or eight cervical; eleven or thirteen thoracic; four to six lumbar. At birth, most of us have twelve pairs of ribs; some, only eleven; some, thirteen.

Seven pairs of ribs join our sternum, or breastbone; there may be only six, there may be eight. The first pair are sometimes mere rudiments. Our floating ribs are not so important as when we walked on all fours; they vary in number and size. The sternum is less important than formerly; it varies enormously. Two little bones sometimes found on its upper border are vestiges of the episternal bones of the lowest mammals.

No man-made column is so delicately adjusted, so slender, or so well balanced as our spine. Its sigmoid, or "S" curve, gives elasticity to our body, grace to our carriage, fine lines to our back, and saves our brain from jar and shock. The really human curves develop after birth, especially the lumbar curve in the "small" of our back. The infant cannot stand straight up because it has not yet acquired a stand-up-straight backbone.

Our backbone ends in small rounded bones about the size of peas. They are the *coccyx*, skeleton of our tail. They may grow fast to the sacrum, and by restricting the size of the pelvic opening give trouble in childbirth. The orang has only three tail bones; we generally have five. Like the apes, we also have vestiges of muscles which once moved the tail, blood vessels which nourished it, nerves which connected it with the brain.

There is no tailed race in Africa—as the ancients believed. Man withdrew his tail beneath his skin before he was really man, but nature now and then forgets to withdraw the fetal tail. One adult tail measured ten inches. Such tails are usually "soft"—no tail bones outside the body. But a two-inch-long tail with bones, nerves, blood vessels, muscles, and hair, is known. Tail or no tail, the hair keeps on growing in a whorl as though the tail were present.

The upper-arm bone assumes its human form only after birth, when it also begins to twist, as does the femur, to conform to its new position at the side of the body. Above its lower articulating surface is a thin and shallow plate, often perforated—as in certain monkeys. Sometimes there is a hole or foramen at the side; it protects a nerve—as it did in our reptilian ancestors ten million years ago.

Human history may not start with man's foot, but our foot is as human as our hands. Its bones show coming and going changes. The big toe is the strongest and is more powerful in man than in any ape: it is coming. But most of it comes after birth; baby's big toe is a poor affair. The little toe is going. In one individual out of every three it has lost a joint. But not on account of tight shoes—they can make corns, but cannot change heredity; the third bone of the little toe is as often absent in feet which were never shod.

Our skull is no more human than are the bones of our foot or of our pelvis. It is shorter in front, longer at the back, better balanced on the spine: adaptations to an upright gait and a larger brain.

Man has a flat face and a sizable chin when he has short jaws. But jaws vary, and long or *prognathic* jaws change the countenance. The roof of our mouth was once longer than broad—U-shaped, as in some men and all apes. With civilized food, the jaws are shortening; the hard palate tends to become elliptical in shape.

In fetal life we have a pair of intermaxillaries between the upper jaw bones. At birth the suture, as skull joints are called, between them can barely be seen; by maturity, not at all. The suture often persists, obviously atavistic. The chin, or *mental point* of the lower jaw, has nothing to do with "mentality." It is a human trait, but not of all men equally. Some have "strong" chins, some next to no chin at all.

We have two nasal bones. But in some men and all monkeys they become one; no real bridge then to the nose. Sometimes the bones are small and flat: no bridge at all.

The brain can grow only as long as the three big sutures of the skull remain open. They begin to close at the age of forty: the one at the back first; the fore part of the brain can keep on growing. In animals the sutures close earlier than in man, the front ones first. They may close early in man; they may persist till old age.

When one or another skull suture closes prematurely, curiously shaped heads result. The "boat-shaped" head is due to premature closing of the parietal suture. When all the sutures close prematurely, the skull becomes solid as though a single bone. The brain can grow no more. Idiocy results—the "Aztec" people of the circus.

The frontal bone begins as two; shortly after birth they have become one, the suture disappears. But the suture may persist throughout life.

Most of us have about 310 muscles on each side of our body. They are subject to such variation that Testut, a noted French anatomist, required 900 pages to describe them. Some of us may have 3 muscles an ape would be ashamed to own, hangovers from such a remote past.

We marvel at the agility of monkeys and are astonished at the human quality of their actions. Do we not often expect them to smile? The smile never comes: they have no muscle to smile with. Even the chimpanzee cannot express with its face the emotions we think it should; its facial muscles are less perfectly developed, less sharply defined, than ours. In monkeys, they are even less differentiated.

One-fourth of all our muscles are in our neck and face! The human face can light up or cloud over because its muscles are attuned for complex action—keyed to the human pitch.

Facial muscles in mammals below man are more simple. We look for intelligence in the eyes of a horse, not in the expression of its face. When it needs to flick a fly from its face or shoulder, it moves a muscle buried in the skin. Such a muscle covers many animals like a blanket.

We all have bits of this skin muscle—some of us more, some less, even on the chest and back. Usually we cannot twitch it; we send a hand after the fly. We have traces of it in our scalp; a few have enough to move the whole scalp. Most of us can wrinkle our forehead—and do, when perplexed. Apes use this muscle both in pleasure and to frighten enemies. We all have vestiges of the muscles dogs use to pull, push, and lift their ears; some can even wriggle them.

So, while the skin muscle of our face and shoulders tends to disappear, the deeper facial muscles show progressive variation. They are among our most recent acquisitions. We

29

retain the muscle by which the dog shows its canine tooth: we can all snarl. But the muscle by which we smile is not so regularly present; the man of gloom may have no *risorius*.

Variations in muscles about the nose and mouth, necessary for speech, are usually forward-looking; they give the "speaking likeness" to man. Often they reveal what the mind is trying to hide. Only as we grow in experience can we make our face a mask to belie our emotions. This is because the face is primarily under the control of the autonomic nerves; they act of their own sweet will and are by nature honest. But by and by our brain learns to get control of them; we force our face to wear a smile when our heart would bid our eyes to weep.

The long flat *rectus* muscles which extend upward from our pubes once helped to support our abdomen. In our upright gait they are of no great use. Usually they end in the fifth, sixth, and seventh ribs; they may end in the fifth; they may extend up to the second, as they do in the lowest monkeys.

The small *pyramidalis* resting on the *rectus abdominis* muscle may be absent on one or on both sides; it may extend a third of the way up to the navel, or all the way. The kangaroo needs it to support the pouch in which she carries her young. Man has carried his young in his arms for ages, but the pyramidalis hangs on like a bad habit. The little *sternalis* muscle of the breast knows it has outworn its usefulness; it is found in one of every twenty-five individuals.

We flex our fingers by delicate muscles beautifully specialized. The long clumsy flexor of our palm was good enough for our ancestors; it is not good enough for us. It is absent in one man out of every ten.

Our arms are free; they have not forgotten that they were once legs. Of 36 bodies examined, 292 variations were found in the arm muscles, 119 in the leg. Our immediate ancestors were four-handed, we are two-footed. But when baby gets on the floor, it pulls with its fore and pushes with its hind limbs: just as we once crawled up out of water on to dry land.

Palmists rarely read the pad at the outer edge of our palm—or know that we have one like it on the sole of our foot; both protect deep-lying muscles from injury in walking. The palm pad has its own palmar muscle in one man out of every ten. It helped to work the pads which 'protected the muscles and tendons beneath. To-day, it is as atavistic as the pad itself; we gave up walking on our hands about 2,000,000 years ago. As for "lines" of fate and marriage, and the "girdle of Venus," they can all be "read" in the hands and feet of monkeys, and to a certain extent in a baby's foot—or in the fetal hands and feet. Palmistry is as dead as phrenology. Anyone who can read "character" or "mental capacity" from head bumps or palm lines is a wizard and should be paid accordingly.

What does it all mean, this astounding range of variation, on which I have barely touched? There they are, by the thousands, by unnumbered thousands. Shall we say that they lie, that our *levator coccygis* never lifted a tail, that our *curvator coccygis* never curved one, and that our *attollens auriculam* never lifted an ear? Or shall we say that we are walking museums of comparative anatomy and try to find out whence we came and whither we are going? This is certain: there is no fixed, standardized, perfect, or biologically ideal human body; there are no two human bodies quite alike. Each one of us reeks with evidence that our ancestors were not the two-handed, two-footed creatures we are now; that they had no talking muscles; that they could not back up their talk with a speaking countenance; and that they could not balance their heads on their spines.

Some variations are *atavistic* or vestigial. Like the buttons on our coat cuffs, they no longer function; like parlor boarders, they often make trouble. They are hangovers from a remote past. They are prone to disease; we should be better off without them. Some are *retrogressive*, weak

31

sisters of our body, functioning in a half-hearted way; we could do without them—many of us do. Some are *progressive*, a little bit more than human; they point to further change in man's physical structure.

Taken together, they bridge every gap and make a complete story. They prove that, while our eyes look forward, our body has not forgotten its humble origin—and carries some dead wood we were well rid of, such as appendix, tail, snarling muscle. Our proneness to hernia and prolapse of the uterus is only one of the many proofs that our body is not yet perfectly adapted to an upright gait.

10

On the day we are born we have used up only 2 per cent of our allotted growth power. We can grow 98 per cent more if we are spared.

We double our weight the first six months; a calf does it in fifty days; a dog, in eight. We increase our weight 200 per cent in the first year, less than 30 in the second, only 5 in the fifth. Increase in weight then picks up again and continues until the tenth year, to drop back from the eleventh to the thirteenth. From the fourteenth to the seventeenth, puberty years, it increases again, to 12 per cent. That is our last spurt. It drops to 4 per cent during the eighteenth year; to 1 per cent during the twenty-second.

Stature also increases by spurts. By the time the infant can walk, it has grown from twenty to thirty-four inches; thereafter, until puberty, it grows between two and three inches a year. The thirteenth is the rapid growing year for girls, the sixteenth for boys. Between fourteen and sixteen the boy increases his stature eight inches. Girls usually attain their full stature by twenty, sometimes by eighteen; boys by twenty-five. But both may continue growth three or four years longer, boys even up to thirty-five.

The newborn's brain is already one-fifth its destined weight, about ten ounces; by the second year two-fifths, or as large as an adult anthropoid ape's. Full brain weight comes before twenty-five; after that it loses weight, rapidly in old age.

The body changes proportions during growth. At twenty-five years the middle point of stature cuts across the pelvis —legs make up half the total length; at birth, only three-eighths; of a two-months' fetus, only one-eighth. Adult man cannot easily walk on all-fours; at birth he is better proportioned for an all-fours gait than a gorilla.

The two elements in growth are weight and height. Weight often continues beyond maturity, long after the body has taken on its last cubit. The giant can grow no taller; the fat lady knows no limit.

In prenatal life weight increases by growth, division, and growth of cells. A bacterium increases its weight by 1,000 per cent in a few hours; the human embryo at first grows at least as fast. Weight after birth increases in the size rather than in the number of the cells of the body.

Stature is determined almost entirely by the skeleton. Only skin and a thin layer of fat cover skull and the bones of the feet; thin cartilage covers the ends of the leg bones; between the vertebræ are thin pads of cartilage. Stature growth, then, is largely a matter of growth of skull, bodies of vertebræ, and especially of the leg bones.

Bones grow from *centers of ossification*. Centers for the principal bones of the body appear by the end of the second month of fetal life; centers for the ends, or *epiphyses*, appear later—many not until puberty, when the skeleton begins to assume its permanent form.

The number of ossification centers varies in different bones. The long bones of the arms and legs have at least three: one in the shaft itself and one at each epiphysis. The humerus at fifteen years is still in three parts: shaft, two heads; but the heads are more closely connected with shaft than at birth.

By maturity, the heads are so united with the shaft that it is not possible to see where they grew on.

In general, facial and skull-dome bones are formed from membrane—"skin" bones; the other bones begin in cartilage. Bone-forming cells multiply by division, absorb lime salts from the blood, ossify, and so continue until the cartilage is replaced by bone. Increase in length ends when the cartilage disappears. In the mature skeleton there can be no further growth in stature or in length of arms. If final conversion of cartilage to bone is delayed, gigantic stature results; if the process is reversed, dwarfs. Only the articulating or joint surfaces of mature bones are covered by cartilage.

Bones increase in girth by additions of bone cells from the surrounding membrane. Long bones are hollow. To preserve their relative proportion of bone wall to cavity, bone cells on the inside are destroyed as fast as cells are added to the outside. Thus the cavity grows with the bone, the form and strength of the bones are preserved. This process keeps up until late in life. With old age the bones become thin and delicate.

11

Complicated changes take place in acquiring the upright gait. A chick can run from its shell; a baby cannot even straighten its legs. They bend in at the knees and are drawn up at the hips, and are only 60 per cent of head-trunk length. By maturity they will be over 100 per cent. As the walking days approach, the legs grow fast. Knee and hip joints change; the legs can now be straightened out. The soles of the feet no longer turn in. The baby at birth can clap its feet almost as easily as its hands.

The spine also changes. It is not solid, but consists of twenty-four vertebræ with pads of cartilage between. At birth a large percentage of the column is cartilage. Powerful muscles develop to hold the spine erect; others, acting on the ribs as levers, to balance the trunk and spine. The last five, or lumbar, vertebræ at birth make up 27 per cent of the total spine length, as in adult chimpanzees; in adults they make up 32 per cent. The first two lumbar vertebræ take on their wedge shape which produces the curve in the small of our back only after birth. When the baby first tries to stand, it bends backward at the loins.

Standing is a complex act involving nearly all our big muscles. When we stand "at attention," powerful ligaments in the hip joint hold the body. This relieves the muscles from strain, but locks the knee joint. We stand easier if the knees are slightly bent and the knee-caps loose.

The feet muscles must bind the many small bones together to give support and form the instep or arch. A man can stand up asleep, but not if muscles of feet or of legs are "asleep."

In walking, each leg rests half the time. We tire standing because neither leg gets rested. The shoulder muscles which hold the head erect also ache from the strain in standing. As we nap in a chair the head nods.

Flat feet are not due to a giving way of ligaments; ligaments limit joint movement. Feet become "flat" when the muscles of the arch fail to support it; the arch breaks down. The result is a mid-tarsal joint. This is most likely to happen in long, narrow feet.

Short feet and high insteps go with large calves. To raise our body on our toes, we lift our heel. The toes are the fulcrum, the power is the calf muscles; the weight falls on the foot at the ankle joint but nearest the power at the heel. Hence the greater need for large calf muscles. But small calves go with long heel bones. As the foot is a lever of the second order, the long heel brings the weight nearer the fulcrum—that is, the toes. Hence "flat-foots" do not step off their toes; the fallen arch destroys the lever of the foot.

We nod our head between skull and first vertebra, or atlas;

35

rotate, between atlas and second vertebra, or axis. Both movements are limited by ligaments; otherwise the spinal cord would be crushed.

The main business of the face is to hold the teeth-bearing jaws; eyes and nose moved in by accident. The infant's face and neck seem small because the brain is so large. Their real growth begins with the eruption of the teeth.

The skull is a fulcrum for the jaw muscles in chewing. Muscles to hold the fulcrum steady develop with the teeth. The neck grows larger. With the teeth all in place the neck reaches normal size, the rounded "baby-face" disappears; strong jaws, powerful muscles, and prominences and ridges on bones of face and head support the muscles of mastication. The tiny mastoid processes below the infant's ears become adult structures as big as thumbs, required for muscle support.

The first, or *milk*, teeth should be in place by the end of the second year. Meanwhile the transverse ridges in the roof of the infant's mouth disappear. The *permanent* dentition begins with the first molars in the seventh year; incisors in the eighth and ninth; premolars in the tenth and eleventh; canine and second molars in the thirteenth to fourteenth; third molars, or wisdom teeth, in the seventeenth to fortieth year.

Startling changes of far-reaching consequence mark the years of adolescence for both sexes. As these changes are both physical and mental, and as they proceed under impulses from the gonads acting as glands of internal secretion, they will be described in the chapter devoted to the endocrine organs.

After maturity the body's chief task is to maintain its equilibrium: produce enough energy and heat to keep up repairs and carry on. But, from ovum to death, the body never ceases to change. Senility may be postponed; the body begins to age the day the ovum begins to grow. Before the newborn can mature, it must grow more human. Before it is twenty years old, it will increase its weight from fifteen to thirty times. Thereafter it grows old at a less rapid rate.

Old-age or senile changes precede natural death. These appear toward the end of a span of life which varies in different species. This span of life for some invertebrates is less than 100 hours; for some insects, 17 years; for some fishes and reptiles, over 200 years; for some birds and mammals, 120 years.

Absolutely authenticated cases of human beings alive beyond 100 years are almost unknown. It is far from certain that Thomas Parr lived 152 years. A critical examination of nearly one million cases of alleged unusual longevity showed none over 100, and only thirty that lived that long; twenty-one were women.

Longevity is not, as Weismann claimed, related to size of body. Some mammals live less than two years, some locusts seventeen. A dog is old at 20. I have seen a parrot 117 years old; it matured in its first year. A tortoise can live 350 years. No elephant known has exceeded 130 years. Nor does death "naturally" follow the reproductive stage; innumerable animals long survive their sex life. But every animal must reach sex maturity or its kind dies with it.

Old age is decrepitude; the body is worn out. The mechanism the infant acquired to walk with breaks down. The spine is not so supple, the cartilage disks between vertebræ shrink. This decreases stature—as much as three inches after fifty. The spine both collapses and "stoops with age." The knees are bent, the hip joints stiff. The muscles shrink. The body loses its natural fat. Folds of skin appear on neck and face. The toothless jaws atrophy and the mouth loses its shape. Cheeks and temples cave in, the bony scaffold beneath stands out.

The brain loses weight—in the last forty years of life as much as three ounces. The heart is enlarged from overaction to keep the blood coursing through thick, hard arteries. The pulse mounts again. It was 134 at birth, 110 at the

end of the first year, 72 at twenty-one. After eighty, it is 80.
The lungs lose their elasticity, the walls become thicker.

Many women after fifty show a thicker neck, hair on the
face, deeper-toned voice, more prominent cheek-bones, ridges
over the eyes. Their "feminine" traits are less feminine. It is
as though the inactivity of the gonads permitted a return to a
neutral condition, halfway between male and female.

Old age, senility, decrepitude; the body is worn out, it can
no longer function. Death.

12

There are no two human beings quite alike; every human
being in the world is unique. And yet there are about seventeen hundred million beings in the world to-day so much
alike in body and behavior that without hesitation we call
them human; they all belong to the human race. Nor is
there any doubt about the striking physical differences between a white-skinned, blue-eyed, fair-haired Scandinavian
and a black-skinned, black-eyed, frizzly-haired Senegambian.
The Scandinavian and the Senegambian are so different that
they could not possibly be mistaken one for the other. Do
they belong to the same *race?*

Recently I came across this heading: "Races Now Well
Defined"; and here is a sample definition: "*Asiatic* or *Mongolian* race—yellowish color, dark hair and brown eyes,
character cruel and avaricious, fond of show, likes to dress
in flowing garments, and is ruled by prevailing opinions!"
This is sheer nonsense. Here is a better one: "*Caucasian* or
European race—white skin, red cheeks, brown hair, round
skull, oval face, smooth forehead, narrow nose, small mouth,
perpendicular front teeth, face symmetrical; and agreeable."
Agreeable race, therefore!

Most of this confusion dates from Blumenbach's scheme
of five races, one for each continent. But as a matter of fact
no anthropologist knows where "Caucasian" leaves off, where

"Mongolian" begins. Boas, our foremost anthropologist, once addressed a Japanese in an Indian tongue of the northwest coast of America—he thought the Jap a native American! I could pick a dozen old women out of Peking, dress their hair and put them in beaded buckskin, and defy Congress to tell whether they are Arapaho, Manchu, Chinese, or "Mongol."

"Race" is a biologic term and has to do with physical characters based on blood relationship. The extent to which environment may alter the physical features we are born with is still an unsolved problem. There is no Aryan or Semitic race, because "Aryan" and "Semitic" are linguistic terms and refer to peoples who learn to speak an Aryan or Semitic dialect. In other words, *race* is the naked body we are born with; language and culture, the duds we learn to wear—often, in civilization, with much discomfort. There are varieties or types of men on the one hand; on the other, groups, tribes, nations, having a common language or a common culture or both. To classify people by language or culture is one thing; to classify man by physical traits is quite another.

There are Negroes in America of African ancestry; they speak English, are civilized, Christian, American. Transplant them to Africa: they cannot get rid of their physical features; they may forget or retain their English or acquire a new tongue—or a half-dozen; they may retain their "civilization"; they may become Mohammedans and adopt Arabic culture; or they may become cannibals and found a slave-trading kingdom.

A man's great-grandmother may have been Indian, his other ancestors mixed Irish, Swedish, Spanish, and Turkish: that man is white, Caucasian, Aryan, and may be "Nordic." For "Indian" substitute "Negro"; if any of the Negro shows through, he is a Negro! This gives us the emotional element; prejudice is at work. Clothes and the barber go far to make the man, but prejudice trains the eye to detect signs that would otherwise never be noticed. A Negro of Atlanta is often a white north of Dixie.

The emotional factor takes it for granted that moral and intellectual values inhere in skin color, language, culture, and nationality. H. G. Wells's heart beats faster in nearly every chapter of his *Outline of History*, because he cannot forget that he is Nordic, Aryan, English, British, white, civilized. *Are these traits innately or necessarily related?*

Assuming, as every biologist does, that man's ancestor was a monkey before he was an ape, is the blond Caucasian a "higher" type than the dark Ethiopian? Is one the end, the other the beginning, of human evolution? In other words, are there *higher* and *lower* races? Common sense says "yes." Common sense also said: There are ghosts. Witches turn milk blue. Any idiot can see that the earth is flat!

If I measure by my foot and weigh by my body, I can grade the whole human race from myself down to the lowest, blackest Pygmy. Man is usually measured and weighed that way, and with the same result: "high"; "low." The "highest" are the whitest; the "lowest," blackest: when the grader is white. It is good psychology—self-love is the first law of life—but not good biology. Imagine dogs graded from "high" to "low" by a Pekinese pug, a Mexican hairless, a Scotch collie, an Australian dingo; or pigeons graded by a pouter, a carrier, a fantail, a tumbler, a rockdove!

Color probably has no biologic significance; it may have physiologic value. Nowhere in the plant or animal world is it a mark of high or low, or of progressive or backward. Man's skin color is partly determined by exposure, mostly by an inherited mechanism which regulates pigment. How or why this mechanism works, how it arose and why it varies as it does in man, we do not know.

Pigment is probably a waste product of cell metabolism; it contains iron; it is possibly a response to living tissue's need for protection from harmful light rays. This does not help much. Why are Eskimos brunettes, Icelanders blonds? Why

40

are the Amazon forest natives "red," those of the Niger forests black?

All humans (except albinos) have skin pigment; it is the amount that counts. A white skin may turn dark bronze in Addison's disease. White skins develop black moles and tumors, and even general *melanosis*—dark pigment is carried by the blood and deposited throughout the body.

Much is known of man's anatomy at the dawn of the human race; the color of his skin and other details are not known. Fossil bones tell a story; they supply "links"; they may help clothe the skeleton with flesh, but not with skin color.

Our ancestral skin was probably dark. The amount of pigment increased in the Negroid type, decreased in the Mongoloid. They represent the two extremes. But "high" and "low" skin color is as sound biology as grading planets by color would be sound astronomy: Venus "highest" because whitest!

Kinky wooly hair is found in no apes or monkeys; straight black hair is. The kink is the "highest" type, the straight black the "lowest." Where shall we put the red—and the tow-heads?

The African's jaws are heavy: they support a first-class set of teeth. The European goes to the dentist to have his jaws stretched; *high*—or merely degenerate? The Negro scores with his thick out-turned lips; no men in the world have such human lips as the blackest Africans. Thin lips are primitive—"low," apish. Even in the bony ridges above the eyes, most Negroes are among the "highest" of man. This ridge is extraordinarily developed in the gorilla; also among the blacks of Australia. But in the gorilla it is a secondary sexual character. It is not found in gorilla children, nor at all in gibbons of either sex.

The earliest human skulls were probably long. Negro skulls are long, but not so long as the Eskimo. There are round heads in Europe; rounder, in China. There is no evidence that big brains are innately associated with long or with round heads; nor any evidence that extreme artificial deformation of infants' skulls (a widespread custom) changes the size of the brain or the capacity for intelligent behavior.

In brain weight, the average of a hundred Europeans would slightly exceed the average of a hundred Africans, but among the Africans many will be found exceeding the European average. The two groups overlap; no sharp line can be drawn. Nor, after diligent search, has any difference been found in brain structure or in convolutions. Intelligence does not depend on size of skull, nor is a big skull any proof of ability. Neanderthal man of fifty thousand years ago had a bigger skull than we have; he disappeared.

The Negro's lumbar vertebræ are of a primitive type; his gait is as upright as the European's. His spine retains more of its original suppleness.

The Negro's nose is primitive; it would not be so primitive if he had less jaw. The more the jaws recede, the more prominent the nose. If a low-bridge nose is "low," the "highest" bridge comes from Asia, through the Jews, acquired from the Hittites.

In long arms as compared with leg length, the African is more primitive than the European; as he is in his longer heel and smaller calves. In size and shape of external ear, he is less primitive than the European.

What is it all about, then? Much of it, convictions; habits of mind; prejudices, emotionally reinforced. There are dozens, perhaps hundreds, of physical types. Some have peculiarly or excessively marked features in one direction, some in another. To have diverged from the parent type means—simply divergence. We read significance into color of skin and other physical traits without knowing the facts behind these traits or the causes of change. There is no known fact of human anatomy or physiology which implies

42

that capacity for culture or civilization or intelligence inheres in this race or that type.

How about the "Nordics," then? How comes it that the Anglo-Saxon is at the top of the heap? Is it not because of his inherited ability that he rides the wave? The answer is to be found in the cultural history of man. What wave did the Anglo-Saxon ride in the days of Tut-ankh-Amen, or of Cæsar, or of William the Conqueror? Are his feet riveted to the crest?

Civilization is young; blood is as old as salt water. Once there was no Anglo-Saxon; but there was "civilization." Were there "higher" and "lower" races then? How "low" the savage European must have seemed to the Nile Valley African, looking north from his pyramid of Cheops!

Divergence, mixture; in isolated spots more divergence, less mixture; and so, sharply defined types—as the Eskimo. No people have a more distinct physical type than they have. I know of no skull more specialized or more easily distinguishable in a collection of skulls than an Eskimo's. They are "pure." Perhaps no people living are purer! No one pretends that there is an Eskimo race.

"Pure" types are *extreme* types. Blue eyes, flaxen hair, white skin, is an extreme type. The huge African with kinky hair, black skin, thick lips, high smooth brow, hairless body, is equally extreme. One is as pure as the other; one is as high as the other.

Huxley classified man by hair; he was too good a zoölogist to classify cats by hair. Hair is only hair. Its color is one thing, due to pigment; its shape is another. Straight hair in cross section is round; kinky hair, flattish. There is straight black hair, black hair that will not stay straight, and curly hair from red to black.

We know too little yet what environmental change does to physical structure, too little of the permanence of types, too little of the causes of change of type. We have no classification of man based on stature, skin color, hair form, head

43

form, proportions of limbs, etc., so correlated that they fit one race and one only. The original divisions of the human race are not yet known. Possibly they never will be known; possibly there were no grand divisions; possibly only minor types developed from time to time. Some of these types became extinct or left only traces which, through intermarriage, have become so hopelessly mixed that they can no longer be distinguished.

Nature is not so prejudiced as we are. She says that there is a human race, that all human beings are of the same genus *Homo*, species *sapiens*. She draws no color line in the human or in any other species. Black and white dogs mix as readily as do blacks and whites when the sex impulse is not outlawed, and are equally fertile.

In biology, fertility is generally regarded as a criterion of species. Using "race" as synonymous with "species," man is of one race. Hence the difficulty in distinguishing even subspecies, subraces, varieties, and types of men; they overlap. The human species has interbred. There are no biologically pure varieties and certainly no pure races, except, possibly, the Pygmy.

13

Open your atlas to a map of the world. Look at the Indian Ocean: on the west, Africa; on the north, the three great southern peninsulas of Asia; on the east, a chain of great islands terminating in Australia. Wherever that Indian Ocean touches land, it finds dark-skinned people with strongly developed jaws, relatively long arms, and kinky or frizzly hair. Call that the Indian Ocean or *Negroid* division of the human race.

Now look at the Pacific Ocean: on the one side, the two Americas; on the other, Asia. (Geographically, Europe is a tail to the Asiatic kite.) The aboriginal population of the Americas and of Asia north of its southern peninsula was a light-skinned people with straight hair, relatively short arms, and a face without prominent jaws. Call that the Pacific Ocean or *Mongoloid* division.

This grouping of man into two grand divisions was proposed by Boas. The scheme has the merit of convenience and is based on facts. Almost every shade of skin color can be found in India. But the early inhabitants of India were black. Their descendants survive to-day on many isolated peaks of Central India. They have Negroid faces, dark skin, woolly hair. In the Malay Peninsula and the Philippine Islands are isolated bands of little blacks or Negritos. The blacks have disappeared from Java, and in Sumatra have left only a tinge. The natives of Australia are black, as were those of Tasmania. The Melanesian Islands north of Australia are, as their name implies, peopled with blacks.

Negroes did not get their skin pigment from any "mark" put on Cain. Bible and biology are silent on Cain's color. Biologically speaking, the white skins of North Europe have lost something. When or where they lost their pigment, and why they lost more than the Asiatics, we may never know. But they have lost enough, in Kroeber's opinion, to suggest that to Boas's Negroid and Mongoloid divisions a third should be added—the *Caucasian.*

Kroeber distinguishes four subtypes: Nordic, Alpine, and Mediterranean in Europe, and Hindu in Asia. What are the facts? In general, skin color deepens and stature diminishes in Europe from north to south. North Germans are Nordic; South Germans, Alpine. The Alpine is broad-headed; the others, long. The Hindu is long-headed and dark-skinned, probably due to mixture with the submerged aborigines. Otherwise we have not moved a foot. It can as easily be shown that between North Europe and India there are only three subtypes—or that there are thirty-three. You can have as many as you like. To use William James's figure, counting "subtypes" is as profitable as counting the stones on a New Hampshire farm. But if any Nordic's pride is soothed by recognizing a Caucasian division and four subtypes, let it be soothed.

The prevailing color of the Mongoloid type is yellow. Malays and American Indians are nearest to the original type. The Chinese are a divergent strain; the Eskimo, a peculiar subvariety. The Negroid type abounds to-day in Africa proper (south of the Sahara) and in Melanesia.

Millions of Europeans are darker in color than millions of Asiatics. The colors overlap along the borders; they will intermarry. The border itself is a political boundary, not a racial barrier. North Europeans were not always as colorless as they are now. Once there was neither Mongoloid nor Negroid. These divisions simply represent directions of development, probably begun on two continents— Asia, Africa. Some diverged from the main line before others; their affiliations cannot be made out.

For example, the Bushmen and Hottentots of South Africa are two distinct Negroid subtypes; yet they are also distinct from typical blacks. Both are yellowish in color, have long heads, short flat ears, short legs. Are they remnants? Of what?

African Negroes and Melanesians of the South Pacific are close kin. The African has a flat nose, the Melanesian aquiline. Why is the Fijian black, his nearest neighbor yellow?

The Australian black is a puzzler. In some ways he is nearer Caucasian than Negroid. He is short, slender, longheaded; has a broad nose, wavy hair. His closest kin are the primitive folk of South Asia: Kolarians of India, Veddas of Ceylon, Sakai of the Malay Peninsula; the group is often called the Indo-Australian. Possibly the Veddas branched from the Caucasian type before it lost its pigment and took on the European type of face.

The Negritos, or Pygmies, are even more puzzling. The average stature of the human race is five feet five inches. Few groups of men vary from this more than two inches. No race averages less than five feet or more than five feet ten inches except the Pygmies of equatorial Africa, the Malay Peninsula, New Guinea, and the Philippine Islands; they are true *dwarfs*. Their average stature is a full foot short of the average of that of man. Many adult Pygmies are only four feet; no males exceed five feet. If stature were held to be a mark of race, there would be only two races—Pygmy; non-Pygmy.

The Pygmies are as black as blacks; they are dwarfs; otherwise they are as human as Nordics. In jaws, lips, and nose, they are more Nordic than African; in relative length of arm to leg they are almost as close to the Chimpanzee as the true Negro.

The Pygmies are spread around a quarter of the globe. They are so alike in physical type that they constitute a real thorn in unraveling the history of man's body. They complicate the general problem of human races; they constitute a distinct problem in themselves. Are they remnants, heritors of the ape crowd that left the trees for good? Possibly. Theirs, perhaps, is the type of body our ancestors tried out ages ago. It was good enough to be human and to survive; it was not good enough to subdue the earth.

Two points seem to stand out over and above every discussion of races and varieties of man: there are areas of characterization—within such areas, especially if isolated for long periods, certain physical traits or varieties become pronounced; these physical traits or varieties are neither necessarily biologically useful nor related to mental capacity or intellectual endowment.

14

Unless well protected, or in rainless Peru or Egypt, or in dry caves, or the cold storage of Arctic ice, or in oil, wax, or amber, the body soon yields to the bacteria of decay or to the teeth of wolves and hyenas. For bone or other tissue to be replaced by mineral whereby it petrifies or "fossilizes," many conditions must be right. The wiser the animal, the less likelihood of its being caught in quicksands or engulfed by the gravel and silt of floods. Primitive man was as little enamored as we are of being buried alive.

Fossil remains of the famous Crô-Magnon man have been found in Wales, and especially in France. Possibly earth never saw finer built human beings. His brain was 15 per cent larger than ours, his stature taller than any living race by two inches. He was clean-limbed, lithe, and swift. He had a good chin, thick and strong jaws. His head was long, his face broad. He buried his dead. He was an artist and an artisan. He lived about 25,000 years ago. Did he become an ordinary European, or did he disappear? No one knows.

Beyond Crô-Magnon, our forbears rather run to brutish casts. Grimaldi man was of the Negroid type. Neanderthal man had a huge head, chipped flint, and buried his dead. He is set down at 50,000 B. C. and left no known heirs. He is the first known cave-man.

The jaw of Heidelberg man fits a gorilla, but the teeth are ours. He is possibly 400,000 years old. Piltdown man is possibly a hundred thousand years older. Some think he was an ape. Some say he was the first Englishman. We have reached a point in time where no one knows who's who.

The champion fossil is *Pithecanthropus erectus* (ape-man erect), discovered by Dubois in Java in 1891. He is certainly a half-million years old; some say a million. He is more pithecoid than any known human being, more anthropoid than any known ape. He was as erect and almost as tall as the average European. He had definitely left the "well-ventilated arboreal tenements." He was a low-browed moron—and may be represented in the living flesh. But whether he was of the direct line that led to man, or only of a line that ended with himself, is not yet definitely known. It is enormously significant that, after a debate lasting more than a quarter of a century, the biologists of the world cannot decide whether *Pithecanthropus erectus* belongs to the first or the second of the earth's First Families. That makes him a pretty good link that is no longer missing.

15

There are six families of Primates, premier order of mammals: 1. *Lemuridae* (lemurs); 2. *Hapalidae* (marmosets); 3. *Cebidae* (monkeys); 4. *Cercopithecidae* (baboons, monkeys, etc.); 5. *Simiidae* (manlike apes); 6. *Hominidae* (men).

To import monkeys for their sex glands is ghastly business, perhaps the lowest that has engaged the cupidity and lust of man, but to shoot down simians as we do mad dogs or boys in uniform is a crime. The four Anthropoid apes are our next-of-kin-living; they should be respected as cousins and not exterminated as vermin or Indians.

Man never was a gorilla, a chimpanzee, an orang, or a gibbon. No biologist ever made such a claim. Whether these apes could have developed into human beings is a different story. They have the makings—all the parts. If we knew how heredity works and could control variation, we might breed from an ape a being that could dig a ditch, play the piano, talk English, and sing the "Messiah." We can teach them to smoke cigarettes, chew tobacco, drink beer, wear clothes, and eat with a knife and fork. We do not yet know the limit of their capacity to learn human ways.

Why do zoölogists put these four apes so close behind us that we can feel their breath and they can catch our diseases? Because they are Anthropoid. Nothing has yet surpassed them in the race to become human. Their anatomy, embryology, histology, morphology, paleontology, physiology, and psychology entitle them to second place in the Ancient and Honorable Order of Firsts.

They vary in their man-likeness; no one is in all ways

closest to man. The orang looks like an Irishman; the gorilla is built like Jack Dempsey; the chimpanzee is the most angelic; the delicate gibbon has a lady-like skull and an upright carriage. The first three—the Great Apes—are the extremes of variation from a generalized ancestor. The gibbon varies least, and to that extent is nearest the tree man climbed down when he decided to stand up and talk.

Except in teeth, the young female gorilla is the most human. Her father is a brute in size and appearance. Only five feet high, he may weigh over 400 pounds: mostly neck, chest, and arms. If his legs were of human proportions, he would stand over seven feet high. His hands and feet are almost man's. His courage is unbounded, his strength prodigious. His humanoid skull has retreated behind enormous jaws and beneath powerful ridges required to support the muscles to work the jaws. He is the blackest Anthropoid; his skin is nearly black; his hair is coarse dark brown, whitening with age.

The chimpanzee, like the gorilla, lives in jungle Africa. Like the gorilla, he has a shuffle-along gait, swinging his body between his long crutch-like arms. He has the gorilla's proportions, but never the great bulk of chest. And so is more at home in the trees, where he builds his nest, as does the orang. The chimpanzee's skull is not unlike the one *ape-man erect* tried on when turning into man—and gave up because it had too much jaw for the teeth required and not enough brain-box for ideas.

Our other two cousins are Asiatics. The larger is that red-headed satire on the human race, the Wild Man of Borneo and Sumatra; known to the natives as orang-utan, to science as *Simia satyrus*. The orang is the original roundhead. He is chunky, rather lazy, but has a good mind. He moves into a new nest when he has eaten up all the figs and young leaves in the neighborhood of the old one. With his four-foot body and his seven-and-a-half-foot arm-spread, he can swing

through the forest faster than a man can run. He slows up
on the ground, where he is less at home.

The gibbon *(Hylobates)* is the prima donna of the Anthropoids. If our weightiest opera star could sing as loud in
proportion to size of body as can the slender three-foot-high
gibbon, she could drown the siren of the *Leviathan.*

There are several varieties of gibbon, marked chiefly by
hair and skin color. None is so dark as the African apes.
With arms relatively longer even than the orang's, they swing
across the forests of south-eastern Asia with amazing skill and
rapidity. For hours on end they clear fifteen-foot spaces;
as much as forty feet when in a hurry.

In shape of skull and character of teeth the gibbon is the
most primitive ape, and thereby the most humanoid and
nearest the source of man's origin. He walks erect, his
arms are free and straight, his brain-centers for touch and
hearing are humanoid. In other words, of our four first
cousins the gibbon has the closest speaking likeness to our
great-grandfather.

The *Cercopithecidae* share with man and man-like apes the
doubtful honor of having thirty-two teeth, a narrow nose, a
tail more ornamental than useful, and a thumb which can
describe a circle. Their big toe is equally opposable, a
trait we generally leave in the cradle. They have no vermiform appendix; as compensation, they have callused rumps.
These, in mandrills, together with the cheeks, are gorgeously
colored; rarely are more brilliant blues, lilacs, and scarlets
found in nature.

The baboon is named *Cynocephalus* from his dog-like head.
He walks on all-fours, has long since abandoned tree life,
and is so strong and savage that he easily holds his own on
the ground. He has the meanest disposition, and, in spite of
fine fur, painted cheeks, and brilliant bottom, is the least
prepossessing of the Primates.

The macaques, of which the Barbary ape of Gibraltar is
the only Primate but man living in Europe in historic times,

are mostly Asiatic. One species lived in Japan, and is preserved in inimitable art. In fact, never did contact between two First Families lead to such happy results as when they posed for Japanese artists.

The two American First Families (2 and 3) are just monkeys. They have broad flat noses, no cheek pouches or callused rumps, tails generally prehensile, and a thumb often tiny and never opposable.

The tiny marmosets are greatly prized by sailors, and, since the opening of the Panama Canal, many spend their last days aboard a warship. They have the same number of teeth a sailor ought to have.

The *Cebidae* include all other New World monkeys. They have thirty-six teeth, humanoid nails—flat, instead of claws— and a tail as good as a fifth hand. The best known Cebida is the *capuchin*, named from its monkish garb—often disguised by the rags of his bondage to an Italian organ-grinder. This contact between First Families may please the children, but has not led to art. Probably a capuchin is no happier on the East Side than is a marmoset on a flagship. Yet the tiny marmoset has the brain of man at the third month of fetal life.

The *lemurs* are our poorest relations—poorest in all that makes for kinship between man and monkey. They live in the trees, prowl around all night, sleep all day. Their body resembles that of a four-footed animal. Their brain also is of low type; the hemispheres of the fore brain are small and do not cover the hind brain. Their second toe is a claw, often weirdly long.

It is a far cry from man to lemurs, but the links yet missing are not between man and the great apes, but between the great apes and the gibbon and between the gibbon and monkeys. In one sense the great apes are halfway between man and gibbon, yet the gibbon is much closer to the three than to monkeys. It is also related in many ways to the New World monkeys. Hence it is likely that gibbon, Old

World monkeys, and New World monkeys all came from a common stock. The New World monkeys developed in one direction, the Old World monkeys in another. But while the gibbon preserved and perfected its purely arboreal mechanism, it also developed an upright posture and, when on the ground, an upright gait. Orang, chimpanzee, and gorilla also specialized, each in its own way. The gorilla evolved the largest brain, but only larger than chimpanzee's as its body is larger.

The gibbon, in common with the great apes, can be inoculated with infectious diseases: syphilis, for example. Such inoculation in monkeys leads only to slight disturbance. Monkeys do not respond to the test for human blood, nor do any other mammals except the four Anthropoids.

The common ancestral stock of man and Anthropoids developed in two directions: the gibbon remained small; the others became heavy and partly took to the earth. Man came from that group and left the trees altogether. But even as he turned in our direction, his equipment was invaluable. His long sojourn in the tree-tops and his agility in swinging through the forest were a great education, for, as Lull says, "every hand-leap required that he instantly solve a compound problem in mathematics made up of distance, trajectory, direction, and strength of limb." When he did not solve that problem, he crashed! Mental preparedness had a high premium in those days.

We often wonder where we get our brain; it was standardized a million years ago. From stock such as the gibbon, man also sprang. That life in the trees gave him his start toward his big brain. There was no "fall"; man climbed down. And that is a story of changing limbs.

16

There is nothing in man's arm, from the muscles by which it is fastened to his head, neck, and spine, to his finger nails, that does not show modification due to change in function since man left the trees. The gibbon line started the changes. He can stand as straight as man; his shoulders have already swung around to the side of his body, his thorax begins to assume the human type.

Our ancestor needed a long forearm and a short upper arm. In swinging through the trees the body, attached to 'he lever at the shoulder, is the weight; the fulcrum is in the elbow; the biceps muscle furnishes the power to the moving lever or upper arm. The greater the distance of this lever from the fulcrum, the greater the power. The biceps muscle in the gibbon has extra heads of insertion, the better to lift the greater weight.

Our ancestral arm became modified to meet a change in occupation. With *hand* work, the movable lever was no longer the upper but the forearm. Men vary greatly in relative length of upper to forearm, but in general our forearm is short and powerful. We do not need the extra heads of insertion for our biceps, but one man in ten still has them.

Why did not man *fly* down? That would have been speedier. In a pinch he could fly up again. To fly is to be free. Bats can fly. They are high mammals; they are marvelously free. But at what a price! They lost their *hands*. They cannot handle things. A baby can; does. That handling of things is a priceless possession, worth more than eagle's wings. With hands the baby brings things up to its eyes, ears, nose, mouth; turns things over, examines them from all sides; prods things to see if they are alive; shakes them to learn if they are hollow; feels them to find out if they are ripe or rotten or hard or smooth or hot; feels its own body, explores itself.

The monkey is no less handy, rather more so; and marvelously quick. The hand of a baboon in a Calcutta zoo shot over a high wire screen and picked my spectacles from my eyes; I knew he had them only when I saw them in his hands. He twisted the wires into a shapeless mess and broke the lenses into tiny bits; nor gave me revenge by cutting his fingers.

It is enormously significant that a normal newborn can hang by its hands for half a minute; three weeks later, for two or possibly three minutes. Not so much? Try it. An average three-weeks-old baby can outhang an average thirty-year-old parent. It is a doting father that encourages baby to get its fingers in his beard; it "hangs on for dear life." So it does. It had to, once, or fall. That was the way it clung to home and mother up a tree.

Primitive peoples to-day walk up and down trees, "like a monkey." Some tribes make their homes in trees. Armless men can learn to write and shave with their toes.

When a boy drops from a limb, his legs bend out at the knee and hip joints. When he falls, he generally breaks something. The legs and feet of a newborn babe are no good at all for walking on a flat surface. The legs are crooked, the feet turn in. When it can walk, it does not walk on the soles of its feet, but on the outer rim of the soles. The bones under that outer rim are the first to appear in fetal life. The baby can wriggle its big toe almost as much as its thumb. Its drawn-up crooked leg, inturned foot, and opposable toe are lingering mementoes of the days when our feet were more at home on the limb of a tree than on the ground. Our hand is very wonderful, but not so "human" as our foot.

Even our ancestral backbone was almost human. It was not arched, as is the dog's; it was already a column. Not for months can the baby stand up, but it can soon sit up. Man sat up on a limb before he stood up on the earth. If we must "point with pride" to some part of our anatomy denied our monkey ancestor, it is not to our spine or to our hand, but to our foot. To become human, the foot had to travel as far as our brain. Yet we hide it in a shoe made on the toe formula of a spider monkey. Our longest toe is our big toe; if not, our foot is a throw-back and a poor relation.

The human foot at best is a misfit and is not improved by being shod. By the time we have lost our lower jaw through disuse, we shall have lost all our toes but the big one. Our foot will then be as highly specialized as a horse's. Of all the Primates, man's foot is the most primitive; next is the gorilla's. Even Pithecanthropus is allowed a human foot because his thigh bone was so human. He walked like a man —and as man cannot at birth.

The great apes' babies also have short and crooked legs, and, like man babies, but unlike monkey babies, cannot hang on to their mothers by their fingers and toes. Their fingers are only fair graspers and their toes worse; their mothers' bodies have not enough hair to hang on to. They must be carried. On that fact rests the foundation of every human home. The first kindergarten of human conduct was in the trees.

A monkey baby clings to the hair of its mother's body by its fingers and toes. Lemur babies wrap their legs around their mother's body, cling with their arms, and anchor themselves by holding on with their mouth to one of the two extra teats in her loins.

Our ancestor neither fell nor dropped from the ancestral tree. He walked down; his brain had become too big for foliage. It was the most important step in the life of the human race. His début as a terrestrial mammal, with nothing but his wits as his principal weapon, was the culminating episode in the drama of life on this planet. It was ages before he became a good actor, but without his schooling in the trees he could hardly have become human in a million years.

17

Man lost his tail and began to acquire his present stature and upright gait, including a tendency to hernia, during an arboreal existence in the Miocene epoch of the Tertiary era from two to three million years ago. During the last million years there has been little change in his stature or size of body. In weight and length of trunk and head, the chimpanzee is as human as we are. The greatest change was in larger head, shorter jaws, shorter body and arms, longer legs.

During the Miocene, New World monkeys became differentiated from lemurs and from the tailed monkeys of the Old World. Small tailless apes not unlike the gibbon had evolved from the Old World monkeys. This was a big step in man's journey up off his belly. Through the ancestor of modern gibbons, man lost his tail and gained his gait.

Dryopithecus, first of the big-bodied apes which eventually led to man, also appeared during the Miocene. He is a pre-*Homo.* His line is quite as important as that of Charlemagne or the *Mayflower.* It divided. One branch is represented by the extinct Paleopithecus of India and the modern great apes. The other branch took to the earth; from it came Pithecanthropus, Piltdown, and Heidelberg man. But a million years elapsed before any ape became so human that he could only be *Homo.*

Was it speech that made man? Speech often leads to his downfall, and in all the world is no mechanism so delicately poised as a woman's tongue. But vocal cords are as old as frogs; and few of us can chatter like a magpie or a monkey. Nor can we howl like a howler-monkey or scream like a gibbon. Fossil men left no voices, nor anything to suggest the nature of their larynx. Yet it is significant that the normal human larynx has no such laryngeal pouch resonators as have many Primates. Man has had to make an amplifier. But no ape has developed speech into such a perfect medium of communication as man. This is not alone due to any imperfection in voice mechanism.

Was man's appearance due to his big brain? The brain

weight of a tuna fish compared to its body weight is as 1 to 37,000; of an ostrich, 1 to 1,200; of a horse, 1 to 500; of a frog, 1 to 170; of a gorilla, 1 to 120; of a lemur, 1 to 40; of man, 1 to 35. But brain weight to body weight in rat and magpie is as 1 to 28; in marmoset, 1 to 22; in capuchin, 1 to 13. The place of honor goes to the humming-bird, 1 to 12.

Imagine a human being with a brain as large in proportion to his body as has a humming-bird!

But in weight of brain in proportion to weight of spinal cord, man exceeds all creation: 50 to 1; in the gorilla, it is 20 to 1; in mammals below Primates, 5 to 1; in birds, between 10 and 2 to 1; in fishes, 1 to 1. Spinal cord is good, but brains are brains. And there is nothing in the world like them.

Longevity among Primates began with the great apes. If adolescence ends with a full set of teeth, adult life in man begins at twenty-two, in the great apes at fourteen. Keith holds that man's age at sixty-six is equivalent to that of the gibbon at eighteen, of the great apes at forty-two; and that a native Australian of forty-two shows the age changes of a European of sixty-two.

There are no marked sexual differences among gibbons; as a rule, the female is a bit heavier. In the chimpanzee, sexual differences are about the same as in man. Orangs and gorillas show marked differences, the gorilla especially. The male is larger, heavier, stronger; his jaws and teeth, especially the canines, are more powerful. He is the fighter.

Secondary sexual characters in man thus appear to be only one or two million years old. They seem to be diminishing. Nature gets rid of useless structures or finds new functions for them. Modern woman shows no great disposition to find any new function for them.

Europe or Asia? Hrdlicka says Europe—through Piltdown man to Dryopithecus, the Miocene ape. Osborn says Asia: "Asia is near a center of evolution of a higher Primate; there we may look for the ancestors not only of prehuman stages like the Pithecanthropus, but of higher and truly human types."

In that case, prehistoric man in Europe was an immigrant from Asia, as was prehistoric man in America. Possibly Asia, in a not too remote age, will lead the race to be more humane.

CHAPTER II

THE EVOLUTION OF THE EARTH, LIFE, AND SEX

1

THE race to be human began with the first living being. That being was possible because the earth brought from the sun some very remarkable elements and because the sun continued to shine. Under its beneficent rays, certain elements became so dynamically constituted that they began to perform like an organic individual. It could do what matter had not done before, behave like a living being. It grew, but its size was limited by its nature, as is that of a raindrop or a drop of oil or a piece of jelly. It split up. It developed new ways of growth, and evolved sex. Various theories have been proposed as to how all this came about; even propaganda for taking the future of the race in our own hands. These are to be our concern in this chapter. A time-table of life will start us off. With that before us, we can soon trace our body back to a bacterium or something just as good. It is a long journey, but we shall try to keep out of blind alleys from which there is no return. Meanwhile, do not forget that the egg with which we begin life has been living since life began; that egg has had a long history and

THE GEOLOGIC TIME-TABLE OF ANIMAL LIFE

(Modified from *Organic Evolution*, by Richard Swan Lull, 1921, by permission of the author and the publishers, The Macmillan Company.)

Era	Epoch or Period	Advances	Years' Duration
Psychozoic Age of Man	Recent	Civilization	25,000
Cenozoic Age of Mammals	(Ice Age) Pleistocene	End of great mammals	9,000,000 (Matthew)
	Pliocene	Man-ape became Man	
	Miocene	Culmination of mammals	——
	Oligocene	Higher mammals	60,000,000 (Barrell)
	Eocene	End of archaic mammals	
Mesozoic Age of Reptiles		Archaic mammals	40,000,000 (Matthew)
	Cretaceous	End of great reptiles	
	Jurassic	Birds	——
	Triassic	Dinosaurs	160,000,000 (Barrell)
Paleozoic Age of Fishes	Carboniferous	End of ancient life	
		Land vertebrates	30,000,000 (Schuchert)
		Primitive reptiles	
		Ancient sharks	
	Devonian	Amphibians	700,000,000 (Barrell)
	Silurian	Lung fishes	
	Ordovician	Armored fishes	
	Cambrian	Shellfish	
Proterozoic		First invertebrates	500,000,000 to 1,000,000,000 (Barrell)
Archeozoic		Unicellular life	

has learned much about life. Otherwise we could not learn to behave like human beings in so short a time.

Our most *human* parts—brain, skull, teeth, voice organs, upright gait, and fingers—are not new, they are not unique, they are not ours exclusively; for life itself they are not even essential. Some human beings never use their brains, their skull is merely a frame for features, they lose all their teeth, and their fingers are all thumbs. No, our most humanoid parts will not give us much clue to the nature of the ceaselessly changing creature that became at last human.

A man, monkey, opossum, lizard, frog, shark, flea, fishworm, oyster, and malaria germ have one thing in common: they must eat and breathe, or die. Every animal must have lungs and stomach, or the equivalent. Call it *viscera*. Viscera are vitals, the something without which there is no living animal. What else have they in common? A motor mechanism to bring the necessary elements of life within reach of the living body's vitals.

The great difference between man and oyster is not viscera, but motor mechanism. That difference is so great that man can catch the oyster and eat it. The most the oyster could catch of man is a finger, and then only if man carries his finger to the oyster and invites the oyster to catch it. Even then the oyster could not eat the finger. The motor mechanism of man and higher animals is knit together by a nervous system, supplemented by vocal organs and presided over by a brain.

The history of our body is primarily that of the mechanism for getting food, ways of avoiding being eaten as food, and method of growth. In other words, the chemical activities whereby living beings maintain life are fundamentally the same in all animals, but the laboratory in which these activities take place and the mechanisms for carrying the laboratory about and for acquiring information as to food, enemies, etc., vary enormously.

Even our Primate ancestor up a tree lacked no parts to

62

become human; certain parts merely had to be altered. Say, two million years. Beyond these two, other millions passed while body and brain bided their time; the earth was not yet quite ready for nature's great experiment.

As Bergson puts it: "Man only realized himself by abandoning a part of himself on the way; he was not yet ready to fight for his life with his mere wits." Wits are his greatest weapon.

We must not think of our body as the most or the best this or that. In many ways the eagle has a more specialized structure; it excels in eyesight, respiratory system, skeleton, and locomotion. Even the bee in its own line, as Thomson says, is hardly inferior to man and represents an achievement that angels might desire to look into.

Life has tried out countless bodies. Certain species of snails and crustacea have survived almost unchanged from pre-Cambrian days, sixty million years ago. Two-million-year-old fossil ants embalmed in amber are so much like ants of to-day that, could they awake from their sleep, they could recognize their descendants, if their noses were not stopped up. They kept to the middle of the road. That man evolved from a lowly Primate means that the Primate itself was neither an accident nor a highbrow, that it was not too far removed from the body its ancestor brought up out of the mud on to the dry land.

Many families of Nature's masterpieces have no living representative because they over-specialized; they gave up so much to tusk, trunk, canine, wing, leg, stomach, size, height, length, or armor, that they had not enough to live on. They put all their eggs in one basket. Earth's crust is full of these fancy forms, so specialized they could not meet change. Man got ahead because he could grasp an idea, could talk it over with his fellow-men and think up new ideas. The amazing thing is not that he became human, but that he can be so inhuman in so many ways.

The fundamentals of living remained unchanged through

vast periods of time, the structure in which vital processes functioned kept changing. When the larder shifted or the nature of its contents changed, the method of keeping the viscera in touch with the larder, or in preparing food so that the viscera could digest it, had to change. Countless animals still solve the problems of life with simple structures. Few went in for brains. None but man ever tried to discover the nature of brains or thought of preserving them in alcohol. He could do this because the body he inherited could be adapted to diverse occupations.

Reading the time-table backward suggests a parallel process which seems to have been at work in human culture: progress by leaps; between, long pauses. The pauses grow shorter as time moves on.

For a hundred thousand years man gets along without steam-control. The steam engine is invented. In the twinkling of an eye steamships plow the seas and every land is ribbed with shining rails. The Age of Steam blossomed out of nothing. Gossip formerly passed from mouth to ear; at breakfast, now, Cape Town reads of the color of the hair of the girl the Prince of Wales danced with the night before on Long Island. This is another New Age.

How did man get along without radio, newspaper, steel, steam, plumbing, arch, calendar, spear, flint knife, fire? He did. But he gets along faster with them. So with life itself. It got along without mammary glands and internal incubators, skull and vertebral column, head and tail, brains. But with brains, head, backbone, and placenta, the procession speeded up, life shot out in new directions.

Progress is often made by lying low; let the other fellow try out Nature's new-fangled notions. By holding out, man came on the stage during the big scene. When the call went forth for clever people who could double, shifty people who could walk back to town if the show "blew," who could catch and fry their own fish in case of need, who could dig out, swim across, climb up and jump down, who were handy with their hands, had good memories and could mix, man appeared.

All this took brains: a big brain, a brain so big it had to wrinkle or burst its case; a brain with frontal lobes so big they dwarf the hind-brain. A brain big in every way; in absolute size and weight, in proportion to spinal cord, in proportion to body.

Think of a jellyfish, a shark, or an elephant with a human brain. The jellyfish has no head to put it in; the shark, no bony skull to protect it; the elephant, no hands to do its bidding. The human brain would be an incumbrance to the jellyfish, a nuisance to the shark, and would drive the elephant crazy.

Nature has made many extraordinary experiments. Some survive: their parts had "survival" value; most of them disappeared. But no great group-experiment was a total failure. Even the Cyclops-eyed reptile of pre-Tertiary times survives in the Sphenodon of New Zealand. The eye itself, as eye, was a failure; we inherit it as endocrine gland!

2

If the hand that rocks the cradle is the hand that rules the world, it will not hurt good government if the hand knows what it rocks; or what the hand came from; or that the first cradle was in a tree-top. The human brain and throat made civilization possible, but it was the hand that built the home, kindled the fire, and made human culture. There are simpler and surer feet than man's, but none has carried such priceless freight or been shod with the wings of a Perseus. The human hand should build a monument to the human foot, for the foot freed the hand!

In a class on Christian Evidences, the President of the college wiggled his thumb and said, triumphantly, "No monkey ever lived that could do that!" Could if it wanted to. Watch a monkey climb a rope: thumb on one side, fingers on the other. Sally, the chimpanzee, grasps the neck of a bottle like a man, and opens a clam shell with the thumbs of her two hands. Watch a monkey on a still hunt through the hair of its mate.

Opposability of thumb is no marvel. The marvel is that an organ modified for grasping limbs can also pick up a pin, throw a stone, wring a chicken's neck, and crack a nut with a rock. Any average monkey has a pair of such marvels. The fact is that if a primitive five-toed foot had not been carried into a tree and there developed along lines of its original pattern, there would be no human hand to grasp to-day. It was figuratively and literally kept in the air. Had it specialized either as grasper or as support, it could not have been turned into the marvelous organ that it is.

The monkey was not the only mammal that took to trees; the whole marsupial family started their career there. The kangaroo came down; his prehensile forefoot lost its offset great toe. The koala remained; his forefoot developed an opposable thumb and an opposable first finger. No vine is a better clinger. When you shoot a koala you climb the tree and pry its fingers loose or it will hang there till it rots. Tree-sloths (cousins to armadillos) also specialized in grasping organs. One has only three fingers, each armed with hook-like claws; its hooks also hang on after death. Our ancestors were *adapted* to an arboreal life; they were not *enslaved* by it.

Some Primates experimented in fingers. A lemur lost his second finger to give the thumb more grasping space. Some tried claws instead of nails. The marmoset has a thumb nail, the other fingers have curved, pointed claws. As Primates progressed, nails replaced claws and all five fingers were put to use. With the gibbon, the prehensile hand was well developed. Early lemurs lived on rather than in the tree-tops. The gibbon does not walk on trees, but swings from limb to limb. Its hand is more specialized than ours,

66

farther evolved from the ancestral type. The orang's thumb is almost gone; often has no nail.

Several animals tried out the prehensile tail: chameleons, opossums, an ant-eater, and some New World monkeys. Old World monkeys were wiser. The spider monkey's marvelous tail cost him two thumbs; in gaining a "fifth hand" his true hands lost their perfection.

Invertebrates are allowed as many legs as they please up to a millipede. The vertebrate limit is four, two pairs. They began with fishes: gills modified for propulsion. Their limbs are oars; the tail is rudder and sculling oar. When fish crawled out of the water on their belly, their limbs were paddles—as are ours in fetal life. Many vertebrates kept on crawling on their bellies, and, like most snakes, lost their paddles. Whales went back to water and turned their front legs into oars again; they lost their hind-limbs.

Man never was a whale or a snake; nor did he ever walk like a horse. He did not go in for stability, as did the horse, cow, and elephant; mobility was his goal. In bones, muscles, and plan, our forelimb is closer to a frog's than to a cow's. It is built on the old fish type handed on by amphibians to reptiles. Compared with the front foot of a horse, our hand is primitive and ancient, closer to the hand of an extinct iguanadon of Jurassic-Cretaceous times.

With that type of limb the first Primates climbed a tree. It was a four-piece arm: humerus, swinging free at the side and held against the shoulder-blade, which in turn was held out and away from the body by the collar-bone acting as a strut; forearm of radius and ulna, making possible the right-side-up, upside-down hand movements; wrist joint of eight bones; five fingers. These bones can all be matched in the "hand" of a mud turtle, but not in the forefoot of a horse. The turtle's wrist has one more bone, the *central*. All men, gorillas, and chimpanzees have it in the fetal hand. It then incorporates with the scaphoid bone. It sometimes forgets to incorporate.

When our ancestor walked down the tree, his forelimb was already an arm and a hand; the tree had saved it from a leg's fate. His hand could grasp the ball; his arm could "wind" it up, as does the pitcher before he puts it over. It did not have far to go to become the hand that rocks the cradle.

A large litter is wasted energy without a suitable nursery. The horse specialized in grass-cutting teeth and fast legs. It has no nursery; the colt can run the day it is born. It must, or the wolves will get it. Our Primate mother had no natural nursery, but she had a natural clinging disposition— as had her baby. As brain and body developed, the baby's dependence on its mother became more profound. Apes carry their young in their arms, as does man. Even a young gibbon is dependent on its mother for seven or eight months; she carries it to the water, bathes it, dries it. A gorilla mother boxes her young hopeful's ears, and the male guides and guards all his children.

Interpret all this in terms of pa, ma, and the baby. The family grows larger. Family circle. Divided cares, mutual responsibility. Human behavior began up there.

The tree-living Marsupial carries her young in a pouch: a marvelous contrivance, a wonder-work of nature. The tree-living Primate carries hers in her lap. She had to sit up: she had to have a columnar instead of an arched spine; hips to hold viscera; head poised at one end of the spine for better control; chest flattened to agree with the columnar spine; diaphragm shifted in position and moorings to conform to the new style of breathing; muscles once needed for breathing now used to hang the arms at the sides of the body and swing them out from the body.

Such were some of the changes required before the primitive mammal that climbed the tree could walk down and conquer the earth. But not until earth became man's home did his trunk reach hour-glass form. Then it was that the mammæ took on well-developed nipples and their encircling areola. But as Woods Jones says, something more subtle than mere change in bone and muscle was involved in man's evolution. The kind of life lived through the ages up the tree made possible the kind of wits needed to live at the foot of it. There were no baby-farms or homes for children of missionaries-abroad or officers-absent-on-foreign-duty, in Miocene times; "mother love" was more necessary then for the lives of young apes than it is to-day for their descendants.

3

In twenty million years the Age of Reptiles produced eighteen orders. Five survive; too much specialization. Osborn named one *Tyrannosaurus rex*. That saurian king was forty-seven feet long, twenty feet high, heavier than an elephant. His teeth were half a foot long; his feet were armed with mighty claws. He was a perfect machine: in speed, size, power, and ferocity, the most destructive engine that ever lived!

He is an also-ran. Inside his thirty-six cubic feet of skull-box he had less than a pound of brains!

The big-bodied pin-headed Reptiles were gigantic failures, as were the first mammals nature experimented with. Both turned to rock and left no descendants to mourn their loss. And yet they had had everything conceivable in dental weapons and heavy armor. Not enough brains!

With Oligocene times began another series of mammals; more brains in proportion to body. Nearly all of them are alive to-day. It was man's salvation to have had a tree-climbing ancestor at that time.

Early land vertebrates smelled their way through life; foods, friends, mates, all through the ends of their noses. Like a dog. The scent was lost in the trees; also the need for a long-drawn-out face, like a horse's, an ant-eater's, or an elephant's. Monkeys do not touch things with their snout, but with their finger tips, which are as good as most animals' tongues for feeling things out.

Sight is much more valuable than smell. Having no need for snouts, Primates shortened their faces. Having little need for feet, they developed their hands. Hands could bring things up to the eyes. Eyes could settle down where they would be handiest. The eyes moved on to the front of the face. Each eye sees an independent picture, but the pictures overlap; the eyes can correlate and blend them into one. Thus, Primates' eyes are binoculars with stereoscopic effect. Many mammals have no such binoculars.

What can an elephant know of its body? It can feel very little of it, see even less. What does a monkey not know of its body? What its hands feel, its eyes can picture. The brain knows nothing of muscles, but it becomes a storehouse of pictured movements.

And so man's headpiece became a compact, snug affair; eyes, ears, nose, tongue, teeth, all close together, easily turned this way or that. With two, sometimes four, hands available to bring things close. The brain grew as its requirements grew. The motor mechanism of the body kept improving; more brain needed to work it. The more it was worked, the better it grew. Its areas of association between hearing and seeing, seeing and touching, etc., kept on growing. These areas are the distinguishing features of man's brain.

If man had received no more than mere bodily form from his monkey ancestor, he might as well have had an opossum for an ancestor. It was not mere body that made monkeys smart; nor their brain that produced their hand. Their brain made the most of their hand, but, as Jones says, while man can play the violin because he has a big brain, what could his brain do if his hand were a horse's foot?

Man's ancestor won his freedom not so much by specialization as because he kept his plasticity, extended his wits, and improved his control.

4

Eocene times knew nothing of tabloid foods and nature herself was the dentist. No teeth, no food; no food, no life. Instead of a knife, the primitive Primate used its incisors; instead of meat-chopper or mortar and pestle, its molars. It stabbed its prey with its hand, but kept the big canine to show what it could do when angry. It saved its teeth by using them. They were not good for anything in particular; they were good enough for almost everything in nature's larder. Our teeth are among the most primitive of all mammals. Our four-cusped molars are more like those of extinct Eocene mammals than they are like those of living apes. We are the shortest-snouted Primate; our teeth, alone of Primates, are in one continuous series. There is a real gap between canine and incisors in apes; also in our milk set—or should be, shorter jaws are lessening the gap.

Our ancestral Primate was a small, warm-blooded, primitive mammal with forty-four teeth, four short legs all alike, and feet with five toes armed with claws. It lived on insects, worms, fruit, and nuts. Who was its ancestor? *How did it become viviparous? Where did it get its mammae?*

Circumstantial evidence points to a dog-toothed, low-browed, Triassic reptile, called *Cynodont*. He is older than the giant reptiles which appeared millions of years later, lower than the reptiles which led to dinosaurs, which in turn led to crocodiles and birds. If not the Cynodonts, then we must assume that mammals started in the Permian period. Some say it was in Africa, but probably Central Asia will prove to be the birthplace of reptiles and mammals.

The reptile that developed into mammal had teeth fit for a mixed diet. It could run, making possible a broader outlook and a surer hold on life. Legs that lifted the belly from the ground made warm blood possible. Warm blood made energy more easily available and personal incubation of the egg possible. And there is no more interesting tale in the

71

book of nature than the one which recounts her experiments in eggs.

Mammals get their name from their *mammae* or milk-glands. All mammals suckle their young, although true teats appear only with marsupials, the second order of mammals. Monotremes, the lowest mammals, lay eggs, as do all birds, amphibians, fishes, and most reptiles.

But there is a vast difference between monotreme, bird, and reptile eggs, and amphibian and fish eggs. The latter are laid in water; they develop in water. Amphibian eggs develop into tadpoles which live like fish; by and by their gills close, their tails are absorbed, their fins become legs; they hop up frogs or toads. But frogs can no more live all their life under water than can whales or porpoises: they must come up for air. Amphibians lead double lives.

As do some men. But our fetal gill-clefts never break through. We can thank our reptile ancestor for that. Nor do reptiles or birds have gill-breathing apparatus. Their young do not metamorphose from a larval stage. The alligator deposits her eggs in dry ground; if deposited in water the eggs would "drown," as would birds' eggs.

Reptiles, ancestors of birds and mammals, invented a new style of egg to get away from the double life led by amphibians. All eggs are complex, but this reptilian egg was the first to have a shell or protective envelope, and a yolk inside: food to tide the embryo over the first stage of life, oxygen until it grows a lung.

The embryo develops an amnion, or protective membrane of two layers; between, amniotic fluid—storm-door and shock-absorber. Also a second membrane, the sac-like allantois. This is connected with the embryo's blood vessels; it is the embryo's "lung." Oxygen, entering through the pores of the eggshell, is picked up by the allantois and carried to the embryo; the returning blood-stream carries carbon dioxide. The egg must have air or the embryo within is asphyxiated.

As the yolk-sac diminishes, the allantois grows in size and efficiency.

Certain snakes and all mammals except monotremes are *viviparous:* their young are born alive. What has happened? The egg is incubated within the maternal body. The lung-like allantois becomes placenta and unbilical cord. The placenta grows fast to the wall of the mother's uterus. Through the connecting umbilicus the embryo gets oxygen and nutrition. Yolk—as in birds' eggs—is not needed. But nature is persistent; the human embryo has a yolk-sac, but no yolk.

This *vade mecum* incubator is a great advance over the reptilian way of letting the sun do it. But reptiles get the credit for the new-style eggs. They were nature's answer to a drought. That drought gave reptiles their great start. Those that developed blunt dagger-like teeth into grinders with cusps, and eggs that could hatch in a desert, were the reptiles that led to mammals and man—and made valuable contributions to science.

Our indebtedness to reptiles, then, is very great: our antenatal robes, four-chambered heart, and a rising temperature leading to warm blood. Some even go so far as to credit a certain reptile with our ideas of the Tree of Knowledge. Our family life was founded in the trees; but it is rooted in the placenta. The long and intimate commingling of parent and fetus had far-reaching consequences. The first placenta was developed in the reptilian ancestor. By the time that reptile had become mammal, it had warm blood, a hairy body, and a muscular diaphragm between lungs and liver.

5

Reptiles developed the habit of living on dry land. An amphibian pointed the way, in the Upper Carboniferous Age. The family name of that amphibian is *Stegocephalia*— because he had a roof over his head. He may date from the Devonian period. He was heavily armored, and a flesh-eater. His four limbs were well developed for crawling; his bones, in number and character, were of the type that millions of years later developed into the prehensile hands and feet of Primates. He retained enough of his fish habits to compel his return to water to deposit the eggs. In the water the young developed.

To that amphibian ancestor we are indebted for four priceless possessions: fingers and toes, true lungs, a wagging tongue, vocal cords. The bullfrog inherits his voice direct, nor is there evidence that he has improved it. It is known that he puts it to the use it had from the start—a mate-call. A vocal mate-call could have been of no use under water; in swampy lands it was a necessity.

Beyond, and older than amphibians, are fishes. Our debt to them is greatest of all: skull, at first a rude brain-box of gristle; true jaws; limbs supported by bones articulating with an axial skeleton. Such parts distinguish us from devil-fish, oysters, clams, barnacles, and fleas. With such parts, nature began to branch out on new lines; new lines had something to go on. They could develop brain, the skull protected it; a real spinal cord, the backbone carried it. With skeleton inside instead of outside the body, and of bone instead of shell, they could develop big strong bodies. With their paired limbs they could travel, explore, experiment. With their new type of mental machinery, they could record new experiences.

What an amazing tribute to the persistence of nature! Every normal human embryo develops a notochord. That notochord is the oldest and only original "backbone," the only backbone to-day of the *amphioxus* or lancelet, possibly the only living representative in direct line of the inventor of the vertebrate idea.

From Cambrian days, when the first notochord was laid in the first fish, possibly a half-billion years were to roll from the scroll of life before man was to puzzle his brain to discover the nature of the creature that decided it would be easier to carry its skeleton inside its body than on its shoulders.

That creature is not yet known. Countless tons of rock weigh it down. It had no bones, possibly no shell. Its remains may never be found; its soft body may have left no remains.

Beyond vertebrates, the skein is tangled. Nature tried many types of bodies before she found one fit for a fish. That was no mean honor. Fishes are highly organized; they stand high in the tree of life. The parts they transmitted to posterity made frogs, lizards, eagles, monkeys, and man possible. No essential part has been acquired since the first fish laid the keel on which every vertebrate builds its body. The very bones of our middle ear began their career in the arch of the gill of a fish. The wonderful mechanism by which we know when we are right side up was invented by a fish.

What makes a body fit for a fish? What did an invertebrate have to have before it could think of becoming a shark or a sturgeon or a cod?

No protozoon would do; it has only one cell. The lowest multi-cellular animals are sponges; but they are primitive and lead a plant's life. Next come jellyfish, polyps, corals. Some drift with the current, others settle down to build coral reefs from their limestone skeletons. They have insides for circulation and digestion, but their body is built on the plan of a tub.

The next three higher groups, flatworms, threadworms, wheelworms, look like something; the first two especially. With them nature tried out an epoch-making experiment— bilateral symmetry: two sides, two ends. They could tell right from left and knew whether they were going ahead or astern. Good-by to the old watchful waiting, or drifting round-the-circle days. Strenuous life moves straight ahead.

Earthworms seem low to us. But a jellyfish would have to look up to them, they are so highly organized; even an amphioxus respects them. They have regular parts; they repair lost parts better than a surgeon. They have a suggestion of a backbone and spinal cord; mouth, esophagus, intestine with posterior opening; nervous system, brain and nerve chain; pulsating vessels to circulate the blood; kidneys; striated muscle. If our vertebrate ancestor was no worm, it was a worm-like form. The fishworm has the form and all the essential parts. It even has two sexes in one body; it is a true hermaphrodite.

With molluscs nature experimented with soft bodies protected by shell armor. It was a pretty idea, and gave us pearls, clams, oysters, and snails; but the shells so slowed them up and weighed them down they could never get away to a fast start or far from the mud.

Starfish represent another experiment. Possibly our decimal system is due to the two five-fingered hands inherited from a starfish ancestor.

Joint-foot arthropods are high invertebrates. Some have very perfect bodies and enough instincts to fill a book. They are segmented and have well-developed legs—though neither grasshopper, cricket, nor locust goes "on all-four," as Leviticus misinforms us. They go on all six; spiders and scorpions, on all eight.

That exhausts the possibilities. But which invertebrate line is founder of vertebrates is not yet determined. It may have been a fishworm. It may have been a scorpion, or a horseshoe crab. It may have been an unknown family which split, one branch leading to the amphioxus, which has a real notochord, but no skull and no red blood.

Poor fish as it is, the amphioxus is the nearest living ancestor of vertebrates. They live a quiet life near the shore, generally buried in sand up to their gills. They have the makings of a true fish, even to the nervous system; but are only a fish in the making. And of all the bodies nature tried out during countless millions of years, no survival has the long, slender, segmented body that so closely resembles the amphioxus as a fishworm.

6

Subkingdom I, Protozoa; subkingdom II, Metazoa. That is all. Man belongs to the second subkingdom: his is a many-celled body, all from an original cell.

Flower in crannied wall may be more poetic, but if we knew all about the one-celled ameba, we should know more about life than we are likely to know for some time. If we knew why several Protozoa decided to found a co-operative society and so the subkingdom Metazoa, and if we had the minutes of their first meeting, we should be able to manufacture animals to suit our fancy. If we knew the nature of the jelly called protoplasm of the ameba's body, we should know what life itself is.

With the mere mention of the word "protoplasm" we have, as the farmers say, a lot of hay down. We cannot get all our "hay" in before it rains; some of it spoils. We call in the biochemist, but by the time he gets it in a test tube or stains it so that he can see it, what was living jelly is dead. He examines only the remains—the "débris," as Lull calls it.

Protoplasm (first-molded-thing) is called living jelly because it is about of the consistency of jelly. It is semi-fluid, generally transparent, and colorless. It may contain granules which make it grayish in color and semi-transparent. Some of these granules may be stained, and are called *chromatin*. This appears as a central spherical mass, and is called the *nucleus* (*nux*, nut); the remainder of the protoplasm is called *cytoplasm*.

Protoplasm is known only by the body it keeps; but whether one cell is the entire body or only one in a body of billions of cells, every cell has certain properties or functions. It is self-supporting; it has its own definite wall, or is so cohesive that its outer surface serves the purpose of a wall. It eats; it must have food or it dies. It must get rid of waste. It moves. Its movements may be of the flowing kind or "ameboid"—part or parts of it flow out in processes, like the movements of the ameba. Or, it may be covered in whole or part with fine cilia which set up whipping movements. It is excitable or irritable: when touched, it moves. It responds to certain stimuli. It has conductivity: a stimulus at one side may lead to movement on the opposite side. It can co-ordinate its movements, as it does in such harmonious actions of the cilia or the pseudopoda in ameboid movements. It grows or has the power of reproduction.

The ameba can be studied only under the microscope. It is literally a speck of living jelly, but it is as "alive" as an elephant or a whale. It goes about for food. It flees from danger. It is sensitive to stimuli from without. It breathes oxygen and gives off carbon dioxide; collects, digests, and distributes food; excretes waste; reproduces its kind. It can learn from experience. It is organized for one purpose only: life. Within that limit it fails in no essential.

What is the ameba? Life. What is life? Protoplasm—ultramicroscopic, unanalyzable; but only living if it behaves like a living being.

Protoplasm is 72 per cent oxygen, 13.5 per cent carbon, 9.1 per cent hydrogen, and 2.5 per cent nitrogen. The remaining 3 per cent consists of sulphur, phosphorus, chlorine, sodium, potassium, calcium, magnesium, iron, and silicon. Add a pinch of fluorine, iodine, and manganese; and that is what little girls are made of.

Such is the stuff of life. How about the staff of life? For, as Huxley said, while a solution of smelling salts in water, with a tiny pinch of some other saline matter, contains all the elements which make up protoplasm, a hogshead of that fluid would not keep a hungry man from starving, nor save any animal from like fate. It is equally true that if animals lived only on dead animals, the animal world would perish through cannibalism. Even nature cannot pull herself up by her bootstraps.

Which takes us out into the open and face to face with life itself. No one quite knows what life is, but there are certain fairly accurate tests for life. One is growth. Are certain bacteria alive? Put them in a suitable medium: if they grow, they are alive; if not, they are dead. We stop growing larger, but when there is no growth anywhere in our body we are dead and our own digestive juices will begin to digest our body.

The point is that plants are older than animals and bacteria older than both; and that there is no sharp line between lowest animals and lowest plants or any general agreement as to whether bacteria are plants or animals. Nor does it make any particular difference to us. What matters is that animals must rely on plants or other animals for their growth-material and that plants are not so dependent; they can live on materials which would be death to animals. With carbon dioxide, water, and nitrogenous salts, a plant will multiply a billion-fold—"building up the matter of life from the common matter of the universe." *But where do they get their nitrogenous salts?*

Bacteria. Their daily bread is a few simple minerals. Without bacteria, air, land, and ocean to-day would be lifeless. They were the primordial chemists, finding food in a foodless world, drawing their energy and their nutrition direct from lifeless compounds. We shall have a closer look at them later. It is enough now to pay a tribute to them for having helped form the crust of the earth and so prepare the land and sea for the evolution of higher life. Without them, life on earth as we know it is inconceivable, nor would life be possible to-day without them.

In other words, this earth was once lifeless and about as big as Mars, half its present size. To imagine it as it was then, Osborn asks us to subtract all mineral deposits of organic origin, such as organic carbonates, phosphates, and lime; carbonaceous shales and limestones; graphites; silicates derived from diatoms; iron deposits; humus of the soil; soil derived from rocks broken down by bacteria; and ooze of the ocean floor. The shells of microscopically small diatoms alone make up 6 per cent of the bottom of ten million square miles of sea!

These *organic* deposits cover the earth miles deep. They fitted it for higher forms of life. And all due to microorganisms. Geikie thinks it might have required four hundred million years.

7

The earth itself, according to Chamberlin, our foremost geologist, is an offspring of the sun; as are the other seven planets, the twenty-six satellites, and the eight hundred planetoids which make up our planetary system. In giving birth to them, the sun parted with less than an eight-hundredth part of its body, the earth itself representing about three-thousandths of 1 per cent of the sun's substance. In other words, our earthly home is considerably less than the proverbial drop in the bucket of our heavenly parent.

Birth of earth and other planets was due to a passing star. It was bigger and denser than the sun and consequently had a greater pull. It attracted little bits of the sun away. One bit is our earth, held to its course by pull, by gravity. Were the pull of the sun to be altered, the orbit our earth makes about the sun would change.

It happened this way. The sun is so hot that it explodes sun-stuff or gas-bolts. They travel 300 miles a second and may project 300,000 miles beyond the sun's surface before they drop back again.

Along came a huge star, itself a sun, bigger, denser, than our little sun. Its pull was so great that the sun stuff that happened to be erupting was drawn so far out it could not fall back. It was mostly gas, the parts nearest the sun hottest.

It kept on moving, condensing; it came finally to be broken up into bits. Each bit kept on traveling in its own orbit about the sun—held by the sun's pull, but each too distant to be pulled back into the sun.

Chamberlin assumes that several gas-bolts were pulled from the sun. From the first grew Neptune and Uranus; from the second, Saturn and Jupiter. These great planets are still hot and gaseous. On the return journey the passing star loosed another gas-bolt; from it grew the *terrestrial* planets: Earth, Venus, Mars, and Mercury.

The earth to-day is five and one-half times heavier than an equal volume of water. At first it was not so dense, more nebulous, and of varying density. Knots of denser matter condensed into liquid or solid cores. These grew by drawing into themselves smaller knots. This could happen because their orbits kept changing according to their change in density. The largest core kept on picking up bits that came in its path. It kept on growing denser. The earth is still growing.

When only a nebulous knot, the earth was magnetic, and is now. It "selected" the matter that was to form its core: iron, nickel, cobalt. It picked up planetesimal dust, meteorites, etc. It began to draw an atmosphere about it. From the atmosphere fell the rain, the primitive waters in the earth's cavities. Thus there came to be a lithosphere, a hydrosphere, an atmosphere.

Our atmosphere is chiefly nitrogen, oxygen, hydrogen, and water-vapor; all were in the original nebulous knot. Some gases were carried into the inside of the earth, to be let loose again by volcanic action. Some simply gathered more and more closely about the earth; the earth's pull was enough to hold them.

When the young earth had reached 30 per cent of its growth, it could begin to draw to it the water-vapor that had been shot from the sun. Thereafter, the water on the earth and in the atmosphere strove to maintain an equilibrium. But the temperature kept changing and the atmosphere kept circulating. The earth has always had its arid as well as its humid areas; it was never enveloped in a "warm moist atmosphere."

Our earth began, then, with a small lithosphere, a small hydrosphere, a small atmosphere. These reacted on each other, always in co-operation, always in competition and antagonism. Even to-day land, water, and air struggle for the mastery. The story of that struggle is the history of the earth. The oldest rock record known shows that the earth was then about as it is to-day, mostly land areas, wide seas. Water and air struggle to wear the land down, only to have it buckle up again in some new mountain range, the waters to retire to new abysmal depths.

As long as volcanoes last, the earth will not get overheated because of pressure toward the core. Through volcanoes, as through the pores of our skin, the earth rids itself of excess heat and fluids. Thus, the earth is always becoming more solid, more rigid; its lighter and more mobile material is constantly being forced to the surface, again to be buried, reheated, reorganized, and part of it to be belched forth again. Its core now is chiefly metallic, its envelope of a fluid-like nature; the whole, immobile, refractory, crystalline.

The gas-bolt that was pulled by a passing star from its parent sun and grew into earth carried the elements of life. When the earth was fit for life, life came; the *inorganic* elements reorganized into *organic* compounds. That was as radical a move in the earth's evolution as was its break from the sun.

8

With the words we build with our A B C's we name the universe nature builds with her L M N's—as the Romans called them, from the letters on the tablets on which children learned to write. The world of matter is what it is because the elements are what they are and what they become when chemically united. Each element is unique and has unique behavior, but matter assumes an infinite variety of forms because two or more elements can surrender their individuality and become a new substance with unique behavior.

A-r-w is a meaningless mixture of letters; w-a-r is a loaded word and has infinite possibilities. With only two elements, thousands of new substances are possible; with three, the possible combinations are enormously increased. With C, H, O, and N, and a pinch of salts, every living thing is possible. Why? It is their *nature*.

"Nature" can mean anything. For example, sodium is a metal, lighter than water; a drop of it on our tongue or on a sweaty hand catches fire and burns a hole. Chlorine is a gas, heavier than air, so corrosive that a few whiffs are fatal; it was the poison gas in the World War. Of these two elements combined in one, we use about thirty million tons a year. It is found on every table, eaten at every meal. Sodium chloride is common everyday table salt: in large quantities, fatal; in moderate amounts, good for man and beast.

What is the nature of salt? Why do we require a certain amount of salt in our diet? Why will salt preserve meat? Why do sodium and chlorine lose their specific characters when united as salt? Why is sodium electrically positive, chlorine negative? Why is the human body rubbed with wool positively charged; rubbed with silk, negatively charged? What is the nature of electricity?

The nature of things is what we know of things. Of some we have the number, we know their law. For example, with hydrogen, chlorine forms hydrochloric (muriatic) acid, so strongly caustic that it will eat the enamel off a tooth or dissolve a bone. Dogs' stomachs secrete more hydrochloric acid than ours; they digest bones better than we do. Why our stomach secretes hydrochloric acid is one question; how our body separates the chlorine out of salt and the hydrogen from water (both difficult chemical processes) and combines them into a powerful acid that will digest gristle, is another. The first question is on a par with thousands of others as yet beyond the pale of science.

What is the nature of elements? The answer is so astounding that the world has hardly yet recovered its breath, so far-reaching in its implications that science has not yet grasped its full significance.

Science recognizes eighty-two and actually knows seventy-nine stable elements. There are, in addition, ten heavy radioactive elements, which, unlike the stable elements, are transmuting themselves into lighter elements.

The unit or smallest quantity of an element which takes part in a chemical reaction is an *atom* (uncutable). Recently, the atom has been "cut." It consists of unit charges of positive and negative electricity called *electrons*. While electrons are alike in strength of electric charge, negative electrons have a mass or inertia 1/1845th of the lightest known atom, hydrogen. In other words, the weight of the negative as compared with the positive electron is almost negligible.

An atom, then, says Millikan, consists of a heavy core or nucleus of free positive electrons about which are grouped enough negative electrons to render the whole atom stable or neutral. "Hence the number of negative electrons outside the nucleus must be such as to have a total charge equal to the free positive charge of the nucleus; otherwise the atom could not be neutral." As the weight of the atom depends almost entirely upon its nucleus, and as hydrogen is the lightest element, the *atomic weight* of other elements is an expression of their weight compared with that of hydrogen.

The *atomic number* of hydrogen is 1. Its nucleus carries one electron of positive charge; outside that nucleus is one electron of negative charge. The two electrons thus neutralize each other; the result is a system, *an atom of hydrogen.* The heaviest known element is uranium; its atomic weight is 238. Its nucleus, therefore, must contain 238 positive electrons. But as its atomic number is 92, its nucleus must carry, in addition, 146 negative electrons to neutralize the 146 positive electrons over and above the 92 positive electrons free to neutralize the 92 negative electrons outside the nucleus. The result is a system, *an atom of uranium.* Remove one free positive electron from the nucleus of that atom; it is no longer an atom of uranium. Remove 10 free positive electrons; it is an atom of lead. Remove 13; it is an atom of gold. Remove 91; it is an atom of hydrogen gas. The 92 elements are determined, says Millikan, simply by the difference between the number of positives and negatives packed into the nucleus. All elements, ideally at least, are transmutable into one another by a simple change in this difference.

Magnify the nucleus of an atom one billion times; it is still too small to be seen in a microscope. Multiply that nucleus ten billion times: the outer electrons are now three feet from the nucleus, but the nucleus itself is not yet as big as a pin-point. The nucleus, then, is less than 1/10,000 the diameter of the atom—and yet it may contain, as does the uranium atom, 384 electrons. No wonder that Millikan can shoot helium atoms by the billion through a thin glass evacuated tube "without leaving any holes behind." Atoms themselves are mostly "holes," as is most of our solar system. The negative electron compared with the size of the atom itself is no larger than is the earth compared with the radius of its orbit about the sun. And yet atoms themselves are "infinitely small"! Electrons must be infinitely smaller. Or rather, smallest conceivable—for the electron itself is now believed to be the indivisible, ultimate unit of matter.

When *matter* in the form of an electron moves, there is an electric current. Which means, says Millikan, that electricity and matter look like different aspects of one and the same thing. There is proof that electricity is material; there is evidence, but not yet proof, that all matter is electrical.

The electron itself, then, is a speck of electricity; it has definite granular structure; it is the primordial stuff of the universe of matter. When specks of electricity are combined in certain ways and proportions, certain neutral systems result, and we have the *atoms* of the elements of all physical bodies which are described in terms of chemistry and physics—matter and energy.

Science knows nothing of the ultimate origin of matter or of the source of energy; it only accepts both as facts and goes on with its business of trying to find out what matter is and what energy can do. In other words, the problem of the origin of life is locked up in the origin of matter and in the nature of energy. But the line between life and death is not unlike that between organic and inorganic, a vague shadowy line crossed from day to day in the chemical laboratory. Life has been produced in no man-made shop; *protoplasm*, the chemical matter of life, has been. *It does everything but live!* It does not seem fit for life.

9

Life cannot live without food. Food cannot be had in a red-hot sun, in the interior of the earth, or in a nebula of gas.

We hear much of "fitness," but always the fitness of the organism. There is another fitness—that of the earth itself. Before trees, there was no arboreal life; before plants, no animals. Only as the fitness of the environment evolved could life evolve. Environment and life go together. Fitness of environment is as essential to life as it is to a snowflake, a salt crystal, a diamond, or a river; nor are these more thinkable out of their environment than is any living being, or more easily "explained" away. The fitness of the earth's environment for life has been beautifully worked out by Henderson.

The earth keeps its atmosphere because of its size and relation to the sun. This fact and the nature of its atmosphere led to winds and clouds, rain, snow and ice, lakes and rivers, oceans and ocean currents, tides, and magnetic and electric phenomena.

In the earth's atmosphere were carbon, hydrogen, and oxygen. From carbon and oxygen came carbon dioxide; from hydrogen and oxygen, water. With water, carbon dioxide, and carbon compounds, living things became possible. These three. The greatest of these is water.

There is nothing like water. Over seventy per cent of our body weight is water. Much of life lives in water and all of life dries up without water. No water, no life. Life as we know it is inconceivable without water. In fact, Prout, the theologian, thought it the most remarkable instance of "design" in all nature: "Something done expressly, and almost (could we conceive such a thing of the Deity) at second thought, to accomplish a particular object."

Why does the highly inflammable gas hydrogen, united in certain proportions to oxygen, another gas and necessary for combustion, always produce water, which is not only not inflammable, but a hindrance to combustion? The "why" of water is unknown. Much is known of its behavior, in some respects more weird than that of a child. We speak of "solving" problems. Water is the great *solvent*. We may not suffer from water on the brain, but conscious brains are 85 per cent water. Were our brains only 60 per cent water, they would be as dense as tendons; if only 20 per cent, as hard as the skull itself; and if 10 per cent, just fat.

More substances will dissolve in water than in any other liquid. Each year the earth's rivers carry to the sea five billion tons of dissolved minerals and other unnumbered millions of tons of carbon compounds. Water is the great dissolvent of food before it is taken into the cells and as it leaves the body through the sweat glands, kidneys, or lungs. Over 90 per cent of the blood of our transport system is water, holding in solution iodine, bromine, iron, sulphates, urea, ammonia, etc. The water excretion of our body carries off in solution countless organic substances, as well as chlorides, bromides, iodides, phosphates, potassium, sodium, ammonia, magnesium, iron, carbon dioxide, nitrogen, argon, etc.

Chemical reactions take place in water; electrical forces are at work, forces which bind atoms into molecules and cause chemical reactions. Acids and salts are electrolytes: they can carry electric currents, they can be dissolved by electric currents. In dissolution, *ions* (goings) are formed; they carry the current.

Life is dynamic. Every living thing is a dynamo. Its electricity, like that of batteries, comes from the ions of atoms of electric charge set free when molecules of acids, bases, and salts are split up. Ions are back of protoplasm and essential to all life processes. Water is the supreme solvent for ionization.

A heart cut from a living body keeps right on beating provided it is kept in proper solution. What is "proper" for a heart? A change in the hydrogen ion concentration of one ten-billionth part in that solution is improper: the heart stops. The control over such salt solutions is now so perfect that glands can be kept alive while awaiting transplantation into foreign bodies.

Water is chemically and physically *stable;* inert in the atmosphere; almost inactive on the surface and in the soil. It changes few substances, it is not easily changed. It is almost everywhere present in the soil; and in the atmosphere as clouds and vapor. Its *high specific heat* tempers both summer and winter. The tropics is a vast warm reservoir; the poles, cold reservoirs. This makes for circulation of the atmosphere and ocean currents. Water's high specific heat also makes it possible for man to produce 2,400 calories a day, enough to raise his temperature to 150 degrees, and yet keep his body at its normal temperature.

Water can be cooled to the freezing point; it can get no colder than ice. With the thermometer forty degrees below zero, a cake of ice is almost the next best thing to a stove. Lakes and oceans cannot get colder than the freezing point of water. This makes water a powerful regulator of the earth's temperature.

Most substances contract with cold. If water obeyed this law, most of life would go out of business every winter. Water loses *density* on cooling; it rises to the top. Lakes and rivers freeze from the top down, not from the bottom up.

Life is colloidal, like glue, jelly, protoplasm; it has no definite, rigid, predetermined form, as has a crystal. Colloid structures are complex beyond man's present capacity to resolve them when in the form of protoplasm. Protoplasm can live because it can absorb food substances. The force which operates upon colloidal structure is *surface tension* of water. Surface tension is at the root of all food metabolism.

In short, water is a vital part of the evolutionary process which fitted the earth to be the home of the life that culminates in man; fit of its very nature, as Henderson says, "with a fitness no less marvelous and varied than that fitness of the organism which has been won in the course of organic evolution."

Every living thing is but a watery solution; man himself, but a porous sack of water. But water alone could not have led to life without carbon dioxide. Carbon dioxide is even more pervasive than water; it is everywhere.

Carbon dioxide (carbonic acid or carbonic acid gas—one atom of carbon, two of oxygen) is colorless, has an acid taste, a pungent smell. Inhaled by animals, death follows from asphyxiation. Eaten by animals, in the sugars and starches of plants, it "burns"; what is left over is carbon dioxide. Were it not a gas, the task of ridding the body of it would be impossible; were it not a freely soluble gas, that task again would be impossible.

Only carbon dioxide enters water as freely as it escapes

from water. As water is made up of hydrogen and oxygen so firmly wedded that only unusual force tears them apart, so water and carbon dioxide are inseparable companions: in water itself, in fire, in air, in the earth. Only its unique mobility and its wide distribution have made plant life possible.

The lilies of the field toil not; the sun does it for them, using carbon dioxide of the air and of the water. The cattle of the field have to go to the lilies: the lilies will not come to them. Cattle toil with the sun's energy of green grass. We too are children of the sun and toil with its energy stored in food plants. For example, a gram of glucose contains 3.7 heat units of solar energy. When a muscle burns that gram, the 3.7 units are spent: the glucose was a temporary depository of energy. The energy was released by burning, *oxidation*.

Glucose is a carbohydrate—$C_6H_{12}O_6$. Ninety-five per cent of our body can be accounted for by these same symbols— C H O; for water, we need only hydrogen and oxygen; for carbon dioxide, only carbon and oxygen.

When heat and energy were liberated from glucose, the oxygen was torn from the carbon and hydrogen. Oxygen is almost unique in its energy-liberating processes. Compounds of carbon, and especially of hydrogen, yield great heat in oxidation. No source of energy so good as oxygen. No transformers of energy so great as hydrogen and carbon. Together, these three elements have unique "fitness for the organic mechanism. They alone are best fitted to form it and set it in motion; and their stable compounds, water and carbon dioxide, which make up the changeless environment, protect and renew it, forever drawing fresh energy from the sunshine."

Water is not an organism; it is not life; it is *inorganic*. Carbon dioxide is not an organism; it is not life; but it is *organic*. The *carbon* makes the vital difference. Protoplasm is a very wonderful substance. Remove its carbon: it is no longer protoplasm; it is not even an "organic" compound. The chemist does not "wonder" about protoplasm; he finds carbon wonderful enough.

What is carbon? The lead in the pencil with which I write, for one thing. Charcoal is carbon. So is lampblack. Also diamonds. What is an element? A system. Each atom of each element is a system. Carbon must be thought of as having form, shape, size, mass, architecture. Build atoms of carbon one way, and you have a molecule of diamond; another way, and you have a molecule of lampblack. Carbon alone among the elements can form the skeleton of the compounds known to organic chemistry. It is a unique substance; in its way, as unique as life itself. It is unique in its capacity to enter into relationships with other elements. One atom of carbon can unite with from one to four other atoms to form a compound. Carbon atoms can form ring compounds, the rings themselves may unite with carbon chains, and so on in bewildering possibilities. With only fourteen atoms of carbon and thirty of hydrogen, it is possible to form 1,855 distinct and stable compounds. The difference between acetylene and paraffin is in the way their carbon and hydrogen atoms are combined.

Add oxygen to carbon and hydrogen: the number of organic compounds possible is at once multiplied enormously. Alcohol, glycerine, lactic acid, ether, carbolic acid, sugar, cotton, camphor, olive oil, starch, oil of wintergreen, vanilla, and the venom of the cobra. What a mess—solids, liquids, gases! Yet only three elements enter into their make-up: carbon, hydrogen, oxygen. The list only suggests the diversity that follows from a few of the thousands of possible combinations of three seemingly simple chemical elements.

About a half-million organic compounds are already known to chemists. Back of all, carbon. Hydrogen and oxygen, next in importance. These three made life possible: as water, the carrier of life; as carbon dioxide, the substance on which life hangs.

91

From such simple carbon compounds as the baby earth inherited from parent sun, grew the more complex and subtle carbon compounds that to-day peer into microscopes at dividing cells and shake test tubes over gas jets to discover what life is.

The earth's physical conditions were always changing. Matter itself kept changing. Earth, energy, matter, are bound together in one continuous change: the history of that change is the story of evolution. In the process of change life itself was evolved. But only after the environment into which life fits itself had evolved to the point that it was fit for life. Fitness of life and fitness for life are two views of the same tale; and both incidents in the greater story which goes back through the young earth to the old sun, and thence out into the wide universe. Forward, to eternity.

10

Snowflake, salt crystal, diamond, are *described* in terms of matter and energy; *explained* in no terms known to science. Life also is described in terms of matter and energy. The form or substance of life is complex, much more complex than snowflake, salt crystal, or diamond.

This complexity of living beings requires a mechanism organized for durability. The lowest plant is a more complex mechanism than is a raindrop, a snowflake, or a crystal. But, like them, living beings are subject to gravity, and if they break the laws of physics and chemistry they no longer live: what was complex and had a certain behavior is now less complex and has a different behavior.

Living things escape the fate of less complex compounds by holding their fate in their own hands to an extent denied inorganic things. Snowflake and bacterium "die" under a sun's ray; an alga synthesizes protoplasm; a lizard crawls into the shade; a man hoists an umbrella. But one action is no more "explicable" than the other.

The lizard's energy is of a different type from that of the bacterium; it has a wider range, it can better adapt itself to its environment. But otherwise its *vital* processes, though of a higher order, must be of the same kind.

Life, in any and all forms, to go on as life, must exchange matter and energy with its environment; it takes in food, excretes waste.

The smallest known molecule—hydrogen—weighs a three-million-million-million-millionth of a gram. It travels a mile a second. Do chemistry and physics "resolve" it? An electron is smaller and travels faster. Is it less mysterious than a seed of mignonette? Why does a molecule of hydrogen have only one kind of behavior, a molecule of oxygen two kinds, a molecule of carbon four kinds? Heredity? Why does one speck of protoplasm grow into mignonette, another into man? Heredity again. But always: matter, energy. The matter is differently combined, the energy comes from different sources.

Thus, plants obtain such matter as carbon dioxide, water, and mineral salts, from the air and soil. With the aid of energy (sunlight) they transform these into such other matter as sugar and oxygen. The oxygen returns to air and renews it. What becomes of the solar energy? Animals eat the sugar; within their body it is burned, setting free as muscular force and heat the energy the plant got from the sun. What becomes of the by-products? Eliminated by the animal as carbon dioxide and water: food fit for plants. The food goes round and round.

Living matter does not produce something out of nothing, neither the matter of its own body nor the energy expended in building its body or in keeping it alive. Plants conserve energy, animals dissipate it.

Nothing is destroyed, nothing lost. What is here has always been here, or gathered up from the dust of the universe. Energy from the sun changes matter, alters it, evolves it. Matter itself is indestructible; the energy itself

93

is transformed, flows in but one direction. There is enough in the sun to keep earth and life going for untold millions of years.

Untold millions of years ago, the sun's rays were impelling forces as they are to-day. Under their influence, the facile carbon took on new and more complex forms as it built into its structure hydrogen, oxygen, nitrogen, sulphur, phosphorus, chlorine, sodium, potassium, calcium, magnesium, and iron.

This took time. But the times were ripe when water began to collect in pools, and there were shores. Circulation, at any rate, went on then. Evaporation made for clouds: water came from above; capillary attraction brought the waters up from below. Wet and dry seasons alternated. The elements favored concentrations and resolutions. All favorable to colloidal growth, to fluent forms, and to pliancy.

The development of colloids must have been as important in the building of life as were the organic compounds. Even early in the earth's growth the organic compounds must have tended toward colloid rather than crystalline direction. Within limits, the colloid was more stable. Crystalloids were subject to dissolution; in solution, they contribute to the upbuilding of colloid capsules.

Conceive of several units or globules of colloidal protoplasm wrapped up in an envelope, and we have a bacterium. Add more protoplasm, rearrange the internal mechanism, and we have a plant cell. Increase the complexity of the internal mechanism, add more colloid globules, and we have an ameba. Give it a definite outer garment, and we have such cells as we are made of.

A true cell differs from a bacterium in its greater complexity of structure and more stable dynamic process; it lives faster because it is better organized to take in what it needs and get rid of the husks. The animal cell has greater flexibility than the plant cell; it can travel as well as grow. It can live faster, spend more, and sleep less. Both differ from a crystal in having a larger number of substances for chemical activities to organize.

While the shape of living beings and crystals, says Loeb, is primarily determined by the chemical nature of their material, their mechanism of growth is different. Crystals grow, and even restore their old form when mutilated; but only in "supersaturated undercooled solutions of the molecules of which they are composed. Living cells grow in solutions of low concentrations of simpler compounds than those of which their cells are composed." They grow because they synthesize large insoluble molecules from comparatively small soluble molecules. The crystal cannot organize in colloid form; it has no such substratum for dynamic changes.

The nature of the earliest form of life we may never know. Of living organisms, bacteria are presumably the lowest, simplest, and most primitive. Sulphur bacteria obtain their energy by the oxidation of sulphuretted hydrogen to sulphuric acid; with that energy they fix nitrogen of the air and synthesize carbon compounds. We may speak of their energy as a bioelectric current; their growth, as electrosynthesis. They deal direct with inorganic matter. They are a link in organic evolution. Whatever life is, they had it. They made more complex bodies possible: lowest plants.

The microscopic one-celled algæ, through their green chlorophyl, began to *store* energy from sunlight. For this they needed only a cell membrane; inside which they fell "asleep in immobility."

The next step was the lowest animal, an organism so complex that it got its energy from plants. It was a new kind of power plant. But it had to go after the energy it put to work; the plant comes to the animal only as borne by the wind or water.

Animal and plant evolution forked—one went one way, the other another. But animals had to know which way the plants went.

The first lesson animals had to learn was, "Keep moving."

The key to their evolution is their specialized ways to find food and go to it, and to know and to avoid their enemies. Plants, on the other hand, were enjoined to keep their place in the sun. The green leaf is the key to their evolution; their interest in locomotion is chiefly confined to their seeds: these must meet their mates and be carried to suitable soil.

The primitive animal cell had the world before it and could go where it liked, always provided it never ceased to function. It had to keep in touch with a commissary department. Life, as well as armies, travels on its belly.

Some dug in, as the Sporozoa; some went in for speed, as the lively Infusoria; some just dragged around, as the ameba does. And these three types of primitive organisms are represented to-day by the encysted, ciliated, and ameboid cells of our body.

Where the single-cell animals began to combine and pool their interests, the tree of life took on new capacities for growth. The sky was the limit—and the bee beat the lark to it.

Both bee and lark are *animated* and have *vital* energy. And that is all there is to Animism and Vitalism.

An ameba engulfs a diatom and casts out the shell. A drop of chloroform suspended in water engulfs a shellac-coated spicule of glass and casts out the spicule. Known laws of physics and chemistry suffice to describe both actions. But neither action can yet be fully described because not all is known of the energies involved in the two actions. More is known about the mechanism in which energy is manifested in the drop of chloroform than in the blob of protoplasm. It is known that the ameba is activated by forces from without, as is the drop of chloroform; not much is yet known of the mechanism of the ameba by which it makes its response. The energies which move it are vital only because complex mechanisms, such as amebæ and other living protoplasm, possess what is known as vitality, life. The rays which blister paint and my skin, dry up amebæ, and impel green leaves to synthesize carbon compounds, come from the same sun. These rays are forms of energy: they do things. They animate nature. When we stop eating that stored energy, we lose our stored vitality and soon become inanimate.

The chemist can synthesize many organic molecules; he cannot yet synthesize a living protein molecule—he does not know its exact composition and architecture. If he could synthesize a living protein molecule, he could probably synthesize protoplasm and build a living cell. If he could build a living cell, there is no telling what he might not do, for, as Millikan says, when nature's inner workings are once laid bare, man finds a way to put his brains inside the machine and drive it whither he will.

In other words, we shall know how life evolved when we can evolve life. That day will probably come; it is yet a long way off.

Facts of evolution, yes; by the million. Museums, libraries, and laboratories full of facts. But no one law yet propounded begins to fit all the facts. Two hypotheses have become famous and have passed into current literature; they have given rise to world-wide controversy. They did not describe evolution; they did serve mightily to open men's minds to new views of life and wider conceptions of nature. Lamarck and Darwin will remain great names in the history of the science to which they gave their lives, but which was to develop into a real science of life only within the last few decades.

11

A fundamental criterion of life is growth. The outstanding phenomena of life are universality and prodigality. The only line life knows is the food line. Nature seems to abhor a lifeless vacuum. Life abounds in deep seas, in hot springs, in ice-cold caves, on the eternal ice of glaciers. There are fish that climb trees, spiders that live under water.

In a three-by-four-inch garden patch Darwin found twenty kinds of flowering plants. There are seven thousand million diatoms in a square yard of pond water. One Alpine glacier supports fifty million wingless insects of a single species. In one bucket of water there may be five million phosphorescent microorganisms. A ship may plow through countless millions of billions of them for hours. In a pinch of soil there may be twenty billion colloidal food particles supporting a hundred million bacteria, fourteen million fungi and algæ, and five thousand protozoa.

Life is a spendthrift breeder. Elephants are the slowest, yet Darwin calculated that one pair in 750 years would have 19,000,000 descendants. Australia has often told the world what one pair of rabbits can do. Fish are worse. A cod can lay 6,000,000 eggs; a ling, 28,000,000. Even the ling would be crowded out of the sea if just one oyster were let alone by all and sundry until it had great-great-grandchildren. If all survived, Lull says, there would be just 66,000,000,000,000,000,000,000,000,000,000,000,000 oysters. Their shells would make a pile eight times the size of the earth!

Oysters only produce 60,000,000 eggs a year. A starfish produces over 200,000,000. But even a starfish's progeny are but a drop in the bucket compared with the yield of one—not a pair, just one—paramecium. This animal, just visible to the naked eye, has been domesticated in a Yale laboratory by Woodruff. He studied its capacity to occupy the whole known universe: not our puny solar system, the universe. At the end of the 9,000th generation there would not be room for a star or a comet or a nebula in the sky. The universe would be solid paramecium.

But the universe is not solid paramecium, nor have there ever been 19,000,000 elephants at large at any one time, nor can we travel from New York to Southampton on a road-bed of oyster shells. Why not? Because, in short, life is a fight. Which survive?

Here is where Darwin got his key to evolution. Nature herself decides; she selects. *Natural Selection.*

But, does not like beget like? Are we not all created free and equal? Darwin knew better; as does every farmer. Animals breed true; but they vary. Peas in a pod vary. Rabbits of a litter vary. Identical twins vary. Without variation, there could be no evolution. Variation is the law of the universe. Living beings vary, the environment varies. There is overproduction, and a struggle for existence. In that struggle the fittest would survive. Harmful variations would be eliminated, beneficial characters intensified and modified; characters neither hurtful nor beneficial would persist through heredity. Man himself carries around two hundred characters he could dispense with, but which are not so unfit that nature weeds them out.

There followed much talk of "survival" values and of "adaptations." One marsupial "survives" because it is a jumper; another, because it is a sprinter; another, because it is a climber. One snake survives by turning a tooth into a hypodermic syringe, his saliva into venom; another keeps his teeth, but changes his skin to look like that of his poisonous brother; another parts with teeth entirely, and develops a spine in his gullet to break birds' eggs. He is "adapted" for climbing.

Remove the "adaptations" from a whale, there is nothing left. Some whales have big teeth in big jaws and a gullet big enough for a Jonah. Their equally big cousins have no teeth and a gullet so small they must strain their food through a whalebone sieve. They are "right" because the right kind to yield lots of blubber and whalebone.

Milton's whale, that "at his gills draws in, and at his trunk spouts out, a sea," would be an "adaptation"! Especially if its young were born alive and took nourishment from mammary glands, as all whales do. Whales have no "gills," no "trunk." They are perfectly good mammals, as mammal as bat, giraffe, or man. Why did they go back on their country and go in for aquatics? Why are some whales as gentle as turtledoves, others as mean as sharks? Why are there Negritos and Nordics? Natural selection must work overtime to answer these questions.

What kind of variation may we expect to find in a land-lubber that takes to water and adapts one branch of its family to fight sharks and another branch to live on nothing that would not pass through a finger ring? Did you ever try to catch food in your mouth and swallow it, fifty feet under water? Any whale can. The first whale that tried that trick drowned: it transmitted nothing, not even a taste for salt water. Think of the "adaptations" a whale had to part with to become adapted to water.

De Vries, a Dutch botanist, suggested the mutation theory as a way out. Life does not always vary by slight change, but sometimes by jumps. Breeders call them "sports." Perhaps the first tailless ape was a sport. Perhaps man himself is.

But can the "sport" hand on the essence of its change? For example, a human sport with four toes can found no four-toed dynasty unless the four-toedness is a transmissible trait. Again, the trait which characterizes the sport may have no "survival" value; it may even prove a handicap in the struggle for existence. In either case, it will lead to no permanent change. It is difficult to see how the mutation theory can work, apart from natural selection.

Some variations are "predetermined": they are inherent in the developing egg. Or they may be "acquired" after birth, called out by outside influence. They may be "chance" variations, subject to no known law; such are the variations "selected" according to the Darwinian law. Or they may be "orthogenetic," as Osborn calls them: they seem to point in some definite direction. Most variations are "continuous" and of slight quantity: these also enter into the Darwinian calculation. Or they may be "discontinuous": of large quantity, the "mutants" of De Vries. Some books on evolution abound in such jargon. It gets us no nearer to the cause of variation.

After the first shock, people began to like Darwin and his fittest doctrine. "Survival of the Fittest! Aren't we here? We are the fittest! Darwin says so." Many O. K.'d Darwin without knowing that merely to be alive under domestication is no proof of fitness, mental, moral, or physical. When they realized that they could not count on Darwin for a Personal Fitness certificate, they lost interest in evolution and blamed Darwin for having taken them in. And grounded their blame on the monstrous proposition that Darwin sought to drive God from the world!

Darwin himself would have been the last soul in the world to do such a thing. He had no wish to disturb anyone's religious beliefs. On the contrary, knowing that the publication of his findings would challenge the Mosaic cosmogony, he held back for twenty years and did not publish until he was actually anticipated by Wallace. And then he said he felt like a murderer! But no scientist ever less deserved the reproach of the Church. Nor does it become the physicist, L. T. More, even in "trying to vindicate the belief in our spiritual nature," to bear false witness against Darwin, as he does in his *Dogma of Evolution*, just issued by the Princeton University Press. Darwin died as he had lived, a Christian gentleman.

Darwin did not discover evolution, but he so presented the facts of and the case for evolution that the world believed. In the fact that Darwin and Lincoln had a common birthday (February 12, 1809), Lull sees Darwin as an "emancipator of human minds from the shackles of slavery to tradition," as Lincoln was the "emancipator of human bodies from a no more real physical bondage." His nobleness of character and generosity of disposition were not less than Lincoln's.

"All that has been acquired or altered in the organization of individuals during their life is preserved by generation and transmitted to new individuals which proceed from those which have undergone change," said Lamarck, a great French naturalist who died nearly one hundred years ago, blind, in poverty, a social outcast—for telling the truth as he saw it! He coined the word "biology"; it thrives. Biologists have driven a hundred daggers into his theory of evolution through the Inheritance of Acquired Characters; the theory is as alive as ever!

To find out if "acquired characters" could be inherited, thousands of animals were mutilated; Weismann himself cut off mice's tails for twenty-two generations! They gave it up, realizing, as Conklin puts it, that wooden legs are not inherited, but wooden heads may be.

I may "acquire" such development of the muscles of my breast and abdomen that I can dance the "hootchy-kootchy"; that is one thing. To have those muscles cut out is something else, certainly not an "acquired" trait. The marvel is that Weismann's silly experiment ever got into print as experimental "evidence" that there is nothing to Lamarck's theory of evolution.

"Every animal climbs up its own genealogical tree," says Thomson. But that no more disproves Lamarck's theory than Weismann's mice that were born with tails. If an animal never takes the first step, it can never take the second. Nothing added to zero gets nowhere; adding more zeros adds nothing; nor climbs any genealogical tree. Something gets added. Otherwise nature could not have made a man out of a monkey or a mammal out of a reptile.

Novelties do get into life. Spinal column, prehensile tail, blue eyes, were once novelties. There was a time when there was no such thing as spine, tail, or eye, in any living being. To say, as Davenport seems to, that they are not really inherited but persist because parent and offspring are "chips from the same old block," is to make the same "old block" a Pandora's box.

Man's arm, bat's wing, horse's leg, whale's flipper, bird's wing, and turtle's paddle, all evolved from the fin of a fish. These are typical "adaptations"; they are characters which have been acquired; whether "inherited" or not, they are transmitted.

But they cannot be transmitted, said Weismann, because the germ-plasm is sacred, immortal, and *continuous*; nothing can get at it, nothing can touch it. Tennyson's immortal brook had nothing on Weismann's germ-plasm. But that brook does become a river; and somehow, some way, a piece of the original life-germ, or germs, has come to be a human being.

Biologically, immortality is a figure of speech, but based on certain facts, namely: all living things grow, and if they cannot grow young they grow old and die. Whatever "immortality" is, then, it involves the process of either remaining young or of growing young, "rejuvenescence." Later, we shall see how man and higher animals renew their youth.

Weismann's doctrine of the "continuity of the germ-plasm" held sway for three decades, and still furnishes texts for well-meaning enthusiasts who have a case to prove. It is an especially useful ingredient in eugenic and political pies. But as we shall see, there is nothing sacred about the germ-plasm, nor is it alone allowed an immortal heritage. Body cells also are potentially immortal. "Immortality"— for germ-cells, for soma cells, for all living organisms—is contingent upon an inherited mechanism and upon physical and chemical conditions of environment.

The old formulæ do not suffice to explain the facts of evolution. The facts have outgrown the old theories. Evolution is up and down, back and forth; a circulating, pulsating, inextricably woven web.

We see life in fragments. Fragments, individuals, arise by fission or reproduction from pre-existing individuals. Each individual must be "adapted" to get food and oxygen. Each individual strives to occupy the earth—as does oxygen or hydrogen; in this it adapts itself to diverse conditions, or it dies. Evolution proceeded not on one but on several lines. The main lines led to food and oxygen, self-protection, reproduction.

There are two great problems: how have individuals become adapted to the conditions in which we find them? Natural Selection seems to have been the *limiting* factor. How have their organs become adapted to the functions they perform? The Inheritance of Acquired Characters seems to have been the *decisive* factor.

The great problem Darwin tried to solve was the origin of species. There are species. Man is a species. The gorilla is a species. How species arose is, after all, only the problem of inheritance, of heredity, of individual variation, writ large. The more this problem is examined, the less simple it seems. It is far from solved. Segregation is an important factor; inbreeding tends to swamp variation.

Probably no one law can be formulated which will adequately describe the processes of evolution. It is obvious that if an animal is not fit to survive it will perish, and that if there were no variations there would be no evolution. Selection does work on variations—in nature as in Wall Street; but as time goes on we shall probably hear less and less of selection, variation, adaptation, etc., and more and more of the nature of the physico-chemical mechanism which exhibits living behavior under livable conditions. Under such conditions living things do certain things, show a certain capacity for a certain range of behavior. One of the striking features of that range of behavior is the power to grow. In fact, nothing so characterizes livingness as its capacity for reproduction. This is so great in lower animals that they are conceived of as endowed with immortality. With higher animals "immortality" becomes a special affair of the so-called germ-cells.

13

The very lowest organisms have nothing comparable to sex. Woodruff's one-celled paramecium is in its 10,000th generation. If each generation equaled man's, his original paramecium would now be well over a quarter of a million years old. Yet it remains eternally young and shows no loss of virility. As fast as one paramecium tires of existence it renews its youth by becoming two, "which go on playing the fascinating game of living here and now."

Some protozoa show the beginnings of sex. Two individuals unite *(conjugate)* to become one; nuclear material is exchanged and divided: one becomes two again and these two grow and divide. Conjugation is evidently a *rejuvenation* process. Other protozoa only partially unite—and again separate, "rejuvenated." In other species, a small individual bores into and buries its body within that of a normal-sized individual; the latter then divides repeatedly.

Thus far there is no division of labor or true sex forms. When two unite the conjugation is an energy stimulus, as though the spring of life needed rewinding. In higher organisms, this rewinding becomes the prime function of the sperm-cell.

In *volvox,* a high protozoon, thousands of cells held together by protoplasmic threads unite into a colony. When the colony is full-grown, certain cells become engorged with food and are of great size. These big cells now divide into many small cells, break away from the parent colony, and form a little colony of their own, where they grow to full size.

But in some volvox colonies, certain cells may divide and form bundles of cells of rod-like bodies with whip-lash tails. One of these now conjugates with a cell of the other type;

105

this then divides and founds a new colony. The cells of the colony which were not concerned in reproduction live awhile longer, and die.

Natural death had appeared. Also *germ-cells:* egg-cells; sperm-cells. The idea of male and female began with a volvox colony of protozoa.

The egg-cells of the volvox colony were large; the sperm-cells, minute. This disproportion in size holds good for the entire animal kingdom. The mammal spermatozoon may be only 1/100,000th part as large as the barely-visible-to-the-naked-eye ovum.

One volvox colony may produce both ova and sperma, or only ova, or only sperma. The volvox, therefore, is either unisexual or hermaphroditic—it is neither male nor female. As the ova themselves can form complete colonies without the need of fertilization, the volvox is also *parthenogenetic* (virgin-reproduction). In short, volvox, as Geddes says, is an "epitome of the evolution of sex."

Many lower metazoa are so small that only with the microscope can males be distinguished from females. There is no mating, no sex complex. Ova and sperma are turned loose to find each other as best they may; for every ovum there are tens of thousands of sperma.

Higher in the scale, sex distinctions tend to be more pronounced, but the evolution of sex forms does not follow a straight line. Sometimes the sexual differences are unnoticeably slight; sometimes they reach absurd and amazing forms. The difference between certain spider males and females is equivalent to a man of normal size married to an eighty-foot-high woman weighing a hundred tons. The female of one species of worms is a hundred times larger than the male; he lives in her oviduct as a parasite.

Difference between the two sexes is most conspicuous in birds. But in rooks, kingfishers, and some parrots, there are no secondary sex characters. Even many mammals show none or almost none: mice, rabbits, cats. In vertebrates as

106

a whole, conspicuous sexual differences are the exception; in the entire animal kingdom similarity is the rule.

Now from this brief *résumé* of the history of sex let us see what is back of it. Are sex and fertilization primary attributes of life?

After years of study Woodruff concludes that "the protoplasm of a single cell may be self-sufficient to reproduce itself indefinitely, under favorable environmental conditions, without recourse to conjugation." In other words, the union of two cells, or two organisms, is not the essential element of new cells or organisms. Proper environment alone is enough to enable the paramecium to reorganize its nucleus and continue dividing indefinitely.

More suggestive is the behavior of simple planarian flatworms, studied for years by Child with interesting results. Life processes in planaria are naturally highest at the head and diminish toward the tail. Cut one into three pieces: the head part grows a tail, the tail grows a head. Normally, a head will grow at the end of the middle piece which was toward the head, a tail at the other end. But Child can reverse this! He can so alter the life process that a head will grow out from the tail end, a tail from the head end. The net result is the same: from one old worm, three new worms. With no more "conjugation" or "fertilization" than a scalpel.

What happens when the professor is not looking? At the end of the season the old planaria break into bits. In the spring, each bit grows into a new worm.

"Germ-cells" are not unlike these bits of worms; they are not young but old cells. They become young by union. In other words, the whole theory of the need of sexed parents for carrying on the spark of life breaks up with planaria. Even the theory of the need of special germ-cells to carry on, falls flat. Any group of planarian body-cells is the potential bearer of immortality.

107

Loeb "fertilized" a frog's egg with a hatpin. Delage had already found that starfish and other marine metazoa could get along without fathers. Eggs could not only be fertilized with various chemicals, but the developing embryos could be turned this way or that, or checked in growth at different stages, or be made to assume monstrous forms, or become twins. With tannin and ammonia he not only "fertilized" starfish eggs, but grew one with six rays—nature allows them but five.

Among mammals, fertilization of ova from one species by sperms from a closely allied species occurs. The hybrid mule is sterile, but the hybrid offspring of a bull and a buffalo is fertile. In lower vertebrates, and especially among invertebrates, there are innumerable cases, according to Marshall, where the sperms of one species can fertilize the ova of other species.

Riddle's ringdove that laid eleven eggs and then began to behave like a male, and was found, after an autopsy, to have lost her ovaries through tuberculosis and to have developed male sex-glands instead, seems to indicate that neither structure nor behavior has a fixed and uncontrollable basis in heredity. The germ-cell chromosomes, or whatever it is that makes for hereditary characters, can be modified and even reversed.

For example, food may cause great change in structure. Tadpoles fed on thymus gland become big, dark tadpoles— but never develop into frogs; if fed adrenal gland, they become very light in color. Larvæ of bees fed royal jelly become queens; on bee bread, unfertile females or workers. Canaries fed on sweet red pepper become red in color. The germ as the "bearer of heredity" is meaningless or monstrous apart from its usual environment.

The egg is the parent of the chicken, and of more eggs. What these eggs will develop into depends on many hitherto unsuspected factors; as yet almost beyond control because so little known. But among these factors is physical and chemical environment.

A male element, as represented either by one of two similar conjugating cells or by a distinctive sperm which "fertilizes," is not a necessary factor in the reproduction of life. But in truly bisexual animals fertilization is a life-saving act, as Loeb calls it; if the germs are not fertilized, they die. Fertilization also seems to be essential for biparental inheritance.

No father, no inheritance from the father's side. Bisexual reproduction made variation possible. Variation is newness. Newness began with life when life was one-celled. That one cell was both germ and body cell combined. It gradually surrendered its functions to daughter cells. Some developed capacities to high degrees; they are fit only for detailed, specialized work. Some remained close to the primitive original form. Groups of such primitive cells can renew their vigor and begin anew.

But in the complex mechanisms of higher vertebrates, the function of propagation came to be reserved for certain cells. At the same time the struggle for life became keener. The male element was a useful mechanism for novelties: it doubled the chance for variation, it made it possible for the organism to acquire something new. If the something new was harmful, nature "selected" it for death.

The first business of sex, then, was to put new energy into life, to release life, to keep it young and flowing. Sex thus appears as one of the many adaptations whereby living beings could become more highly organized and so carry on on a higher scale. The development of special organs for reproduction is comparable to the development of special organs for digestion, for respiration, etc. It was not until evolution was well advanced that the sperm or male element assumed a share in the burden of heredity. This assumption was a great step in the evolution of higher organisms.

14

A fragment cut from a single-celled animal can move, but cannot grow unless it contains part of the nucleus of the animal. Every living cell (except red blood-cells) of every living body, and every body of one cell, has a dense central part, called a *nucleus*. No one knows just what the nucleus is, but it is the essential part of all cells. A one-thirtieth part of a sea-urchin's egg will live, grow, and develop into a complete sea-urchin, if that thirtieth part contains a portion of the nucleus. That thirtieth part of an egg is germ-plasm. Any protoplasm is germ-plasm if it can grow a new individual.

Ordinarily, cells divide by what is known as *direct* division—a constriction appears at the middle of the cell, increasing until finally the cell separates into two distinct cells. But in fertilized ova, the division is indirect or *mitotic* (thread-like).

As the nucleus seems to be the vital spot of the germ, and as a certain part of it stains beautifully and so looms up under the microscope, it is called *chromatin* (colored stuff). No germ-cell divides until this chromatin performs. At first a mere network, the chromatin becomes a long, continuous, tangled skein. Then it breaks into bits, or units, called *chromosomes* (colored bodies); they are always the same in each species and vary in number from two to several hundreds—six in mosquitoes, sixteen in rats, twenty-four in mice, forty-eight in man, etc. Further, these units assume definite shapes in different species, and are always in pairs.

Just outside the nucleus is a small granule called the *centrosome*. While the chromatin is taking its definite thread shape, the centrosome divides into two, which migrate to opposite sides of the ovum. Meanwhile, the nuclear wall disappears and its fluid mingles freely with the surrounding protoplasm. From each centrosome spindles radiate out toward the center of the cell. At this equator and to the ends of the spindles the chromosomes now arrange themselves; and divide—each chromosome splits lengthwise and becomes two! The two sets of chromosomes now begin to withdraw from each other toward the centrosomes.

Meanwhile, the round ovum begins to lengthen, then begins to constrict at the equator. The chromosomes begin to increase in size until each becomes as big as the parent chromosome. The spindle fibers disappear. A wall begins to form around the chromosomes. The cell's equator has grown smaller; it is an hour-glass form. It breaks in two. The one ovum has become two cells. The chromosomes again become mere chromatin, vaguely seen in the dense mass of the nucleus, for the surrounding wall is now complete.

What was one is now two, each complete: blob of protoplasm, nucleus, everything. The most wonderful thing in the world. It is potentially a full-grown animal, complete unto itself. All it needs is food and safety.

That is the way we grew up: one cell became two, two became four, four . . .

The oocytes from which ova develop, and the spermatogonia which become sperms, are present at the time of birth. Although they are among the last of the cells of the body to mature, they are set aside early in embryonic development. The big difference between sperm and ovum is size and behavior. The ovum has much protoplasm and no means of locomotion. The sperm is all nucleus—except its long tail of cytoplasm, as protoplasm outside the nucleus is called. By this whip-lash tail it travels.

Before the parent sperm and ovum unite, they go through a *maturation* or ripening process whereby the number of chromosomes in each germ-cell is cut in two. The fertilized human ovum thus starts with the original number of chromosomes—forty-eight, half being contributed by each parent germ-cell. The maturation process is in general like that of ordinary division by mitosis. But the chromosomes unite in pairs; thus, one of each paired unit passes to each cell formed by the division.

During fertilization the head and "middle piece" of the sperm enter the ovum, the head being equivalent to the divided nucleus of an ordinary cell in process of mitosis. The middle piece becomes the centrosome—in maturing, the ovum lost its own centrosome. It is this new centrosome that divides as above described, each new body taking position as in ordinary mitosis. The chromatin of the two nuclei now splits into chromosomes, etc. What was a fertilized ovum is two cells. The development of a rat, an elephant, or a human being, has begun.

The fertilized human ovum has forty-eight chromosomes, twenty-four from each parent germ. Here is where heredity is supposed to get in its work, and Mendel's law is supposed to preside over the cutting of the inheritance.

15

We all inherit something, if only crooked legs or a tendency to twins. And we all have ancestors: in fact, a surprising number if they had not intermarried. Reckoning three generations to a century, each of us to-day is entitled to 120,000,000,000,000 lineal ancestors in A. D. 1. They intermarried. At no time has this earth seen 120,000,000,000 people, much less 120,000,000,000,000. Kaiser Wilhelm had 162 ancestors ten generations ago—he was entitled to 512. All Anglo-Saxons are at least thirtieth cousins.

We have ancestors. We inherit features, traits, characters, peculiarities—marks of individuality whereby each of us is not only a separate entity, but different in detail from every other individual on earth.

How do we get these traits? What traits are heritable, what are not? The game of heredity was evolved to answer these questions. The game presupposes a knowledge of germ-cell division, a speaking acquaintance with chromo-

112

somes, the assumption that they are made up of countless distinct and definite chromomeres, and faith in two theories—germ-plasm, eternal and inviolable; chromomeres, the "ultimate" bearers of heredity. Thomson recommends also two ordinary packs of playing cards from which the kings have been removed. Why kings is not explained. Each is now a short deck—forty-eight cards. How many chromosomes in the human body? Forty-eight.

We inherit twenty-four maternal and twenty-four paternal chromosomes: possible permutations, 16,777,216. That is nothing. That only refers to possible permutations for one single specific pair of individual germs. Counting potential germ capacity for the life of one pair of parents gives us the tidy range of total possible different combinations in all the fertilizable ova as 300,000,000,000,000.

Now imagine that we deal not with a mere forty-eight-chromosome permutation system, but with forty-eight chromosomes each consisting of "countless" chromomeres, each a possible bearer of heredity! In that case, as Thomson says, every human germ-cell would be "absolutely unique"—and undoubtedly is.

Some biologists play this game because they feel impelled to have a frame on which they can hang heredity. They are not agreed as to what heredity is. But there are the "colored bodies." They do not know what they are. All right. Hang heredity on them. Solve the mystery by multiplying it by forty-eight unknowns.

What is heredity? Heredity is germ-plasm. How does heredity work? By the beads on the thread of chromatin. Maybe. Maybe heredity counts its beads: one bead for each generation. The question is: does this hypothesis get us farther into life than Darwin's "gemmules" or Weismann's "biophores"? I do not see that it does. It does seem to get us in deeper.

Now for the "traits." Are you a female? It is a "Mendelian" trait. Are you bald-headed? See Mendel. Are

113

your fingers all thumbs? "Mendelian" dominance. Davenport, specialist in heredity, no longer finds anything mysterious in the sudden appearance of *atavistic* characters. We are full of such "grandpa" characters: they are "latent"; they appear according to Mendel's law of heredity. Mendel would be surprised if he could come back!

Gregor Mendel was a monk, lived in a cloister, taught school, and had a hobby—garden peas. He died in 1884 at the age of sixty-two, and was promptly forgotten. What he found out about peas and buried in a little article in 1866 was not discovered until 1900—the world had been too busy with Darwin. What this discovery started is still going. Mendel is less abused to-day than Darwin; some think he made a greater discovery. He certainly is a cult.

Walter thus formulates Mendel's "law": "When parents that are unlike with respect to any character are crossed, the progeny of the first generation will be like the dominant parent with respect to the character in question. When the hybrid offspring of this first generation are crossed with each other, they will produce a mixed progeny: 25 per cent will be like the dominant grandparent; 25 per cent like the other grandparent; 50 per cent like the parents resembling the dominant grandparent."

And plenty of stuffed mice and guinea-pig martyrs-to-science in museum cases prove that Mendel's law works. It stands on three legs:

1. Independent unit characters. While we inherit a general plan of structure, we inherit details, or *traits*, as "independent units."

2. Dominance. Brown eyes marry blue: offspring all brown-eyed. Brown is a positive character, *dominant*; blue is negative, "recessive." By the fact of its dominance, brown appears. The blue may be present in the germ-plasm, but as long as the "determiner" is also present, blue will be unable to show itself. "Unit" characters are inherited through "determiners" in the germ-plasm.

3. Segregation, or purity of the germ-cells. A sperm cell or an ovum can have only one of two "alternating characters." For example, either blue-eyed or brown, but not both. Cross a blue-eyed with a brown-eyed: the fertilized ovum will contain both blue and brown units; the offspring will be brown-eyed; brown is the determiner. But half this offspring's germ-cells will possess the blue-eyed unit; half, the brown-eyed; no one germ-cell will have both. The "alternating" characters will have been *segregated*.

This segregation of alternate characters was Mendel's chief point. The way the chromosomes divide in the maturing germ-cell seemed a good machine to try it on. Investigators began to count chromosomes, and on each hang a "unit" character. As there were more "units" than chromosomes, they postulated chromomeres. As these could not be seen and so checked up, they could postulate as many as they wanted.

But experiments show much conflict, nor are experimenters agreed as to results or general conclusions. They can rarely know, if ever, whether the stock is "pure," a hybrid, or a blend. New "Mendelian" factors have been added: "complementary," "supplementary," "inhibitory," "cumulative," "lethal." "Units" may be "independent" as to quality or as to quantity; or a unit may function by being "absent"! A "dominant" character that performed true to form for three generations practically gave up in the seventh generation; showing a discrepancy between man's and nature's idea of "dominance." There seems often no real stability in the parent type. On cross-mating it breaks down; the component characters recombine into different or new types.

If man bred as fast as mice and guinea-pigs, we should know more about our own Mendelian "units" than we do now. Enough is known, however, to support a Eugenics Society. Its motto is: When in doubt, marry a dissimilar; you may thereby skip a generation with a wooden head.

115

16

Can we control our own evolution? Do we want to? To what end? In which direction? Presumably we could; and this is as far as eugenics has any standing in a court of science. All the rest of eugenics is politics—based on assumptions open to opposite views or on race prejudice pure and simple.

Man could probably breed a race of human beings with the following "traits": bald, fat, long chest, short and crooked legs, left-handed, six-fingered and all fingers thumbs and webbed, near-sighted, deaf and dumb, feeble-minded, curly haired, cataract, albino, long-lived, and prolific, with a tendency to twins; at any rate, these are a few of the many so-called Mendelian traits capable of transmission. There are said to be at least thirty-four different hereditary eye defects alone, eight of which can produce blindness.

With nothing more to work with than normal variation in wild rock pigeons, man has bred over twenty races of pigeons. What could he not do with the human race if . . . ! The "if" introduces politics. And to "breed" a race of humans involves a decision as to what is desirable; a thousand-year-long dynasty of cast-iron despots with such power over subjects as Herod never hoped for or breeder of slaves dared exercise.

What are we to breed at? What is the new race to go in for? Stature, tow hair, blue eyes, eight fingers, toothless, one toe, fecundity, mental precocity? The list of heritable traits is indefinite. "Marry dissimilars" is probably good eugenic advice if we are not bent on handing down our own personal traits—but most people are satisfied with their traits. At any rate, the sex impulse itself generally chooses its mate, and that impulse is not primarily concerned in offspring.

Take stature. If height is the criterion for desirable citizens, early-and-often marriage should be encouraged in Iowa, Kentucky, and Missouri; made late and rare in New York,

Pennsylvania, and Massachusetts; and prohibited in Rhode Island. Meanwhile, close Ellis Island to all but native Patagonians.

What shall we do with the Attic Greeks? Raise their "quota," or exclude them because they do not look like the Harvard graduate who fathers an average of only three-fourths of a son and the Vassar graduate who mothers one-half of a daughter?

If there is anything in the "continuity of the germ-plasm" theory, there should be some good germs left in a country which in 150 years produced such statesmen as Miltiades, Themistocles, Aristides, and Pericles; such poets as Aeschylus, Euripides, and Sophocles; such scientists as Socrates, Plato, and Aristotle; such artists as Phidias and Praxiteles; such historians as Thucydides and Xenophon; such orators as Aeschines, Demosthenes, and Lysias. The whole earth, in no centuries before or since, declared Galton, produced such a galaxy of illustrious men.

Some of that germ-plasm may be blacking boots to-day on a Staten Island ferry or running a short-order restaurant in El Reno. Who knows? One thing is certain: if it is, it is more interested in a short shine or a long order than it is in eugenics.

Could anyone, even Francis Galton himself, from the hill behind Athens in the year 600 B. C., have predicted that within a hundred years the little Rhode-Island-sized state of Attica would begin to bud genius so fast and so big that the world has not stopped wondering about it yet?

Could Galton have predicted Lincoln? Could Ellis Island? Can Ellis Island spot the Jukes from the Altmans, or have the faintest idea when it holds up a Steinmetz—or an Edward Bok?

The Jukes case is notorious—and illuminating, and was thoroughly investigated by Davenport. The case began about 150 years ago with a lazy, mentally defective "Max" who settled not far from New York City. His two sons married

117

into a family of six sisters, all harlots. One of them was known as "Margaret, the mother of criminals."

Of the 2,094 progeny of the Jukes sisters, 1,258 were living in 1915: 65 were "good citizens"; 600 were feeble-minded and epileptic. "Criminal," "harlot," "mentally defective," "drunkard," "pauper," recur in their records again and again; now and then, "murderer." In seventy-five years alone, Max's feeble-minded pauper progeny cost New York State a million and a quarter of dollars.

Looks like a plain case—segregation or a surgeon. And yet a Jukes's descendant may be a governor and several of them may be in Congress. Some say they are. Conceivably, a Jukes might become a second Pasteur—and save more lives than were lost in the World War. This is certain: the state or nation which permits marriage between mental defectives and deaf mutes will have to provide for deaf mutes and feeble-minded. We may improve the breed of figs and eradicate thistles, but never will we gather figs from thistles or good figs from poor fig stock.

What carries eugenics into politics is that the Jukes are neither figs nor thistles, and we do not yet know just how feeble a mind has to be before it has to be locked up to protect those who have minds and refuse to use them.

Many Jukes have too much brain to be segregated, not enough to carry a rifle to the front. Selection. That kind of selection is a modern specialty. The sound-minded able-bodied get shot, the priests and scholars will not marry, and the ambitious women and the selfish men transmit their names but not their germs.

Is civilization now breeding a "pure" Andy Gump type— no teeth, no lower jaw? Cigarettes may save the lower lip, and chewing gum may save enough of the lower jaw to support a chewing gum. But a full and sound set of teeth these days is about as primitive as is a perforated olecranon fossa of the humerus.

Natural selection is always at work. In every million

births, not counting stillborns, there are 2,687 deaths the first year from congenital malformation. A certain other small percentage who can never be happy or useful, are nursed along for a varying number of years. This fraction is undoubtedly larger in civilized than in natural conditions; it is probably increasing. It offers a social and biologic problem. That problem is not likely to be solved in the near future because we have too many abstract formulæ about humanity and too little common sense for solving concrete social problems.

But the "racial purity" and the "racial inferiority" behind such books as McDougall's *Is America Safe for Democracy?* Chamberlain's *Foundations of Nineteenth Century Civilization;* Grant's *The Passing of the Great Race;* Wiggam's *The New Decalogue of Science;* Gould's *America a Family Matter;* and East's *Mankind at the Crossroads,* are bunk pure and simple. If these United States wish to restrict immigration to "Nordics" or to this or that political group, why not say so and be done with it? To bolster up racial prejudice or a Nordic or a Puritan complex by false and misleading inferences drawn from "intelligence tests" or from pseudo-biology and ethnology, is to throw away science and fall back on the mentality of primitive savagery.

Evolution produced a human brain, our only remarkable inheritance. Nothing else counts. Body is simply brain's servant. Treat the body right, of course; no brain can function well without good service. But why worry more about the looks, color, and clothes of the servant than the service it performs?

CHAPTER III

THE PROCESSES OF LIVING AND THE GERMS OF DISEASE

1. Life Is Change and Requires Energy. *2.* The Body Is a Living Machine. *3.* It Requires Calories. *4.* Why We Must Digest Food. *5.* The Digestive System. *6.* Our Daily Bread and Water. *7.* Seeing Food Through the Canal. *8.* How Food is Absorbed. *9.* The Flesh Is in the Blood. *10.* How the "Flesh" Is Transported. *11.* Giving the Blood the Air. *12.* The Great Blood Purifier. *13.* The Red Blood-Cells. *14.* The Body Thermostat. *15.* The Rôle of the Duct Glands. *16.* The "Little Fleas." *17.* The Deadly Germs.

1

ALL change implies resistance overcome, work done, energy. Energy is ability to work. Without energy there is no work done or change in any living being. Change in living beings takes many forms. Growth, maintenance, repair, regulation, secretion, chemical synthesis, muscular activity, contraction and relaxation, heat production—all these are changes, living processes. They require energy.

Energy required for engines is stored in fuel—organic compounds such as coal, wood, oil, etc. Energy used for life processes is also stored in fuel—organic compounds fed into the body as sugars and fats. Most of our food is physiological fuel. This fuel is "burned" in the body, releasing energy. This burning is called *oxidation.* Our vitality can be measured by the rate of oxidation. When oxidation ceases, animation ceases. Even individual cells die when deprived of oxygen. In dividing cells the rate of oxidation is speeded up.

Oxidation is a chemical change and takes place only under certain conditions, temperature, etc. During oxidation heat is released, as it is every time we bat an eye, lift a finger, or think; batting an eye, lifting a finger, and thinking are forms of work, energy-consuming processes.

What is oxidation? It can be seen in a furnace; it has never been seen in a living organism. But during oxidation something becomes something else, presumably by means of an ion or carrier of a charge of electricity; something increases its electrical charge; the electrical charge of something else decreases; oxygen unites with something else, forming an *oxide*. We constantly exhale carbon dioxide—the end-product of the oxidation of carbon. Heat is always liberated during oxidation; our exhaled air is always warm air.

Our viscera consume much energy in capturing oxygen and in converting foods into physiological fuel, especially into a sugar called glucose, or when stored in the liver, muscles, or other tissues, called glycogen. Stimulate the splanchnic nerve with electricity, and the liver will convert glycogen to glucose—by hydrolysis; rearrange the molecules of glucose, it becomes lactic acid, which by dehydrogenation becomes pyruvic acid. This, oxidized, becomes acetaldehyde. This, oxidized, becomes carbon dioxide and water—materials to be eliminated from the body that plants may reincorporate them into sugar-cane or grapes or potatoes.

When man digs up the potato, the "potato" that is in his arm as glycogen is oxidized, but only partially. The fate of the lactic acid that is left over is not quite known, but oxidation processes are known to be involved.

What is oxidation, then? Every process involved in digging up potatoes or in thinking about potatoes. Potatoes themselves are stored energy. Cut one open; it turns black—that also is oxidation.

A helping of mashed potatoes contains enough energy to raise the temperature of about 400 pounds of water about two degrees, or to enable a man to sweat enough to keep his body cool for one hour's work digging potatoes.

The potatoes carried to the cellar will lie dormant, if the cellar is not too warm and damp, until the following spring.

Then, cut into bits and put into warm, moist ground, they will begin to grow. Each "eye" of each potato will grow; it is a "germ." Every living germ, whether plant or animal, contains enough stored energy to enable it to respond to vital situations. In its responses or actions it will capture more energy. The capacity of growing things for work is perhaps the most astounding phenomenon in the universe. Growing trees can split rocks with their roots and lift tons of matter hundreds of feet above the ground. Swelling peas in an iron pot lifted a cover weighted with 160 pounds.

Now here is a curious thing. The potato digger dies when his heart stops beating. He is dead; but millions and millions of cells of his dead body will remain alive for hours—they have not yet exhausted their oxygen and fuel. Aseptically removed from the body and kept moist on ice, some tissue cells will remain alive for ten days. If placed in a certain solution and oxygen, their life can be prolonged indefinitely. Connective tissue cells have been cultivated for years. All they seem to require is proper environment. Their capacity to live and multiply outside man's body has opened new conceptions of life.

Life is a dynamic relationship between structure and environment. We do not live long when the oxygen of our environment is shut off. The faster we live, the more oxygen we require. When our reptilian ancestor improved the mechanism begun by amphibia for capturing oxygen from the air instead of from the water, an enormously important step in life was made. When our mammalian ancestor, by supplying a diaphragm, perfected that mechanism, breathing became a delight and oxygen easy to get. Fast living became possible. But whether we live fast or slow, and whether we work with our hands or with our brains, or do no work at all, our living body must work to keep alive. We must have energy. We cannot get it from an electric current, we cannot get it from mere gravity, we cannot get it from the rays of the sun as plants can, but get it we must or die. As our bodily mechanism and all animal bodies are internal-combustion engines, we get our energy from the oxidation of foodstuffs converted into physiological fuel. The capture and transformation of energy is the most fundamental of all living processes. How food and oxygen are made available for consumption in our growing-going bodily mechanism is a process of fundamental importance.

2

When we finish our day's work, we walk to our car and drive home. (We may have no car: we allow ourselves one for purposes of illustration.)

The motor-mechanism with which we walk to our car weighs about eighty pounds: sixty of muscle, twenty of bones. With every step we take, about 300 muscles are in action. Only as muscles contract and relax can we move. By contracting, muscles shorten—they do not push, they *pull*. The bones support the muscles, the muscles move the bones as levers.

Muscles are in opposing groups. With a certain group we turn our head; mere relaxing of this group will not restore the head to its original position: we must use the other group. To balance our head on our spine, we use 20 muscles; to balance our spine with each step, 144 muscles.

Muscles are engines, each made up of hundreds of thousands of tiny individual muscle-cell engines. With each step, over one hundred million engines are at work.

When muscle responds to stimulus of nerve or electrode of an induction coil, lactic and perhaps some other acid is liberated from some compound in the muscle itself. This reaction changes the hydrogen ion concentration in the muscle cell; it contracts, shortens. Some of the lactic acid is oxidized and heat is formed, the remaining lactic acid is restored to the compound from which it was used. Meanwhile, the glycogen stored in the muscle has been called on to supply

123

the energy of the transaction. With the disappearance of the lactic acid, the muscle returns to its former resting condition; it relaxes. All this takes place in all the half-million or more muscle cells of every single muscle involved.

Microscopically small blood vessels bring oxygen and fuel which is "burned" with the aid of oxygen, without which there is no combustion in muscle or auto engine. Microscopically small veins carry away the products of combustion, the same in muscle as in the auto engine—water and carbon dioxide. In the kidneys the blood is relieved of the water; in the lungs, of the carbon dioxide.

The blood itself is driven about by the heart, an engine of such tiny muscle engines so fused together that they cannot be teased apart with the finest needle. Marvelous it is that the heart knows how fast it must do its work if it is to give adequate service. While quiet at our desk, the heart pours about five pints of blood into our aorta every minute. When we run uphill, the heart will drive blood into the aorta seven times that fast—thirty-five pints a minute! And from the great aorta the blood will be carried to every one of the millions of millions of cells in the body. Wherever the body is scratched, wherever the mosquito dips his bill, there blood is found.

Running uphill requires much energy: much sugar is oxidized, much carbon dioxide is generated. Hence the faster heartbeat, to hurry the blood to get more oxygen and fuel, to get rid of more carbon dioxide. The extra sugar needed is picked up from the sugar-bin in the liver; the oxygen is got from the lungs. While the red blood-cells are reloading oxygen from the six million air-sacs in the lungs, the blood itself is giving up its excess carbon dioxide.

These air-sacs are always ready to do their duty. That is why the bellows moved by twenty-four levers of bone must work faster in uphill work; they must keep the air in the lung air-sacs constant; not have more than 5 per cent of carbon dioxide. But as running uphill burned up seven

124

times as much fuel as sitting at rest, there was seven times as much waste product of combustion to be got rid of. That makes us "pant": our bellows work faster and keep up the pace until the normal proportion of carbon dioxide is restored in the little air-sacs.

We need about thirty ounces of fuel a day to keep our body machine in good trim. The combustion of that fuel makes just the same amount of heat in our body engines as if burned in any other engine. In fact, so much of our fuel goes into heat that if we could not get rid of the surplus generated in running or in any hard work, our blood would jell.

One ameba has been seen to chase another ameba, catch up with it, begin to swallow it, lose it, chase it again, recapture it, lose it, chase it, capture it, and "swallow" it: by flowing around it and thus inclosing it within its own body. By and by the little cannibal opened up its body and moved away from the débris of the dead ameba. A little later it divided and then there were two. (Few of us can do more than that in a day—some do less in a lifetime and leave nothing behind but the débris of their dead protoplasm.) That ameba has no liver, no alimentary canal, heart, lungs, gills, or mouth. Yet in that little body of one cell every essential phenomenon of life takes place. It functions, even as a human being.

The difference between ameba and man is not unlike that between a tiny motor-boat and the biggest ship afloat. Man has more parts, the parts are vastly more intricate. He carries a heavier load, moves faster, goes farther.

All this requires great energy. But we no more make energy than a motor or a dynamo. We must capture it first, then convert it. Every move we make, every word we speak, every thought that passes through our brain, every beat of our heart, every breath we draw awake or asleep, requires energy; and all the while we must run a refrigerating plant or boil over, and a heating plant or freeze to death. Our motor mechanism must be oiled at every point of friction. Our nervous system must be protected, cleaned, and kept in repair. Because we are fearfully and wonderfully made, we must have much energy merely to keep alive.

But as long as we are alive, and whether afoot or on horseback, awake or asleep, we are going machines: the chest rises and falls, the heart beats, the blood circulates, metabolism goes on, life functions; energy is required. But however energetic we may feel, we cannot will our heart to stop beating or commit suicide by holding our breath; we may hold our breath long enough to lose consciousness: our lungs then will resume rising and falling. Back of conscious effort, and so well organized that conscious effort may be dispensed with, is a human body which functions as long as it is fed and can maintain itself in a state of dynamic equilibrium.

Our inheritance seems to have set a limit to the duration of that equilibrium. To discover its nature and how to maintain it is the great problem. Now that we have ceased to be merely objects of religious superstition or of philosophic speculation, we can take our lease on life into a court where it can have a fair trial. That court has already solved great problems formerly held in awe and garbed in mystery. There is no known inherent reason why the problem of dynamic equilibrium in living organisms should not be solved.

The ameba solved it; man solves it for fragments (the germ-cells) of his body. Even tumor cells are potentially immortal. Much, if not all, of the tissue of our body is potentially tumor. If ameba solved it, why not man?

The goal is such knowledge of the living that disease may be prevented and the grave robbed of its victory. We of this generation shall not attain that goal, but it is a goal toward which humanity may turn with much hope and some confidence. Meanwhile, there is the immediate problem of hanging on to such lease of life as has been bequeathed to us. As a nation with unlimited resources and as a race with large brains, we abuse our lease of life, often with fatal results. Many preserve their strength merely to make their lungs breathe and their heart beat. The evolution that ended with reptiles sufficed for such processes; human brains were evolved for higher forms of life.

3

You may be growing: you require food to build up tissue. You may be going: you require energy. Both growing and going are change, *metabolism*. But building is an assimilation process; you construct or repair something: that is constructive metabolism, or *anabolism*. But the exhibition of energy involves dissimilation; by converting complex substances into simple ones you destroy something: that is destructive metabolism, or *katabolism*. In both metabolic processes there is a residue: husks not used in assimilation, others left from the destruction. These are excretions and must be eliminated from the body.

Our energy is derived from fuel in the form of food. Our daily fuel needs vary according to our age, size, sex, and especially the amount of energy we expend. A lumberjack expends more energy than a lounge-lizard.

A pound of sugar burned in our body yields as much heat as a pound of sugar burned in a chemical oven. Heat is a form of energy, and when measured in units required to raise the temperature of one kilogram (about two pints) of water from $0°$ to $1°$ Centigrade (about 2 degrees), is called a *calorie,* or "great calorie."

Sugar burned in our body makes energy available. Of such fuel we normally have in reserve and stored in muscles and the liver about ten ounces, or 1,200 calories. That is potential energy. Suppose we *burn* it, as we do when chopping wood; how much energy would we get? Enough to lift a weight of one hundred tons to a height of three feet. That is our normal potential energy reserve.

To do nothing, just to keep alive, quiet, flat on our back, we require about 1,700 calories a day, enough to lift nearly two hundred tons one foot. That amount of energy goes into heartbeat, breathing, keeping the body at a constant temperature and alive. It is called *basal metabolism.*

The energy consumption, in calories, per kilogram in doubling the birth body weight is: colts, 4,512; lambs, 4,243; kittens, 4,554; babies, 28,864. It is biologically significant that the child of man requires six times more energy to grow a pound than a calf does. And for every calf of stunted growth in the world there are 600 stunted children! Basal metabolism, as we might expect, is highest in childhood. After the fifteenth year it drops sharply to twenty, thereafter it slowly declines throughout life. The growing body stores up energy in the form of new tissue.

We eat a meal; digestion is metabolism also, work. For the work of digesting a meal, 170 calories must be added to the 1,700 needed for basal metabolism. Reading is work: for two hours, add 10 calories more; for a five-mile walk or two hours at golf, 300 calories; for twelve hours swivel-chair work (mostly expended in muscle work in holding the body in the chair), 250 calories. Total, 2,450 calories; or say 2,500 for an average man. In a body completely relaxed but with the brain actively at work, so little extra energy is consumed that the calorimeter cannot find it! The more active the work, the more calories required. A farmer will use up 1,000 more calories a day than a bookkeeper. A lumberman may use up 7,000 in one day; a six-day bicyclist, 10,000.

Food consumed in excess of energy required is stored as fat: under the skin, around the abdomen, between the muscles; but not in the more active tissues—even a "fat-head" has little fat in his brain.

Du Bois points out that when a man has maintained a weight of 165 pounds for twenty years—as many do—it means that of a total consumption of 18,250,000 calories he has not stored or lost more than 9,300, enough calories for two pounds of fat—"an exactness equaled by few mechanical devices and almost no other biologic process." But suppose a man of 165 pounds doubles his weight in twenty years; that means that he has added 22 pounds of fatty tissue and 133 pounds of fat. And one small extra pat of butter a day will do it; there is enough energy in that pat of butter to walk one and one-third miles. As Du Bois says, he ate eleven grams too much butter, or walked one and one-third miles too little.

Sitting up in a chair is work: muscles are contracted, energy is liberated as heat and as work performed. Both can be measured in calories, the work calories in terms of the mechanical equivalent of heat. This has practical value. A machine that develops three heat to one work calorie is 25 per cent efficient. Muscles holding up the body in a chair develop three heat-calories to one of work. Our muscles are about 25 per cent efficient. But a *trained* muscle is 40 per cent efficient. A habitual chair-worker requires less energy to sit still than does one accustomed to being on his feet. Some men find sitting in a chair for any length of time really hard work.

Two men at the same work, blow for blow, stroke for stroke, step for step: one sweats; the other is cool as a cucumber. One was not used to it, was not trained; many of his calories went into heat. The other was trained, it was his steady job; he got more work out of his calories.

To get more work out of our calories is to function better. To function better is to live longer. If we find that the thing we trust to pick the mother of our children is simply a double-barreled pump, knowledge of our heart or the liquid refreshment it pumps to our brain will not grow more nerve cells, but it should make us less nervous and more respectful of the pump and the refreshment it delivers; when it stops, the brain starves to death.

129

4

Water, carbon dioxide, and nitrogen made life possible. Bacteria make plants possible. Plants make animals possible. Did it ever occur to you that, apart from a few but necessary mineral salts, everything we eat is or has been alive? About 50 per cent of our body is carbon. We are oxidizing carbon every moment of our life. We must have carbon. We can *eat* lampblack, charcoal, and diamond dust (all carbon); we cannot *digest* them. Anything we eat and do not digest remains a foreign substance that must be eliminated. There is carbon dioxide in the air we breathe, but we cannot build the carbon of that compound into our body or burn it for its energy with the aid of the oxygen of the water we drink. In short, we are dependent on shoddy, second-hand material. Plants are closer to Nature and not so dependent.

To *photograph* is to light-write; to *photosynthesize* is to light-put-together. With sunlight through a green filter called chlorophyl (green-leaf) plants decompose the carbon dioxide of the air and combine its carbon with the oxygen and hydrogen of water to make carbohydrates (carbon-water), so named because they always contain hydrogen and oxygen in the same proportions as they are found in water—twice as much hydrogen as oxygen.

The simplest carbohydrate is sugar. But sugar is soluble and easily washed away. When plants need to store sugar, they change it to a starch. Starch is a more complex sugar, same kind of atoms but combined into different molecules. By further combinations of the same elements, plants form *fats* or oils. Plants can synthesize sugars and fats because water of soil and carbon dioxide of air are available and because plants can use the sun's energy through their photosynthetic power. If the plant had not thus made carbon fit to eat, this earth would be a No-man's land. Ninety-five per cent of the materials of our body are made available by plants' photosynthetic power.

Another 2 per cent of us is nitrogen—small but important. *There is no flesh and no protoplasm without nitrogen.* The air we breathe contains nitrogen, but we can no more use it than we can the carbon dioxide of air. We get our nitrogen also from plants, or from animals which originally got it from plants. Foods which contain nitrogen are *proteins* (*protos*, first) or nitrogenous foods.

Proteins, while enormously complex, are only compounds of the same three elements found in sugars and fats plus nitrogen and mineral salts. Here is where bacteria come in. Plants can *fix* their own carbon, but they must go to bacteria for their nitrogen. As a dead horse contains more nitrogen than an acre of wheat, his nitrogen must be kept in circulation. Bacteria do the work. They are the "middlemen of the nutritive chain."

In one gram of soil, says Jordan, the following bacteria have been found: peptone-decomposing, 3,750,000; urea-decomposing, 50,000; denitrifying, 50,000; nitrifying, 7,500; nitrogen-fixing, 25. Just how bacteria wreck a dead horse is not known, because so little is known as to the structure of the protein molecule. But "eventually, out of the seething caldron of molecular disintegration, emerge such relatively simple bodies as organic acids and amins, mercaptan, sulphuretted hydrogen, carbon dioxide, and ammonia."

The ammonia may be oxidized to nitrites, and the nitrites oxidized to nitrates. This is *nitrification*, and enormously important for the food supply of the world; otherwise, the ammonia from decaying plant life and from manures would not be available for living plants. Sulphur bacteria change the sulphuretted hydrogen of mineral springs and decaying tissue to sulphur, which oxidizes to sulphuric acid. This, uniting with certain other substances, forms sulphates; in this form plants can build them into tissue. The nitrogen-fixing bacteria get their nitrogen direct from the air mixed in with the soil. They make their home in little nodules of the roots of such plants as clover and beans, and by enriching the soil with nitrogenous compounds make higher plant life possible.

Bacteria are also the great scavengers of the sea, turning loose carbon dioxide, ammonia, and ammoniate materials which algæ build into food compounds which make higher sea life possible.

Thomson relates how boxes of mud and manure were set alongside a fish pond which was about to give out. Bacteria multiplied, making food for tiny protozoa. These overflowed into the pond and were eaten by tiny crustacea and similar small fry. There was now food for fish. They multiplied, and were eaten by man. Fish is said to be food for brains.

It is not. But what looked like mud became part of man. And at last man used his brain, invented a microscope, discovered bacteria, and opened a new account with life.

To return to our mutton. Plants find nitrates in the soil, also sulphates and phosphates. These they combine with the elements they photosynthesize into carbohydrates and fats to make proteins. Any bean can. But before we can build the protein of a bean or a peanut, or of milk or an egg or a chop, into our own protoplasm, we must reduce these complex substances to simpler ones. This building of protein into our body is *synthesis,* but our synthetic power is far below that of plants. We must first wreck a body that was alive to get the material with which to build our own living body.

For example. We eat a mutton chop; we do not build a mutton chop into our body. As mutton, it is of no value to us; we can only use the materials mutton is made of. By the time that chop is carted around by the blood and delivered at cell doorsteps, it is no more mutton than a string-bean is a fish. We make our own flesh out of the same materials fish, beans, and sheep use in making their body. We recombine these materials according to our own formulæ. But we can only recombine them when we have torn them down, reduced them to materials the cells of our body know how to use.

That is why we must digest food, that is what our digestive system is for: to wreck the dead that it may be absorbed into the living. Anything that can be absorbed is food. The wrecking process is digestion, work; energy is consumed. Food is also stored energy. But before that energy is available for us, we must reduce it to physiological fuel in our alimentary canal.

5

A white blood-corpuscle swallows a bacterium whole. It breaks it up into bits: *digestion.* Of these bits it selects such as it requires: *absorption.* It opens its body and moves away from such bits as it does not require: *excretion.* Simple enough. Really, enormously complicated. Perhaps the most complicated process known to man; and no man knows much about it, even in phagocyte or ameba.

Each cell in our body is also a living animal and must have its bits: building materials and energy for building and for regulation. To prepare bits fit for cell requirements is the special job of a special group of cells arranged in special tissues and equipped for this particular purpose: the alimentary canal and accessories, the *digestive* system. Its sole business is to reduce dead matter to such standard sub stances as can be delivered by the blood and can be used by living cells for vital processes. Any matter which can be thus reduced and utilized by living organisms for vital processes is *food.*

The alimentary canal is a single thirty-foot-long tube open at both ends; most of it is coiled up in the abdomen. It is lined with mucous membrane and coated with muscle which contracts and relaxes, forcing food forward. These muscles work ceaselessly under the drive of their own engines, of which there are about 2,000,000 per inch of canal. Valves prevent food moving in the opposite direction. Below the diaphragm the canal's outer muscle coat is *serous*, moistened from the serum of lymph, as is also the mesentery or ruffled peritoneal fold which connects the intestine with the back of the abdominal wall. This makes them smooth and slippery; they keep up their ceaseless movements and are not worn out by friction.

Food is sampled in the mouth. If O.K.'d, it is chewed fine and mixed with saliva, a secretion of the salivary glands. This breaks it up, aerates it, moistens it, and makes it go down easily: first step in reduction. That step signals the stomach, "Get ready, food coming down"; the stomach begins to secrete gastric juice.

From the mouth, food enters the cone-shaped pharynx suspended from the skull—the busiest spot in the body at meal times, especially if there is conversation. Its upper mucous lining contains much lymphoid tissue. In that children develop *adenoids*—best "outgrown" with a knife. Adenoid growths may cause children to become "mouth breathers," thereby opening the mouth to do the nose's work, which is to prepare the air for the lungs.

Put your hand on your Adam's apple and swallow. Easy as pie, but one of the most complicated processes in nature. The esophagus must be opened, and passages to mouth, nose, and windpipe must be closed. If the windpipe-man is asleep, food starts for the lungs instead of the stomach. In the lungs it is still out-of-doors, subject to any vulture that happens along. We cough it up only when the windpipe cilia raise it up within coughing distance. Fortunately, our swallowing apparatus works so well that we do not often have to cough it up. In fact, it is so complicated and does its work so well that a *swallowing center* in the brain is assumed.

Once food reaches the esophagus or gullet, it is gone. The mere act of swallowing suffices to shoot it to the upper or sphincter end of the stomach. Time, one-tenth of a second. If the food is semi-solid, it is forced down by peristaltic waves in the circular muscles of the esophagus. Time, six seconds. Whether food is held up by the sphincter before passing into the stomach proper (and if so, how long) is disputed.

As ours is a mixed diet, we do not require such huge compound stomachs as the hay-feeders have. Ours is a simple stomach with a five-pint or six-hour capacity. That enables us to give much time to other organs. Without a stomach, we should have to nibble all the time.

Although simple, our stomach is not so well understood as it might be. It has three muscle layers, lengthwise, oblique, and circular. They vary in thickness in different regions, and contract and expand according to the work they have to perform. Thus, carbohydrates receive stomach treatment different from that given to proteins and fats. But contractions begin a few minutes after food enters the stomach, thereby further reducing it and mixing it with gastric juice, which consists of mucin and pepsin. Pepsin is a combination of hydrochloric acid and pepsinogen. All three juices are secreted by glands.

As a result of mixture and contractions, the more liquid food, called *chyme*, is forced toward the lower or *pyloric* (gatekeeper) end of the stomach. The pylorus opens—so it is believed—when the chyme pressing against it has reached a certain degree of acidity. It now enters the twenty-foot-long small intestine—the main seat of digestion and absorption, the cleverest analytical chemical laboratory known to science. Into this intestine a few inches from the stomach also come bile from the liver and a fluid from the pancreas, also the *intestinal juice* secreted by millions of tiny glands. Also, now and then, the bacillus of typhoid fever or the ameba of dysentery.

The lining or mucous coat of the small intestine is easily one of the marvels of the world—in structure and accomplishment. It is thrown into innumerable irregular but permanent folds. These increase the surface of the mucous coat and

135

slow up the passage of food. The surface itself is like velvet or a bath-towel, due to four million minute finger-like projections, or *villi*. Each villus is connected with a lymph vessel, an arteriole, and a vein; is inclosed in a layer of epithelium; and contains a muscle. Under a microscope, each villus can be seen to lash about and "pump" up and down.

Beyond is the large intestine (cecum, colon, rectum), from five to six feet in length and from two and one-half to a half-inch in diameter. Digestive and absorption processes are concluded here. The cecum (blind) begins as a pouch, the small intestine opening into it on the side. At the "blind" end is the opening of the vermiform appendix, also *blind*, also a threat, and of no known use to man except as a happy hunting ground for gangrene and other bacteria.

Both small and large intestines have two muscle coats: the outer, longitudinal; the inner, circular. They produce two kinds of movements: *peristaltic*, or waves of constriction which force food onward; *rhythmic*—local constrictions which mass food in spots or areas and then break up the masses. Such segregations, Cannon finds, occur every two seconds. An animate churn, as it were; and "keep moving" is its motto.

The two great *organs* of digestion are pancreas and liver, both marvelous chemists. The pancreas secretes enzymes or ferments; the liver works over materials brought by venous blood from intestines, stomach, spleen, and pancreas. It manufactures bile; turns glucose into glycogen; reconverts glycogen into glucose when ordered; and converts by-products into urea. It is an enormously busy organ; the fires under its retort are always burning; its blood requirements alone account for one-fourth the entire volume of blood in the body, or more than may be found in heart, lungs, and great blood vessels at any given moment.

No heat, no digestion; digestion stops with ice water, resumes when the blood has warmed the water to blood-heat. If the blood gets chilled, it can find a warm spot in the liver.

First on life's bill of fare is water. No water, no life. A man of 150 pounds thoroughly dried out weighs 50 pounds; he has evaporated that much water. Bones are nearly half water; our blood, 90 per cent; the three-months' human fetus, 94 per cent. And half the entire water content of the body is found in muscles. Without water, no living process takes place; nothing can take its place for washing away our body's sins. Except for the early hunger pangs we can starve to death in peace, burning our body for its energy, dehydrating our tissue for its water. But without water and on the desert we perish miserably within a few days, the agony growing with the hours.

Other important *inorganic* foods are mineral salts: calcium, iron, magnesium, chlorine, phosphorus, sulphur, sodium, potassium. They play important rôles in vital processes and are found in all protoplasm. Silicon and fluorine are found in certain tissues and are presumably necessary for our existence.

Iron in the protein of the red blood-cell carries oxygen. Fluorine is a minor tooth-and-bone builder and possibly helps form the cement which holds the cells together. Iodine is found in the thyroid gland. Silicon is found in bones, hair, and the crystalline lens of our eye. Chlorine is necessary for the hydrochloric acid of gastric juice. Calcium and phosphorus are necessary for bone. There is no end to the importance of these inorganic compounds or the uses the body makes of them. Some are especially essential during growth. They are found in the organic compounds of plant or animal bodies which we eat as food; they are set free in digestion and are available for growth and repair.

The three food groups proper are *organic* compounds: carbohydrates, fats, proteins. We eat more carbohydrates than fats or proteins, but they do not remain with us long:

we keep using them up day by day. They are the body's primary sources of fuel.

Carbohydrates consist of sugars and starches and related substances. Their *chemistry* is fairly simple, their *structure* complex. To get an inkling of this structure is to begin to understand several important biologic and physiologic phenomena and will help explain why we cannot, for example, digest sawdust, and why our liver must convert sugar to starch or we die—without insulin.

Note, again, that carbon atoms alone can form such diverse substances as lampblack and diamonds; the real difference is in the way the carbon atoms are combined into molecules. Carbon atoms are constituent elements of all carbohydrates; the hydrogen and oxygen atoms present are always in the proportions found in water. But with these water elements the carbon enters to form structures not only of great complexity, but (and this is the main point) of such structure that the molecules cannot pass through the wall of the intestine into the blood or can pass through the filter membrane of the kidneys. In the one case the molecule never gets into circulation, in the other it passes out of circulation before the body cells can use it.

In other words, *food* is not what we eat, but what can be so altered in the alimentary canal that it can pass through the canal wall into the blood-stream and can be used by the body mechanism for building, fuel, or storage purposes. Most foods are insoluble colloids or colloidal in nature: during digestion they are converted into soluble crystalloids; as such they can pass into the blood-stream; as colloids they cannot. By rough analogy, diamonds are crystalloid, lampblack is colloidal. If our digestive laboratory could wreck the crystalloid structure of a diamond molecule so that the carbon atoms could pass into our blood-stream, we could be said to digest diamonds. It cannot use the carbon atoms in a diamond because it cannot wreck the diamond molecule. The same clay-pit may furnish the mud for a hovel and the brick for a Michigan Avenue French château.

We tap a maple tree and collect the sap; boil it down to sugar, which crystallizes and is soluble. We eat the sugar; reduced further in the alimentary canal, it passes into the blood-stream and is converted in the liver to glycogen (animal starch), colloidal, insoluble; it can now be stored, in muscle, for example. The sap flows up the tree, the tree converts it into cellulose and other complex starches; for the tree, the sugar is immediate or reserve food and cellulose.

There is almost no end to the specific carbohydrates in the plant world. Of these, some twenty important kinds are recognized and are divided into three groups.

The *monosaccharides,* glucoses, or simple sugars, generally contain six atoms of carbon (the hexoses); a few, only five (the pentoses). Glucose, dextrose, or "grape-sugar," is found in all animal tissues and in all fruit juices. Commercial glucose is manufactured from starch. Fructose, or "fruit-sugar," is found in honey and many plant juices. Galactose is found in such combinations as the cerebrosides of the brain and in vegetable gums. Arabinose is found in gum-arabic and cherry-tree gum.

The *disaccharides,* or complex sugars, are formed by the combination of two monosaccharide molecules, with the elimination of a water molecule. The three important complex sugars are: sucrose or cane-sugar, in sweet juices of plants, especially in sugar-cane, sorghum cane, sugar maple, and sugar beet; lactose or milk-sugar, in milk; and maltose or malt-sugar, in malted grains.

The *polysaccharides* are still more complex. They are formed of monosaccharides by combining variable numbers of sugar molecules and eliminating a corresponding number of water molecules. The formula of some polysaccharides is so complex as thus far to baffle analysis. Starch, found in grains, tubers, roots, etc., as stored energy for growth, occurs in two forms, but whether the difference is chemical or merely physical, and whether there are one or many kinds of starch, is not known. But every kind of plant has its own distinctive starch grain—otherwise we should not know whether our "tapioca" is sago or mere potato. The starch grain of a bean is as unlike the starch grain of corn as a grain of corn is unlike a bean. Three-fourths of the potato and more than half of cereals is starch. Sago, tapioca, and arrowroot are almost pure starch.

Other "starches" are glycogen, found in all animal tissues and in yeast; agar-agar, found in seaweeds; lichenin, found in Iceland moss; gum-arabic, found in certain trees; and cellulose.

Cellulose forms the cell-wall of plants, the hard part, the fiber; cotton, linen, straw, wood. Celery, beets, and turnips contain more cellulose than fruits, potatoes, or flour. What bone is to animals, cellulose is to plants. That is why we cannot digest it and why trees are possible. If we could digest it, sugar would be as cheap as sawdust. Herbivorous animals can utilize it because they have a large cecum where cellulose can be retained for a long enough time to be fermented by bacteria. Our cecum is relatively smaller and does not retain food so long; the cellulose we ingest is excreted.

Yet chemically, cellulose is potential sugar. Why, then, the peculiar qualities of *wood*, and why can we not digest sawdust? Because, as Sponsler has recently shown, of its peculiar architecture. We cannot wreck it. The atoms in a cellulose molecule are arranged on an up-and-down plan like beads on a string, and the beads cling together for dear life. In an inch-long piece of match there are many strings of "beads"; each string or column contains about 50,000,000 molecules end to end. They are pulled apart only with great difficulty. Wood is more easily split lengthwise than broken across, more easily crushed lengthwise than pulled asunder, swells sidewise but not lengthwise, and is digested by no animal higher than protozoa. Even termites or "white ants" cannot eat up furniture and houses without the assistance of the microorganisms which infest their alimentary canal; deprived of their parasitic digesters, they starve to death within a month.

The second great group of organic foods is *fats;* "comparatively inert substances with long, complicated formulæ," Du Bois characterizes them. They consist of one molecule of glycerin (an alcohol) and three of a fatty acid: palmitic, stearic, oleic, etc. Oleic acid is found in vegetable oils: olive, peanut, corn, etc. In process of digestion such foods—under the body's own steam, water, enzymes, and mineral acids— are reduced to glycerin and fatty acids. Outside the body, they are reduced to glycerin and soap. The late World War fat shortage was due to the wholesale wreckage of fats to recover the glycerin to make into nitroglycerin.

Lipoids are complex fats, so complex that their chemistry is not well understood. One group contain phosphorus and are thought to occur in every living cell, especially in nerve tissues. Lipoids are found also in the liver, muscles, and yolk of eggs.

Bulk for bulk, no food contains so much potential energy as solid fats and oils. When eaten, fat can be burned or stored. The Eskimo eat it to keep warm. Whales wrap a foot-thick layer around their bodies for the same purpose— fat is a great insulator. Certain Ungulates have special fat reservoirs for lean days: the humps of camels and dromedaries and of the humped or sacred cattle of India, and the tails of fat-tailed sheep.

Proteins are complex beyond end. For example, a molecule of cane-sugar has a molecular weight of 342; of hemoglobin, 16,669. But that gives little suggestion of their dissimilar organization. It is like comparing a grain of sugar with an egg.

Protein, freed of all else, is colorless, tasteless, odorless; and the basis of every cell in life from bacterium and alga to giant redwood and man. Apart from water, protein is the big constituent of eggs, cereals, peas, beans, lentils, peanuts, fish, flesh, and meat. The building-blocks of proteins are *amino acids,* organic compounds in which one hydrogen atom is replaced by a chemical compound closely related to ammonia.

Twenty different amino acids are known. Most of these have been discovered in the protein of milk, wheat, corn, gelatin, chicken, and beef. But foods vary in the number of their amino acids and the relative amounts of each. The possibilities in their combinations are staggering, chemically practically infinite. There is milk and milk, and flesh and flesh, and eggs and eggs: each of its own kind. Just as mutton fat built into the human body becomes quite a different kind of fat, so with protein. From the legumin of beans or the albumen of the white of an egg, or the gluten of wheat, or the gelatin of an ox's tendon, man builds his own protein structure.

But we could not do it without *vitamins.* Until recently no one had ever seen a vitamin, nor had the chemical laboratory isolated one; sixteen years ago no one had ever heard of one. And yet a real science of food is impossible without a knowledge of vitamins. Without vitamins (or something just as good) there is no normal growth, health, reproduction, or living out the span of life.

Scurvy was known to the ancient Greeks, and through the centuries ravaged armies, crews of ships, and explorers cut off from fresh fruit and vegetables; seven years ago no one suspected the existence of the antiscorbutic vitamin. Thousands of children have hobbled out a pitiable existence on a rickety frame; until recently no one suspected it was because of lack of a specific mysterious antirachitic vitamin now known to exist in certain foods. About thirty years ago it was known that chickens fed on polished rice developed beriberi, and that the same chickens fed on whole rice recovered; but no one then suspected the existence of an antineuritic vitamin in the polishings of rice or in milk.

Innumerable experiments have now proved the existence of

142

four, and possibly five, vitamins, and their necessity for human life and the metabolism of all food. Because of their minute amounts, their close association with the complex food substances, their proneness to disappear under manipulation, and because no good controls could be devised in testing, they defied isolation. But, by relying on feeding and by huge industry and patience, definite results have been obtained—and civilization again catches up with desiccated and tin-canned progress. In other words, the human body could find all it needed in the old vegetable garden and shambles; when food began to be refined, the vitamins were thrown out with the screenings.

Fat-soluble A (because soluble in fat), or antirachitic vitamin, is probably first in importance. All animals experimentally treated die if their diet contains no vitamin A. It is presumably necessary for all higher animal life. It is known to be necessary for growth. Rachitic children presumably suffer from lack, among other things, of vitamin A. With vitamin A their bones assume normal growth. Rachitic children were numerous in parts of Europe during the World War; when the milk supply became normal, the rickets disappeared.

Vitamin A abounds in milk, cream, butter, egg yolk, cod-liver oil, and presumably all animal fat except pork. It is less abundant in spinach, tomatoes, cabbage, and lettuce. It is not destroyed by ordinary cooking, but is destroyed by great heat.

According to a recent announcement, a semi-crystalline product containing carbon, hydrogen, and oxygen has lately been isolated by Takahashi and Kawakami from cod-liver oil, butter, and egg yolk. Presumably it is vitamin A in nearly pure form. Mice nearly dead from lack of fat-soluble A have been completely restored to health by small doses of the substance.

Water-soluble B, or antineuritic vitamin, is found in eggs and seeds. It is essential to growth, and lack of it is known to produce beri-beri. Seidell has recently isolated in nearly pure form from brewers' yeast a substance which has antineuritic properties. Presumably it is vitamin B.

Water-soluble C, or antiscorbutic vitamin, has thus far defied isolation in any form. It is easily destroyed by alkalies and by oxidation. It is found especially in lemons, oranges, and tomatoes; also in all fruits, leaves, and root vegetables. Without such foods, scurvy. In the World War Mesopotamian campaign, Indian troops suffered from scurvy, British troops from beri-beri. The Indians were living on dried beans and peas, the British on tinned beef and biscuit. The dried beans and peas had lost their antiscorbutic vitamin, the white flour its antiberi-beri vitamin.

Vitamin D, known to accelerate growth, is probably identical with *bios,* a substance that promotes the growth of the yeast plant. Its molecule consists of five atoms of carbon, eleven of hydrogen, one of nitrogen, and three of oxygen. Enough *bios* to cover a pin-point will restore normal growth in a young animal stunted by a diet which does not have proper vitamins.

Vitamin X is the latest. Evans has been experimenting with rats. If they get no vitamin X, they become sterile. He has also proved that natural foods contain a substance or substances essential for the normal functioning of the mammary gland. But certain substances (for example, vegetable oils) which promote fecundity do not necessarily improve lactation.

In short, there are foods and foods: water, mineral salts, carbohydrates, fats, proteins, vitamins. Is sunlight a "food" also? It depends. Children and hogs that play in the sun need no antirachitic vitamin; they do not develop rickets. Light is a marvelous oxidizing agent. Foods with no known vitamin A can by ultra-violet radiation become possessed of antirachitic property. These same rays get into our skin and "sunburn" us; they will paralyze an ameba in a quarter of a second, or kill and tear its body asunder like a bolt of lightning in three seconds.

How much of this or how much of that is good or necessary or lethal for us is a kind of knowledge that did not seriously trouble our remote ancestors, but which, with our increasing tendency to get away from cows, chickens, and gardens, and from natural conditions in general, becomes of first-rate importance. There was a time when a cook was a cook, good or bad as the case might be; to-day a cook should be a first-class chemist, the kitchen a chemical laboratory.

Meanwhile, before we journey through the canal with food, it will be well to recall a fact of great importance. *We* eat food—and should enjoy it; it is the individual, microscopically small cells of our body that are the ultimate consumers of that food. If these cells cannot use it (oxidize it for its working energy, or build it into themselves in repair and growth), we may have enjoyed our meal, but our body is as unnourished as though we had fasted and is poorer by the amount of energy expended in passing it through the mill. It is one thing for us to eat food and for our digestive system to analyze it; it is quite another matter (possibly the least understood phenomenon of living beings) for the cells of our body to synthesize it. Their astounding capacity to find what they want in astonishingly dilute solutions!

With one part of carbon dioxide in 6,000,000 of water, an alga can grow. An ameba can find enough nitrogen in a solution which contains one part nitrate per million of water. Formaldehyde, if it exceeds one part in a thousand, is poison for an alga, yet when the solution of formaldehyde is less than lethal it will synthesize sugar, if deprived of carbon dioxide, from the vapor of formaldehyde. These figures, from McCollum, help us to realize that our digestive system must not only so reduce complex molecules that they lose their original structure, but that the resultant substances must be furnished to the cells of the body in proper solutions and "at a favorable rate."

145

The *mechanics* of digestion is simple. Food is chewed and swallowed. Esophagus drives it to the stomach. Stomach kneads it. Intestines roll it over and around and about, thoroughly mixing it with the juices of digestion.

The *chemistry* of digestion is the removal of one or more molecules of water (hydrolysis) through the operation of enzymes. Thus, foods are so reduced that the substances of which they are composed can be absorbed by the tissues of the body or used for fuel to make heat or energy.

In these processes, carbohydrates are reduced to "simple sugars"; fats, to glycerin and fatty acids; proteins, to amino acids. These are purely chemical processes. The alimentary canal is the chemical laboratory where these processes take place; especially the small intestine. In chemical laboratories outside the body, such processes take place only with high temperature and *catalyzers* (dissolvers).

Catalysts are curious in this: they hurry the reaction, are themselves unaltered by it, and to that extent do not actually take part in it. Thus, phosphorus will burn in oxygen in the presence of water, the water is unchanged; without the water, the phosphorus will not burn. The water was a catalyzer. Again, cane-sugar (sucrose) hydrolyzed with hydrochloric acid is reduced to glucose and fructose; at the end of the reaction there is as much hydrochloric acid as there was before, unchanged, as good as new, ready to do the same thing again when called upon. But as it passes on into the intestine with food it must be absorbed—presumably as something else—and again put into the stomach through the secretion of glands. Sucrose can also be reduced to glucose and fructose in boiling water, but it is a slow process. The catalyzer (hydrochloric acid) speeded the reaction, as will any acid that has electrically charged hydrogen ions. All carbohydrates, fats, and proteins can be hydrolyzed with great heat, or with catalysts.

146

During *hydrolysis,* whether by boiling or with a catalyst, the compound loses one or more of its molecules of water. The polysaccharides hydrolyze into several and the disaccharides into two monosaccharide molecules.

Our body temperature is so regulated as to remain constant at about 99 degrees. We cannot boil foods in our body laboratory. The body prepares its own catalysts: enzymes, chemical reagents that preside over every chemical reaction in living organisms.

Enzyme means "in-leaven"; because, like yeast, it causes fermentation. But yeasts are unicellular plants and make their own enzyme, zymase; with that as catalyst, they ferment sugar to alcohol, carbon dioxide, etc.

No one has yet seen or isolated an enzyme; perhaps no one ever will. It is said that ultra-violet light rays of suitable length will bring about all the reactions which can be produced by catalyzers; but that gives us no light at all on how enzymes perform in living bodies.

An acid or an alkali reagent splitting a complex molecule has been compared to a hammer which smashes a clock and then picks up the undamaged particles. But enzymes, says Bechold, are more delicate tools: they are like keys which may unlock a thousand locks and fail when worn out.

Armstrong thinks it possible that enzymes do not exist as entities: that they are part of a larger colloid complex; and that enzyme action is an interaction in which water is either distributed upon a single molecule which is thereby resolved into two others, or divided between two molecules, so that one is hydroxylated and the other is hydrogenated. In the strict sense of the term, then, an enzyme is not an entity, although it may have a double function: it attracts the hydrolyte, it determines its hydrolysis—it is both *acceptor* and *agent.* Armstrong suggests that synthesis in living cells is also brought about by enzyme action. Possibly all metabolic activity within or between the cells of the body may be due to enzyme action. In other words, the enzyme can not only

147

smash the clock but can make one, provided it has the materials.

Enzymes are relatively unstable and limited in their action, specifically selective and mainly hydrolytic. They activate water molecules. Hence it is assumed that they are structurally related to the substances *(substrates)* on which they act. It is their selective activity which forms the mechanism of metabolic regulations; otherwise katabolic or destructive changes would be uncontrolled. "Once the enzyme complex is formed, an electrochemical current in which active water molecules take part is completed; the energy being supplied . . . disruptive changes take place, leaving the enzyme free to form a fresh complex."

Reference has been made to the storage of sugars and fats in roots and seeds of plants. Something happens to these stored foods when the roots or seeds begin to sprout or germinate. The change that then takes place is due to enzyme action. A potato, for example, in a dry, cool cellar, breathes —absorbs oxygen, gives off carbon dioxide. Its enzymes are quiet. But suppose that the potato is frozen; its enzymes become active. Its amylase digests its starch to sugar, it becomes sweet; its protease reduces its proteins to aminoacids, it becomes bitter. But freezing has killed its germ: it is a *dead* potato; it can no longer defend itself against bacteria and, as McCollum says, soon rots.

It is presumed that the enzymes in the potato were in an inactive state. Freezing activated them. During freezing, a crystalloid was added to the colloid complex enzyme—it became "activated." Such an activator of an enzyme is a *zymogen*.

Pepsin, for example, is active in the alimentary canal only when activated by hydrochloric acid. The zymogen of pepsin is pepsinogen. Again, oxidases make biologic oxidations possible presumably by forming a system of organic substances which can take up molecular oxygen to form peroxide and part with one or both atoms to another substance, the transfer being hastened by a zymogen, peroxidase.

The enzymes in the potato in the cellar were inactive, *inhibited*. They are destroyed at the temperature of boiling water—the boiled potato is still starch and protein. All enzymes act best at certain temperatures. The enzymes of our body find such optimum temperature because of the capacity of the blood to maintain a temperature at which they work best. Enzymes are also governed by their hydrogen ion concentration. Enzymes that have an optimum reaction in an acid solution will become less active, or active not at all, in an alkaline solution. The mouth juices are alkaline, the gastric juices acid; we shall not expect to find the same enzymes in the mouth that we do in the stomach.

Howell divides enzymes into the following seven groups: proteolytic or protein-splitting; amylolytic or starch-splitting; lipolytic or fat-splitting; sugar-splitting; coagulating (rennin, for example, which coagulates a soluble to an insoluble protein); oxidizing, or oxidases; and deaminizing—whereby amonia, for example, is split from alanin, which is thereby reduced to lactic acid.

The first four groups are the important digestive enzymes. But they are not confined to the alimentary canal. Presumably both fat-and sugar-splitting enzymes are present in the blood and other tissues, especially muscle.

The fact that many enzymes exist in an inactive or zymogen stage both in secreting cells and after secretion and require activating before they function, suggests another interesting and important biologic phenomenon: the capacity of the blood and other tissues to form dissolvers or antibodies to foreign protein substances. We shall have a look at these antibodies presently; we now resume our voyage through the alimentary canal.

During digestion, food is mechanically reduced to particles that can be carried in the watery fluid of the canal. In the canal, it is mauled about and churned up with the agents and

149

reagents of chemical action. It is always meeting new phy. sical and chemical conditions. In the mouth food is mixed with saliva, of which we secrete from one to two quarts a day. It contains two enzymes (*ptyalin* changes starch to dextrin and maltose, *maltase* changes maltose to glucose) and *mucin*, a lubricator.

Saliva is slightly alkaline; the gastric juice of the stomach is strongly acid and contains three enzymes: *pepsin*, splits proteins; *rennin*, coagulates milk and converts casein to paracasein; *lipase*, splits fats in emulsion, such as cream. The stomach, then, is the important digester of proteins, especially meat, flesh, fowl, fish, eggs, and milk. How the stomach can secrete a free *acid* such as hydrochloric from blood which is a *neutral* fluid, is as yet an unsolved mystery. It does. That acid is a fine antiseptic or disinfectant and checks bacterial growth, except that which causes acid fermentation. But too much acid makes for hyperacidity: gastritis, gastric ulcers. The flow of gastric juice is inhibited by emotional stress and pain, by anything which rouses the sympathetic nervous system to activity.

When food reaches the intestine it has lost its looks and much of its nature—digestion *begins* in the mouth. In the intestine it loses everything it was as food for eye or mouth, to become something that a cell can use or spend. It meets with about a pint and a half of pancreatic juice: very alkaline, rather sticky, and charged with three enzymes: *trypsin*, leaves the pancreas as trypsinogen (a zymogen) and becomes trypsin in the small intestine; it is a proteoclast, breaks down proteins into their constituent amino-acids; *amylase*, acts like ptyalin, hydrolyzing starch to maltose; and *lipase* or steapsin, which hydrolyzes or saponifies fats into glycerin and their constituent fatty acids. Lipase is also found in the mammary glands, muscles, liver, blood, etc. It seems that it also acts as enzyme in the synthetic processes involved in reconverting the glycerin and fatty acids of lard, butter, cream, oil, etc., into the kind of fat we store in our adipose tissue.

Food in the small intestine also meets a secretion of the glands of the intestine, the *succus entericus*. That intestinal juice contains six enzymes: *enterokinase,* a zymogen which converts trypsinogen to trypsin; *erepsin,* completes any unfinished business of trypsin and pepsin; *nuclease,* acts on the nucleic acids of the nucleoproteins; *maltase,* converts the maltose and dextrin of starches to dextrose; *invertase,* converts cane-sugar to dextrose and levulose; *lactase,* converts milk-sugar to dextrose and galactose.

Secretin is also an assumed constituent of intestinal juice. Its chemical nature is not known. It is probably not an enzyme. It seems to act as a messenger. Carried to the pancreas, it stimulates that gland to send its juice to the intestine.

Food in the small intestine also meets the bile, a constant secretion of the liver, stored in the gall-bladder, and delivered periodically to the intestine when needed. Bile is a thick, bitter, alkaline liquid. Its color, varying from golden yellow to dark olive green, is due to iron pigments from broken-down red blood-cells. Some of these pigments are returned to the liver *via* the portal vein; some are eliminated by the alimentary canal and color the excreta. Bile pigment which gets into the skin colors it yellow and is called jaundice, but is not infectional jaundice.

Bile also carries two acids or "salts," secretions of the liver cells. Their function is not definitely known. They are partly returned from the intestine to the liver and presumably stimulate the liver to further activity. They probably assist in turning fat into soap in the small intestine and so make its absorption possible. They apparently help dissolve cholesterol.

Cholesterol, a "solid alcohol," is ingested with food, but, as shown by Gall, can be synthesized by the liver. It occurs in every cell of our body, especially in nerve cells; it is found in the secretions of the fat or oil glands of the skin (in sheep's wool also, and, when extracted, called lanolin); it is found in blood, milk, yolk of egg, kidneys, and adrenal glands. It stimulates growth of cancer. When it crystallizes in the human gall-bladder, it is called cholelith (gallstone); when in the sperm whale, ambergris. Why gallstones, and all that cholesterol is or does, are not well known; this is partly due to its stubborn resistance to biological and chemical reactions.

"Synthesized by the liver"—I should have said "liver cell." Of which there are many many millions, for the liver is the largest gland in the body. Each liver cell is an "organ." In each cell (according to Bechold) are 225,000 million water molecules, 2,900 million crystalloid molecules, 166 million fat molecules, and 53 million protein molecules; and each molecule bafflingly complex beyond power of description! That cell is more than a mere cell; it is a busy little world. No wonder that a liver which has to handle copper from worm-stills or copper vessels for twenty years gets discouraged and catches *atrophic cirrhosis*. The human liver is organized to deal with iron, sugar, etc., but not with copper. Presumably this copper hastens the break-up of red-blood cells. Too much pigment in the liver. The cells sicken and die.

All in all, a normal adult pours about five quarts of digestive juices into his intestine each day. About four and one-half quarts of these juices are reabsorbed and presumably worked over again for secretion by the various glands of digestion.

Why does not the intestine digest itself? Or tapeworms—they are in the presence of trypsin, a powerful enzyme? But juice of a dead tapeworm mixed with juice of the pancreas stops trypsin action. It seems as though the tapeworm has a substance which inhibits the action of trypsin; with that it saves itself from being digested. Otherwise it could not stop the action of the enzyme.

The alimentary canal does not digest itself because it is protected by the slimy coat of mucus secreted by its living lining cells. But when there is nothing in the canal for the secretions to work on and the pancreas is artificially stimulated to discharge its secretion into the canal, an irritation is set up as though brought about by digestion.

Food begins to enter the large intestine about two hours after it passes the mouth, but not until about ten hours later has the last of the meal left the small intestine. The secretion of the large intestine is alkaline, contains mucin, but no enzymes. The digestive enzymes from the small intestine continue if there is any unfinished business. The time required for food to make the entire canal journey is from twenty-four to thirty-six hours.

The chief digestive change in the large intestine is probably due to bacteria, the "intestinal flora." These multiply so rapidly that about half the contents of the lower part of the large intestine are bacteria, excreted at the rate of about 130,000,000,000,000 a day. They are of no *known* positive benefit. They *may* act on otherwise indigestible cellulose; they *may* synthesize proteins from ammonium salts in such form that the protein can be absorbed; in which case they should not be outlawed, because bacteria are cheaper than enzymes.

The small intestine also has its bacterial colonies which are responsible for ammonia and at least five kinds of intestinal gases. Their action is chemically not unlike that of enzymes; but whether bacteria are positively harmful in our alimentary canal is as yet a moot and unsettled problem. As the stomach is sterilized by the gastric juice, bacteria do not grow there and it is comparatively free of bacteria. But they may escape the action of hydrochloric acid inside solids or undigested particles, and so pass on into the small intestine, where they can grow. Bacteria are sometimes found in hens' eggs; they got in during the hours the egg was in transit from the ovary and before the shell was formed.

8

Digested food in the alimentary canal is as useful to the body as when in the butcher shop or grocery store. It must pass from the canal into the blood before the body can eat it. This is called absorption.

What is absorbed? What is a "square meal" when digested? Sugars and starches have become "simple" sugars; fats have become glycerin and fatty acids. Huge protein molecules of from 12,000 to 15,000 weight and consisting of a hundred or more amino-acid molecules linked together, have been dehydrolyzed into their eighteen to twenty constituent amino-acids and certain mineral salts. One of these salts may be silicon—invaluable for glass eyes and all glass; absorbed within the blood and carried to the eye, it is built into the crystalline lens. Only the diamond is harder than silicon. We cannot eat silicon; our digester finds it in milk and bamboo shoots.

Alcohol, pepper, mustard, etc., are absorbed in the stomach; especially alcohol, and so readily that little of it reaches the small intestine. Water is not absorbed in the stomach, nor to any great extent in the small intestine; chiefly from the large intestine.

The small intestine, with its sixteen square feet of absorbing surface, is the great absorber, as it is the great digester, of food. During absorption, the sugars and amino-acids pass from intestine to the capillaries in its walls and are then passed into general circulation? Not at all; they are carried by the portal vein to the great pool in the blood stream, the liver. We shall see why presently. During absorption, soaps, fatty acids, and glycerol are resorbed and are carried away as *chyle* to the lacteals of the lymphatic system and so into general circulation *via* the lungs. It is this neutral or "emulsified" fat that gives chyle its milky look, hence the lymphatics of the intestine are called *lacteals*.

But how? The intestine is not a tube of blotting paper or of charcoal; its surface is a solid wall of living cells. How do these lifeless building-blocks get through that wall?

Over a salt solution in a bowl place a layer of pure water. Salt molecules enter the top layer. This is *diffusion*. Water and oil do not mix; such a liquid is indiffusible.

On one side of a membrane in a bowl place a salt solution; on the other side, pure water. Water molecules will enter the salt solution. This is *osmosis:* the less dense solution (water) will pass toward the stronger solution. Osmotic pressure lifts water from the soil to the top of the highest tree.

On one side of the membrane place a solution of white of egg and salt; on the other side, water. Salt will leave the egg and enter the water until the concentration of salt on each side is equal. This is *dialysis*.

These three laws of physics help us to understand what goes on during absorption. But there are difficulties.

Why did the salt only leave the egg, why did not the egg also pass through the membrane? Egg is colloidal. Its molecules are too large to diffuse through membranes. Inorganic salts are diffusible: they are crystalloids; their molecules are relatively small. *Digestion* is largely a process of breaking large molecules into their constituent relatively small molecules.

It is one thing to know that a certain organic compound building-block called an amino-acid is set free in the process of digestion; it is quite another question how this block gets through that wall of live cells. And still another question— and one of life's deep secrets—how this or that cell builds that block into its own structure and at the same time stamps it with its seal of individuality so that it is now unique both for the species and for the kind of tissue it is in. What was

a non-specific simple compound has now been synthesized
by the cell into its own complicated specific self. When
we learn how the cell does that, we may hope to build a
living cell.

Consider that the sugars, amino-acids, and fatty acids have
passed that wall of living cells, what then? Much is known.

The sugar or glucose is stored by the liver as glycogen.
Why stored, why glycogen? Sugar is crystalline, soluble;
if left in the blood, it would be washed out in the urine;
glycogen is colloidal, insoluble. As a result of this storage,
the blood sugar concentration may remain normal at one
part in a thousand. When the body needs fuel, the liver
reconverts glycogen to sugar and sends it out into the blood.
Small amounts of glycogen are also stored in the muscles
and all active tissues. Excess sugars are synthesized into
fat.

The fats are carried about by the blood and taken up by
the tissues that need fuel; oxidized, they supply energy.
When thus burned, the "ashes" are carbon dioxide and water.
All fat not required is stored: *adipose* tissue. Fat. People
get fat because they eat more sugars and fats than they use—
and unless they contemplate fasting or fear starvation, they
carry a senseless and an unnatural burden.

For biologic oxidations, fats are relatively the most important foods. One pound of fat has a fuel value equal to two
and one-quarter pounds of carbohydrates or proteins.

No body is built, or kept alive and warm, without energy.
The body requires enough energy: to keep alive (depending
on age and other factors) and to run the digestive system
(often called "cost of digestion"); to work; to keep in repair.
Say 2,500 calories for a man of 170 pounds. Of these
calories, from 10 to 15 per cent should be in proteins. If
one does manual work, or loves to store fat, the calories may
be increased up to 10,000.

The sugars are carried to the liver first; so are the amino-
acids, the raw material from which the body builds itself,

with which it keeps itself in repair. "Repair" is not to be thought of merely as new tissue to heal a wound or new protoplasm to replace that being constantly shed by nails, hair, and the epidermis of the skin. There must be the raw materials for the building of new blood-cells, for glandular action, for hormones and enzymes, and for the eternal wear and tear of heart, nerve tissues, and all the organs which function ceaselessly until chilled in death. *The blood is their environment.* From the blood they must obtain such amino-acids as they require, when they require, and in proper solution. Too great concentration is fatal to certain tissues, fatal to heartbeat; too great concentration of the end-product of their metabolism, ammonia, is likewise fatal. The kidneys play their part, but they can be damaged by too much of the digested products as well as by too much of the end-products of metabolism. It is because the liver receives the amino-acids direct from the small intestine that they pass into general circulation slowly and in proper concentration. When the liver functions badly from disease, the amino-acids are fed into general circulation faster than the tissues can use them up; they escape in abnormal amounts through the kidneys. While amino-acids have no "threshold value" for the kidney filter, we lose little if they enter the blood-stream slowly.

In the blood-stream, the amino-acids are carried about for the use of such tissues as require them. What is not required is normally broken down in the liver—"deaminized." The non-nitrogenous element is then useful for fuel and may be converted by the liver into glycogen and stored. The nitrogenous element, ammonia, is turned into urea and handed over to the kidneys for elimination.

When the body eliminates as much nitrogen as it receives in the form of protein nitrogen, the body is in "nitrogen equilibrium": it is not burning flesh, but fuel. If the balance is in favor of intake, the body is growing: "taking on" flesh. Flesh is not fat, although it can be burned as fat, as it is during starvation.

Why so much bother? Why not eat glucose, glycerin, soap, and amino-acids, and save wear and tear of teeth, action of thirty feet of canal, and secretions of countless glands? Why not *predigested* food? Sounds reasonable. But try it. Try a meal of amino-acids. Even a rat will starve to death rather than eat a mixture of amino-acids. They are about as unpalatable as anything could be; in milk, ham and eggs, string beans, lamb chops, and the innumerable forms in which we ingest amino-acids, they are palatable.

Even pure sugar as the sole source of carbohydrates would soon sicken us—nor could we taste anything else. Starches—in dozens of forms—are in themselves tasteless, but carry odors and flavors which make them appetizing. And as for a diet of fatty acids and soaps! Good butter is good, but its butyric, caproic, caprylic, and capric acids taste bad and smell worse.

Further, foods in concentrated crystalloidal form would irritate the mucous lining of the canal and cause the blood to give up its salts to the canal. A bacterium cannot digest salt or sugar; salt or sugar can "digest" a bacterium, absorb its juices; but a bacterium can live in a weak solution of sugar or salt.

In short, as McCollum (from whom I have drawn freely) says, it is neither possible nor desirable to nourish the body with predigested foods. But when it becomes necessary to resort to rectal feeding, predigested foods are necessary; otherwise they could not be absorbed, because the large intestine is little concerned in digestive processes.

Life is protoplasm. Protoplasm is a solution—mostly water. Water comes before and after food in life. In all, from eight to ten glasses a day or the equivalent in water-laden food. If alcohol is consumed, less water is required; the end-products of an alcohol "jag" are carbon dioxide and water. This brings us back to the blood again.

There are more things in the blood than were dreamt of in Horatio's philosophy or Moses could have imagined when he said that "the life of the flesh is in the blood." Had blood been better understood in 1799, Washington would not have been bled to death to cure him.

While it is important that we do not lose sight of the individuality of the body or of the organism as a whole, and the fact that parts, organs, even cells, as parts, organs, or cells, are meaningless, it is equally important to remember that the body is made up of *cells*. These cells have surrendered certain functions to groups of cells, tissues, and organs, but they are the ultimate living units of the living body; they must get their face next to food, air, and water, and have their garbage removed. The blood performs this service. The blood is their physical and chemical environment. It is an integrating organ to the extent that it keeps the cells at a proper temperature and furnishes them with the proper hydrogen ion concentration, the right kind of mineral salts, sufficient oxygen and fuel for energy requirements, and the proper amounts of brick and mortar for growth and repair. A single-celled organism has such matters in its own hands, but the cells in our body depend on the blood. The blood is their world; without the blood they are as hopelessly isolated from life-yielding energies as would be a child on a cake of ice in an antarctic sea. The blood itself, without arteries, veins, capillaries, and lymphatics, is as valueless as spilled milk; it can function only in its own transportation system. That functioning depends, as does cell and tissue metabolism, on the fact that the membranes of cells and tissues have different degrees of permeability to different substances.

In one sense blood itself is a *tissue;* it has its own metabolism, it has its millions of living cells. But its main function is transportation; it carries that out through the transportation or circulatory system. That system maintains a day and night service, remarkable as system and in the nature of the material it brings to the door of the myriad cells of our body. It does more than deliver: it collects poisonous wastes and hands them over to the kidneys to get rid of. That system breaks down with fatal results.

A 160-pound man has about eight pounds, or four quarts, of blood. He may lose up to one and one-half quarts at one time and recover. Within a day or two he has as much blood as before; it may be a week before his blood regains its former composition.

Under the microscope, blood is a pale yellowish fluid in which float two kinds of minute cells, the red and white corpuscles. The fluid is the *plasma;* 90 per cent water, 10 per cent reduced groceries and meats, chemicals, drugs. It also contains many substances the physiologist is unable to make or to isolate. Whatever it is that the endocrines secrete, and whatever it is that enzymes are, the blood transports them. It also transports such gases as oxygen, carbon dioxide, and nitrogen; such inorganic salts as chloride, carbonate, sulphate, and phosphate of sodium, calcium, magnesium, potassium, and iron; such nitrogenous extracts as urea, uric acid, creatinin, ammonia salts, amino-acids, and phosphatives; many proteins; sugars, fats, lactates, and cholesterol; five or six antibodies, and special substances supposed to be concerned in the clotting of the blood.

Blood issuing from an open blood vessel (or drawn from the body) clots, *jells;* this closes or seals the wound. This clotting is a unique process, though gums play a similar rôle in the vegetable kingdom. The very act of opening a blood vessel seems to set up a reaction in the blood itself. The blood contains an enzyme called *thrombin* (clot), which, in shed blood, activates a soluble fibrinogen in the blood to become an insoluble fibrin of very fine needle-like crystals.

Fibrin collects at the wound and permits the passage of the watery serum, but holds back the red corpuscles and the platelets. They become enmeshed in the fibers, "clot"; the opened blood vessel is sealed, the flow of blood is stayed. But the white corpuscles squirm through the fibrin, as a snake does through a brush heap.

Clotting may generally be hastened by hot towels or contact with any foreign substance, by rest, and by the poison from certain snakes. But the blood of some individuals clots dangerously slowly; they may even bleed to death from a slight wound. True *hemophilia* (bleeder's disease) is said to be hereditary.

Clotting can be prevented by a secretion called *hirudin* from the mouth glands of the pond leech; it is important to a leech that its victim's blood should not clot! It is important that our blood should clot when a blood vessel is injured. Presumably the adrenal gland is responsible for heightening the capacity of the blood to clot under certain psychological stresses. But a foreign substance, even a bubble of air, in a blood vessel may cause a clot, *thrombosis*. If the blood can absorb the clot, no damage is done; if not, and if the clot is carried to some point where it blocks circulation, it is fatal. A clot on the brain or in the heart is almost always fatal.

The personal service of collection and delivery is made by the *lymph*, the body's middleman, the final link in our transportation system.

We rarely see lymph. Rarely hear of it until it goes wrong, then we know it as *edema*, or dropsy; if it is in the legs, as *elephantiasis*—legs as big as elephants'. Something stops up the lymphatics; lymph collects, the part of the body affected swells up with lymph.

Lymph (water) is blood plasma that filters through the microscopic walls of the capillaries. It bathes the cells and effects exchange of materials, leaving behind what the cells need, carrying off what is not needed. Then it joins the great drainage system whereby blood is returned to the heart.

Lymph has its own system, *lymph vascular system*. This

begins with minute lymph capillaries into which the lymph passes by filtration. These unite in larger vessels, the lymphatics; these empty into ducts which pour their contents into two large veins which unite to form the upper *vena cava*. Thus the blood has made a round trip: it is again in the heart. Before it is put into general circulation again, it must be aired.

Why do we not all have elephantiasis? What keeps the lymph moving? Movement, for one thing. Every body movement alters the shape and size of many muscles. This puts pressure on the lymph vessels, which grow larger toward the main ducts emptying into the veins. The lymph cannot flow backward—or downhill, as it should because of gravity—because the lymphatics are beset with valves, as are the veins, especially in the arms and legs. The valves lie flat against the wall of the vessels as long as the current flows in the right direction. Reversing the current forces the valves out and closes the tube. Lymph can only flow in one direction, toward the heart.

In joining the larger lymphatics, lymph passes through one or more of our 700 *lymph-nodes*. Some are no bigger than pinheads, some as large as olive seeds. They abound in the armpits, groins, thorax, neck, and mesentery. They are not true "glands"; they secrete nothing. But they are our good friends. They police the blood. Outposts held by sentinels that never sleep; always on the lookout for foreign substances, especially bacteria.

In fact, a lymph-node is barbed-wire entanglement for bacteria; they never get beyond a node without a fight. The fight is bloodless, for neither combatant has any blood, but it is always a fight to the death. Then it is that we discover our lymph-nodes: the fight inside causes the node to swell with inflammation. We met such inflamed nodes in childhood and called them "waxing-kernels."

The fight is between white corpuscles and bacteria. If the cells win, we hear no more about it. If bacteria win, they tell us. There is nothing so immodest or shameless as an average bacterium, or can do so much good and so much damage in proportion to its size. It can move mountains and destroy cities.

If lymph is blood filtered through tissue, how do white corpuscles get into lymph? The same way: they lengthen and filter through. We hear much of these white corpuscles or *leukocytes* (white cells). They are not well understood, nor is it known how many kinds there are, where they originate, how long they live, why they multiply—now rapidly, now slowly—and what finally becomes of them. Some are believed to originate in bone marrow, others in lymph-nodes. They lead a fairly independent existence.

Presumably they break down dead tissue cells, carry fat from the intestines into the lymph and so to the blood, help stabilize the protein content of the blood, and possibly liberate a substance which assists in blood clotting. They may destroy the worn-out red cells in the spleen and liver. Some eat bacteria.

Evidently bacteria *au naturel* are not palatable and somewhat indigestible. One kind of leukocyte is supposed to remedy that. The blood plasma itself is credited with a substance which makes *phagocytes,* as the "eater-cells" are called, greedy for bacteria. This substance is called *opsonin,* Greek for "preparing a banquet." With no opsonin in the blood, a phagocyte eats only one bacterium at a time; with opsonin, he takes them on in bunches, possibly because it causes bacteria to herd. The result is the same: the phagocytes engulf them faster.

Injury to or inflammation in any part of the body sets up irritation. Blood hustles phagocytes up to the injured part; it gets red from the red corpuscles of the blood. If bacteria are present, a fight is on. If phagocytes win, they crawl back into the blood again. If they lose, the bacteria kill them and also tissue cells. Pus forms. Pus is dead tissue and white corpuscles, plasma from injured blood vessels, and dead and living bacteria. A scar on the neck may mark the spot where tubercular bacilli were held up by a lymph gland and lost a fight with phagocytes.

Our "resisting power" is good when we have enough leukocytes. We generally have enough when our transportation system is all in order.

10

The business of the transportation system is to deliver fresh blood—"pasteurized," aërated, and heated to the proper temperature—to several billion cells twice a minute, every minute of life. That is big business and of vital importance; and no man-made transportation system comes within miles of it for honesty, accuracy, or efficiency. Nor has man yet made as fine a tube as an artery or as good a pump as the heart.

Cut a thin section across a small artery and put it under a microscope. It has three coats of muscle. The fibers of the outer coat run lengthwise and are dense; they strengthen the artery, enable it to resist undue expansion, make it hard to cut or tear. The inner or lining coat is extraordinarily smooth; the blood hustles on with next to no friction. The middle coat is in two layers of fine muscle fibers circularly interlaced; one layer is elastic, the other contractile. The thickness of this coat varies according to the traffic it bears; the larger the artery, the thicker its walls.

With every heartbeat, every inch of artery in the body expands and contracts. In fifty years they have expanded and contracted about three billion times. When this middle coat clogs up with lime salts they harden, lose their elasticity. *Arteriosclerosis* probably increases the rate of flow in the arteries—but does not make for "high blood pressure." Fat does.

Arteries carry blood from the heart. The great artery, or *aorta*, leading direct from the heart, is about an inch in diameter. It soon branches; the branches branch; on and on; they become smaller, smaller, and finally discharge their tiny rivulets into capillaries so minute that it would take thousands of them to hold as much blood as the aorta. Even the corpuscles in the blood must travel through them Indian file, and at that it is often a tight squeeze.

The heart is simply the central power house; the arteries, simply the tubes. But with the capillaries the transport system becomes a special service; without them, the blood could not do its big work. They form a vast network throughout the entire body except in hair, nails, cuticle, cornea of the eye, and cartilage; that is why cartilage is so white.

The blood returns through veins, also tubes and very tiny at first where they begin to gather up the minute trickles after the blood has done its work in the capillaries. The tubes grow larger and larger as vein after vein keeps discharging its contents, and become at last the two great *venæ cavæ* which deliver the blood to the heart.

The heart is easily understood if one does not look at it; then it seems hopelessly complicated. Think of it as two pairs of cubes, one pair on top of the other. The two top cubes are shaped like ears, hence their name, *auricles*. They *receive* blood: the left auricle, from the lungs by means of the two pulmonary veins; the right auricle, from the upper and lower part of the body by the two *venæ cavæ*.

The two bottom cubes are round like little bellies, hence their name, *ventricles*. They *expel* blood: the left ventricle, to the body *via* the aorta; the right ventricle, to the lungs *via* the pulmonary artery.

Why does the heart beat 75 times every minute? How does the blood know where to go? The second question is easy, the first is now being solved. But beat it does, from four months before birth until life snuffs out with its last beat. Forty million times a year. The work it does is literally staggering. More amazing is the fact that it will go right on beating after it has been removed from the body;

kept moist in a neutral salt solution (sodium, calcium, and potassium salts) and fed a little sugar, it will beat for days. Muscle tissue cut from the body will also grow and beat rhythmically under stimulus, but there is an automatic action to the heartbeat which as yet has not been solved.

The heart is striated and "involuntary" muscle—not under control of the will. Only the heart has this combination. The result is a specific dynamic system which functions in connection with certain nutrients and ions. Seventy-five beats per minute is a normal average; but among the soldiers of a single company, all presumably normal and all under similar conditions, it was found to vary from 42 to 108.

The heart beats according to its past as well as to its present experiences; emotions, diseases, narcotics, drugs, muscular activity, rate of metabolism, etc., all enter into the count. The bigger the body, the slower the beat: 25 per minute for an elephant; 50 for a donkey; 70 for men; 80 for women; 90 for youth; 140 for a newborn; 150 for a rabbit; 175 for a mouse. The more active the body, the faster the heartbeat. I can save my heart 20,000 beats a day by remaining quietly in bed. It has been experimentally determined that when the pulse is forced up to 135 per minute, the subject becomes uncomfortable; above 160 it is very distressing and fairly unbearable, although one was recorded of 184 per minute.

The blood-stream is kept to its course by valves. For example, blood returned from the body by the two *venæ cavæ* fills the right auricle and the right ventricle: the two at the time are one chamber. The auricle contracts, forcing more blood into the ventricle below. As the contraction slows up, a valve between auricle and ventricle is forced shut by the pressure of blood in the ventricle. This ventricle now contracts, forcing the blood through the now open valves into the pulmonary artery and so on into the lungs. It is returned by the pulmonary veins, and enters the left auricle and ventricle. Left auricle contracts, distending the left

166

ventricle; then the valve between them closes. Then the left ventricle contracts, forcing the blood into the aorta. After it has traversed the body it is returned by the *venæ cavæ* to the right auricle.

Around it goes. It cannot go astray, for it circulates in a closed system; valves in the heart and in the veins prevent it from going in the wrong direction. The heartbeat forces it to keep moving. The vasomotor apparatus, through nerve connections with the muscle walls of the arterial system, controls the amounts of blood flow to the various tissues and organs of the body.

This transportation system must supply its own needs also. Arteries and veins are tubes of living tissue; they must have their blood. They receive it from their own system of arteries, capillaries, and veins: the *vasa vasorum*, blood vessels which supply nourishment to the coats of other blood vessels.

11

The left half of the heart contains arterial blood; the right, venous. The walls of the two auricles are relatively thin; of the ventricles, thick—that of the left three times that of the right; it has three times as big a job. The left ventricle drives blood into the aorta with a velocity of about thirty feet a second. But before that blood returns to the left ventricle, it must make two long journeys. First it visits every nook and cranny in the body, and is returned by the *venæ cavæ to the right auricle*. That completes the *systemic* or general circulation and requires twenty-three seconds.

From the right auricle the blood passes down into the right ventricle, and by it is driven through the pulmonary arteries to the lungs. There it takes the air. It then returns by the two pulmonary veins to the left auricle, and thence into the left ventricle. That completes the *pulmonary* circulation and requires about fifteen seconds. The blood is now ready to be expelled by the left ventricle into the aorta, to be put again into general circulation.

"Taking the air" is a vital process—in fact, no process is more vital; but before looking at it, let us see how the newborn prepares for that momentous first step, one of the most interesting adaptations in life.

The four-months-old fetus is attached by its umbilical cord to the now fully formed placenta, consisting largely of connective tissue and blood vessels which interlace with blood vessels in the uterus. But there is no direct exchange of fetal blood with that of the host; only by diffusion through permeable membranes can the fetus derive nourishment and oxygen from its host's blood vessels. This it does through the umbilical vein. Through the two umbilical arteries it delivers to the placenta the end-products of fetal metabolism—chiefly carbon dioxide, which diffuses from placental blood vessels into the blood vessels of the host and is by her eliminated in her lungs.

After birth, the umbilical cord is tied and cut. This cuts off the newborn's oxygen intake and carbon dioxide outlet; it must make vital rearrangements. Quick.

A blood clot forms between the navel and the liver in what was the umbilical vein; that stops circulation in that direction and prevents the infant from bleeding to death. As a result of that clot, two blood vessels cease to function and pass off the stage forever. Another clot forms in the vessel which connected the aorta with the pulmonary artery; and it goes out of circulation. Two other clots form; and two other vessels begin to obliterate themselves.

One other change is necessary before the infant is a full-fledged air-breather. Up to the time of birth there is an opening between the right and left auricles, the *foramen ovale*. But with the closing of the vessel from the pulmonary artery to the aorta the blood is forced into the lungs, thence into the pulmonary veins, thence into the left auricle. Pressure in the left auricle closes the foramen ovale between the two auricles. It stays closed; thereafter there is no opening between left and right auricles. Sometimes it does not close tight; venous blood mixes with arterial. The result of this mixture is impure blood; *cyanosis*—"blue babies," even blue adults. If the opening is too great, the mixture is fatal; not enough blood gets the air.

This separation of the heart into right and left halves, thereby keeping venous from arterial blood, made constantly *warm* blood possible, and is found only in birds and mammals. Lower vertebrates have impure blood, and change their temperature with the thermometer. Failure of the newborn's foramen ovale to close is a memento of reptilian days; death follows because our metabolic processes are set for pure warm blood.

The clots and the closure of certain blood vessels and foramen ovale completely alter the newborn's circulation; it must now get its oxygen by its own efforts. It draws its first breath.

This is a big job for a small child. Lungs at birth are solid; they must be shaken out, filled up, as one would a balloon. The balloon the infant has to fill is several times larger than its body. Lungs are like enormously complex sponges—minute pockets or air cells, all opening into funnels, these into tubes or bronchioles, these into right and left bronchi, these finally into the trachea or windpipe.

Trachea and bronchi are lined with the microscopic chimney-sweep cilia. They move foreign particles up within reach of the coughing mechanism. When the cilia are damaged by bad-cold germs, we cough up floods of mucus, dead cilia cells.

If the infant takes its first breath through its nose, it sets a good example for itself; that is what the nose is for. Internal-combustion engines work best if given warm air. The infant is such an engine. Its nose is like a scroll radiator, thereby exposing a large area of membrane to contact with its first and every breath. That breath drawn through the nose filters, warms, and moistens the air, important qualities for every breath. The nose prepares the air for the lungs as the mouth prepares food for the stomach. It "samples" air by the sense of smell, as the mouth samples food by the sense of taste. If the air is no good, we hold our nose; if the air is cold, the vasomotor system sends more blood to the nasal membrane.

The infant is in contact with the air through the skin of its body. When its lungs are expanded, another surface is in contact with the air; this lung surface is from ninety to one hundred times greater than body surface. An average man has about one square yard of skin surface, about ninety square yards of lung surface.

12

After our first breath, our lungs are never again free from air. They must have thin walls, to let oxygen into the blood and carbon dioxide out; without air they would collapse. The passages leading to the air-sacs do not collapse, because they are held open by stout rings of cartilage. Even if removed from the body and punctured, the collapse of the small tubes entraps air into the air-sacs. Lungs that will float *cannot* have belonged to a stillborn; butchers call them "lights"—they are lighter than water.

There are always about two pints of *residual* air that we cannot budge. But with great effort we can expel the *supplemental* air—about three pints. With no effort at all we inhale and exhale *tidal* air—about one pint. With another effort we can inhale about three pints more—*complemental* air. The maximum amount of air that can be forcibly expelled after a deep inspiration is about one gallon. This is *vital capacity*; it differs with individuals, and diminishes if we give our lungs no hard work to do.

We breathe faster when a certain nerve center in the brain tells the inspiration muscles to speed up. The nerve gets its cue from carbon dioxide. There is always carbon dioxide in the blood, but it plays second fiddle to oxygen. When there is too little oxygen or too much carbon dioxide, we breathe faster. The air we inhale has 21 per cent of oxygen, .04 per cent carbon dioxide. The air we exhale has 16 per cent oxygen, 4 per cent carbon dioxide, which means that in the lungs the air lost 5 per cent of its oxygen and gained 4 per cent carbon dioxide. No matter how cold and dry the inhaled air, the expired air is blood hot and saturated with moisture.

A thin, moist membrane of the lungs separates air from blood. On the air side is a high percentage of oxygen. On the blood side, a high percentage of carbon dioxide. An exchange of gases takes place through the membrane. As a result, the blood brought to the lungs by the pulmonary arteries loses about 10 per cent of carbon dioxide; the blood carried back to the heart by the pulmonary veins gains about 10 per cent of oxygen.

It requires less than two seconds for the blood to take the air and exchange its crimson for a scarlet hue. Arterial blood is scarlet. If "blue" blood is a caste sign, certain shell-fish are the Brahmins of creation; their blood oxygen-carrier is not the iron of hemoglobin, but the copper of hemocyanin. This copper is blue in the crab and tastes like copper in the European oyster.

Aërated blood begins its long round through the body as soon as it is shot into the aorta by the left ventricle. The blood delivers its oxygen as the iceman leaves ice—according to the needs of families on its route, making the round trip every half minute. An organ, gland, muscle at rest does not need much, but activity anywhere—in organ, gland, muscle, what not—means an extra supply. The heart itself will use twice the oxygen at one time it does at another. At meal times the intestines require extra large supplies. Even mild thinking causes the brain to double its usual demand. "Fast thinking" may even require fast breathing. Whatever consciousness is, it goes out like a candle when the oxygen is cut off.

Oxygen. Oxygen. Everywhere we go, every time we turn around, always, as long as we live, the tissues of our body are crying for oxygen and freedom from carbon dioxide, else they choke to death. And our bellows keep working away: 60 breaths a minute for the newborn, 40 for the child, 20 for the adolescent, 16 to 18 for the adult. About one breath for every four heartbeats is a normal average.

The air we breathe is about 80 per cent nitrogen; as it is an inert gas, we absorb none of it. But under high atmospheric pressure, as in a diving bell or caisson, nitrogen is dissolved in the blood and in the tissues. If the pressure is suddenly released, the gas cannot remain in solution but forms bubbles, and the blood effervesces like a bottle of pop. (A nitrogen bubble lodged in a vital spot is as fatal as a blood clot.) This makes for stiff muscle joints—"bends," the workmen call them. If the pressure is slowly relaxed, bubbles do not form, and the gas in the tissues is carried by the blood to the lungs and nitrogen equilibrium with the gases of the atmosphere is again restored.

Equilibrium. The body is wonderfully balanced. Vital processes other than growth are equilibrizing processes. When the equilibrium is upset, the body begins to readjust. It works like a defensive army, massing its forces against the greatest dangers. The blood is the marvelous distributor, regulator, restorer, provider, of forces. When one thinks of the billions of individual cells the blood serves, it is truly the Little Friend of All the World.

It is significant that too much carbon dioxide rather than too little oxygen sets the bellows working faster. If we are only short of oxygen we can fall asleep, even in death; the lungs rise and fall until the last. We can burn ourselves up slowly; but from the smoke of the fires of action we must be promptly delivered.

Not, Give the lungs air; but, Give the air carbon dioxide.

172

That purifies the blood. And if respiration cannot be resumed otherwise in an asphyxiated person, give his respiratory center carbon dioxide—then it will order the lungs to action. But if the respiratory center is dead, it is too late.

13

Abel withdrew from one dog in one day twice the volume of its blood. The dog should have died twice, but inasmuch as the professor collected and returned all its red blood corpuscles, it lived. When he withdrew only 60 per cent of the dog's blood and did not promptly restore the red corpuscles to its blood, it died.

Our lungs are valuable, but we really breathe through the hemoglobin, or *respiratory pigment* of the red corpuscles. Blood plasma is complex; the red corpuscles, or *erythrocytes* (red-cells), are inconceivably complex. They are born in the red marrow of bones and have nuclei as have other cells. On entering the blood stream they lose their nuclei and assume their characteristic disk or muffin shape; they can no longer grow, and, after ten or fifteen days' work, die and are broken up in the liver or spleen. In fishes, amphibia, and camels, the nuclei are not lost in the blood.

Each red corpuscle is about 1/3200 of an inch in diameter, 1/12400 of an inch thick. Yet they make up about 35 per cent of the volume of the blood—or enough to fill a pint cup. In a spoonful of blood there are about 30,000,000,000, or in an adult male about 25,000,000,000,000; a few billions less in an adult female. Her blood and her lips are no less red, nor has she less capacity to blush or acquire a red nose, nor has she less iron in her constitution; simply less body, and consequently need for less blood. Anemic persons have either fewer red cells or less iron in the cells they have. The proportionate number present at any one time varies according to many factors—constitution, nutrition, and especially with age, being most numerous in fetal life. In women, they increase in number during menstruation, diminish during pregnancy.

Red blood-cells carry oxygen. That makes them red and they make the blood red. They are soft, flexible, elastic. Had a camel these qualities equally highly developed, he could easily pass the needle's eye. Carried by the blood to the lungs, they squeeze through spaces as small as the universe is big, resuming their disk-like shape. With nothing between them and the air but a thin membrane, they detach oxygen and squeeze through into the blood again. They are small, but their combined surface area is nearly 4,000 square yards, with nearly 90 square yards of lungs for them to operate on. Of course, only a small portion of them are present in the lungs at any one instant. The blood lugs them about from cell to cell. Any cell needing fresh air then and there gets it; and gets rid of carbon dioxide, which the blood carries to the lungs. If it carries much we take a long breath, or several.

While it has long been known that the hemoglobin carries oxygen, it has only recently been established that it also carries most of the carbon dioxide. According to Du Bois, sufferers from faulty circulation show lack of oxygen and excess of carbon dioxide; their blood does not move fast enough through the lungs for the red-cells to get rid of their carbon dioxide. When the saturation of oxygen in venous blood falls below 20 per cent, cyanosis results.

Ordinarily, it is not lack of oxygen or excess of carbon dioxide in crowded rooms that makes for distress; it is the heat, humidity, and odors of unwashed bodies. Gases diffuse through insignificant cracks in walls, around windows, under doors. It was the heat and humidity that were so frightfully fatal to the crowd in Calcutta's Black Hole, not lack of oxygen or excess of carbon dioxide.

While the air we breathe ordinarily contains about .04 per cent of carbon dioxide, a submarine crew will work for days in air containing 2.5 per cent and suffer no ill effect. With

5 per cent carbon dioxide in the air, we double our rate of breathing; when it rises above 8 per cent, we are in real distress. Further increase begins to slow up the rate of breathing, with death when it reaches 40 per cent.

Too much oxygen is equally fatal. Ordinarily, air contains about 21 per cent of oxygen—more than we need or can use. Nor does breathing pure oxygen increase the oxygen-content of the hemoglobin (oxyhemoglobin). But pure oxygen at a pressure of three atmospheres (one for every thirty-three feet) leads to convulsions and death. Workers in caissons, diving bells, and submarines may die from oxygen poisoning in ordinary air at five atmospheric pressure; fifteen atmospheres is always fatal.

At about 26,000 feet above sea-level, the oxygen concentration falls to 7 per cent—a test for an aviator's fitness. Even at 15,000 feet many suffer severe "mountain sickness" (anoxemia), and lose consciousness above 20,000 feet. But by compensatory action in heart and blood vessels, most people can soon become "acclimated" to mountain heights.

Just how the respiratory pigment jettisons carbon dioxide and takes on a cargo of oxygen while in the lungs is no more known than just how an ameba or a cold potato breathes, or how the cells of the tissues of our body exchange carbon dioxide for oxygen. But they do, and we breathe easier.

In one red blood-cell are unnumbered millions of millions of molecules of hemoglobin. Each molecule is of huge size and of such complexity as to baffle the imagination. Here is its supposed molecular formula: $C_{758}H_{1203}N_{195}S_3FeO_{218}$; molecular weight, 16,669. Only three atoms of sulphur, one of iron. But iron is iron and a little of it goes a long way in the affairs of life—and leads to some amazing performances.

Most of hemoglobin is globin, a protein, as might be inferred from the nitrogen and sulphur in the molecule. The remaining 5 per cent is iron salts or hematin with a comparatively simple molecular formula of $C_{34}H_{34}N_4FeO_5$. That

175

hematin will crystallize we have seen; the crystals themselves are as specific for species as are starch grains. A horse's hemoglobin crystal no more looks like that of a human being than a man looks like a horse; but a mule's crystal is half-way between that of a donkey and a horse. Why not? There are such relationships as blood.

Blood is blood and that of all mammals has the same constituents in about the same proportions. Yet blood is specific for different species, and the amount of difference suffices to prove that man is closer blood kin to Old than to New World monkeys. By means of a blood test it was proved that the malaria-carrying mosquito feeds on pigs and cattle as well as on man; by that test horse-meat has been distinguished from beef; blood on a cleaver proved to be deer's blood, and not wild duck's, as the man accused of poaching swore it was; and a stain was proved to be human blood after a lapse of sixty-six years.

All of which opens up a large vein in life—ranging from murder trials to immunity from bacteria.

Any foreign protein element in a blood-stream is a foreign body, an *antigen*. An antigen will provoke an *antibody*. A foreign red blood-cell is an antigen; the antibody it provokes is a *hemolytic*, a dissolver of foreign red blood-cells. Bacteria in a blood-stream are antigens; the blood's reply is four kinds of antibodies: *opsonin*, makes them tasty to the phagocytes; *agglutinin*, causes them to herd together and consequently likely to be engulfed in lots; *precipitin*, causes them to settle down or precipitate when held in solution; and *lysin*, which dissolves bacteria. Lysins, opsonins, agglutinins, precipitins, etc., are specific antibodies, chemical systems which induce specific reactions. When bacteria are agglutinated, thinks Jordan, their negative charge of electricity is reduced; they are thereby more subject to the precipitating action of salts. The net result of the action of the antibodies is to destroy the antigens or so alter their

176

nature that they are more easily handled by the phagocytes, or police of the blood.

Bacteria, red blood-cells, spermatozoa, even pepsin, injected into the blood-stream, evoke specific antibodies; one kills the bacteria, one dissolves red blood-cells, one disintegrates spermatozoa, one neutralizes the enzyme pepsin. On this capacity of the blood (and of other tissues) to react to antigens is based the whole practice of *acquiring* immunity in bacterial diseases by the use of cell-dissolving sera.

Is it *human* blood? If there is enough of it the question is easily answered; injected into the body of a rabbit, the rabbit dies. But suppose there is only a drop of it, or the decomposed remains of one blood clot? The test is simple. Into a rabbit or similar laboratory convenience inject a nonlethal dose of human blood (or ape's—they are so closely related they are almost twins). The rabbit's blood develops a specific antigen for human red blood-cells—it is *immune* against human blood. To some of this rabbit's immune serum add the "suspect," and incubate; if there is a flocculent precipitate, the suspect blood is human (or ape) blood.

Is it *blood?* There may be only a stain on the floor, a shred of stained cloth, or perhaps only one drop of water left in the bottom of the tub in which the suspected murderer bathed. Such tests for blood can be made. They depend on the ability of an inconceivably small amount of hemin to make itself known by showing its specific color when submitted to delicate chemical tests.

14

Breathing is action in a mechanism and implies work; and that suggests heat. Only at *absolute zero* do molecules cease to vibrate. They *cannot* vibrate; they have no heat. Heat, in other words, is a form of energy. And a thermometer is a device for measuring its energy.

For example, the heat under my tongue at this moment

suffices to expand mercury (raise its temperature) until it registers 98.36 degrees. The heat of the skin of my hand is not so great; it would be even less if I were making snowballs. But the temperature at this moment of my body in general is not far from 100 degrees; call it 100 for short.

Heat, as we saw, can also be measured in terms of calories—one calorie being the amount involved in raising the temperature of about two pounds of water about two degrees. If my temperature is 100 degrees, my body contains a certain number of calories—heat or energy units. Suppose I drop dead; my body begins to cool. If it is in a warm room it will lose 550 calories within twenty-four hours; if in a cold room, 1,000 calories. Where has the heat gone? Where does the heat of a red-hot poker go? Same place. It has flowed out, radiated, been conducted. My dead body in a room with a temperature of 100 degrees would lose no calories—there could be no *flow* of heat, because heat flows only from a region of high to a region of low temperature. But suppose I am not dead yet, but have only lost a leg; my temperature remains about the same, but I have diminished the calories in my body—I have less body. Heat would still be conducted from my body; there would not be so much heat to conduct.

Heat, being a form of energy, does things, causes change—a rise in temperature, a change in state, a chemical change, etc. If I apply enough heat to it a piece of coal, its carbon finally combines with the oxygen of the air: it burns; I need apply no more heat—the heat developed by the oxidation of the carbon will suffice to continue the reaction until the carbon is all oxidized.

Our daily intake of fuel-food is, let us say, 2,500 calories. Assuming that we are not taking on fat, but just holding our own, what becomes of these 2,500 calories? If at the end of the twenty-four hours we have neither gained nor lost weight, and have added 2,500 heat units to a body already at a temperature of 100 degrees and it is still at that same temperature, these ingested calories must be somewhere—and they *cannot* be inside us. We lose them in two ways: radiation and conduction from the skin, about 73 per cent, or 1,795 calories; through loss of materials from our body, about 27 per cent, or 705 calories. Whatever leaves our body carries with it body-temperature heat. Thus through saliva, excreta, etc., we lose about 50 calories; through expired air, about 265 calories; and by sweat, about 365 calories. These are all heat losses, means of ridding the body of the heat liberated in the 2,500 calories of ingested food.

All this is simple enough. It is equally obvious that engines work best under certain temperature conditions. Motor engines must be protected from too great heat by cooling devices, airplane engines from too great cold by heating devices. A big tree will sweat a half-ton of water on a hot day to keep its temperature down. Our body engine will not work at all if our temperature varies a few degrees from normal. We freeze to death when we cannot make enough heat, and die of fever or sunstroke when we cannot get rid of enough heat. At 105 degrees enzyme action ceases through autodestruction, the brain engine cannot work; above 105 degrees, the brain begins to be destroyed.

Which means that our body functions best at a certain average temperature. When our temperature varies more than 2.5 degrees from that normal average, our oxygen metabolism is upset and our body is abnormal. We birds and mammals are not so much *warm*-blooded animals as we are *constant*-temperature animals.

How does our body so regulate its heat production and its heat loss that its vital parts are kept at a practically constant temperature? It is easy enough to see how ingesting more calories, taking more exercise and consequent burning of stored calories, and clothing keep up warm enough though we are breathing the frosty air of 40 below zero; but how do we keep cool when the thermometer stands at 120—as they do in Death Valley?

Simply by getting rid of more heat.

Heat loss through expired air is fairly constant and little subject to change in outside temperature. Expired air is always warmer than inspired air; it is almost saturated with vapor. We expire about a pint of water a day; each gram of water vaporized required one-half of a calorie, 180 in all. To warm the inspired air consumed 85 calories.

The blood is the go-between for all parts of the body. Heat generated in any part of the body will heat the blood that passes by. The water in the blood is the transporter and distributor of heat. But the blood also reaches about sixteen square feet of skin and about ninety square yards of lung lining. In both skin and lungs it comes close to outdoor temperature. Through the vasomotor nerves the supply of blood to the skin is under automatic reflex control. The vasomotor system, then, is the principal regulating mechanism. In air close to body temperature there can be but little loss of heat from skin by radiation and conduction; in cold atmosphere the loss will be excessive. The vasomotor system must arrange for compensation. The details are not yet known, but the results can be seen.

Sweat, for example. We have about 2,000,000 tiny pores, or sweat-glands, in our skin, about 500 to the square inch, about 2,000 per square inch in the palms of our hands and the soles of our feet. Sweat is 99 per cent water, 1 per cent salt, a small portion being urea. An average man on a mild summer day will sweat about two pints. He can sweat as much as ten pints; in that case 10 per cent of his urea excretion would pass out through the sweat-glands.

Cats and dogs do most of their sweating through pads on their feet. A dog also opens his mouth wide and sweat—in the form of saliva—drips from his outstretched tongue. Both dog and man also pant, thereby increasing lung ventilation. If the outside humidity is not great, panting increases

180

the amount of evaporation of water from the blood in the lungs.

In the dry air of Death Valley deserts, with the temperature at 120, we do not "sweat a drop." We do; the sweat evaporates as fast as it is secreted. On hot, moist days it evaporates slowly because air can only take up so much moisture. Moist air itself is a fine conductor of heat. Hence more sunstroke with moderate heat and great humidity than with great heat and slight humidity.

Sweating, then, is an active transfer of fluid from inside the body to the surface of the body, where it is vaporized, a heat-consuming process. The sweat that is not vaporized drips from the skin, but, as Du Bois points out, it "removes no heat from the body except as it diminishes the weight of the body." *Sweating* is a different matter from the mere evaporation of water from a non-sweating skin.

When air temperature reaches 86 or more, or when ordinary vaporization from lungs and skin and the amount which can be lost by radiation and conduction falls below the amount of heat that must be eliminated, the sweat-glands begin to pour out water. Actual sweat is the body's last resort in keeping down the temperature. A flushed face covered with sweat is a skin losing hot water because it cannot lose steam fast enough. Usually our skin is "slightly moist, moister than a dead animal, not as moist as meat in a butcher shop."

The actual secretion of sweat is controlled by sweat nerves. The secretion itself increases the heat loss. Rarely individuals are found without sweat-glands—*icthyosis hysterix*. They cannot work in summer or in heat where a normal man would sweat. In one well-known case even slight work would send the individual's temperature up to 105 degrees.

There is always blood in the skin. On warm days the capillaries are gorged with blood; if the air is not too hot, much heat is lost by radiation and conduction and by vaporization. On cold days the blood is withdrawn from the skin;

as Du Bois says, we change our skin into a suit of clothes and withdraw the zone where the blood is cooled to a level some distance below the surface.

This change in volume (and possibly in concentration) of peripheral blood is a matter of vasomotor function, but what part the *hot* and *cold* points in our skin play is not yet known. When air below 60 degrees strikes an unprotected body, the cold points are stimulated. They tell the muscles to shiver; that is their way of getting warm. Shivering is a heat-producing device. Presumably the blood itself has become more concentrated, water has been withdrawn; it is "thicker"—less heat is carried to the radiating surfaces. A man up to his neck in a bath of 104 degrees stops sweating on his forehead as soon as one hand is plunged in cold water. Same reason. Sweat-gland nerves also work according to temperature stimuli. The cold point nerves now cry louder than the hot point.

Heat *production* is a chemical regulation—action in neuromuscular system, action of food on metabolism; heat *loss* is physical regulation—sweat centers and nerves, vasomotor center and nerves, respiratory center, water-content of the blood. So marvelously do these mechanisms work in harmony, and so wonderfully are they co-ordinated, that Howell believes it necessary to assume the existence of a heat-regulating center in the brain. Where it is and how it works, if there is such a center, are not yet known. It is assumed that that center is upset during fever.

Temperature above normal not caused by food, work, or outside temperature, is fever. The cause of fever is not known.

We sometimes shiver during a fever. Fever disturbs the vasomotor system; the blood supply to the skin is reduced. This makes the skin cool. Its "cold points" are stimulated. The blood concentration is increased; this may be useful in overcoming the effects of toxins in the body. A rise of two degrees of temperature in one hour means an increase of fifty-eight surplus calories stored in the body. The body, as Du Bois puts it, has become a reservoir in which extra heat is stored; it is released when the temperature of the body falls two degrees.

Subnormal temperature accompanies starvation; less heat produced because less oxidation. The body has run out of good fuel; it begins to burn itself; its proteins are not good fuel, they do not oxidize well. First to go are the glycogen deposits, next the stored fats. Intestine, lungs, pancreas, brain and spinal cord, and heart, go last of all, and in the order named. Heart last of all. Even the liver is of little use to a starving man but as firewood; half of it is burned up before the heart has contributed more than 2 per cent of itself to the smoldering flame. Twenty-five per cent of the blood of the body may be found in a normal liver; its activity releases much energy, it is a reservoir of heat. But robbed of its materials, it is an idle shop. The starving body burns it to keep the brain and heart warm. In all the world of warm blood there is nothing so dead as a cold heart.

15

Glands are no more unique in life than any other structure or organ evolved for living purposes. We find no glands in an ameba, but the ameba has a full set of test tubes for chemical reactions. At any rate, it oxidizes carbon for vital purposes and synthesizes dead into living protoplasm. A cow also does that, and manages to get most of the necessities of life into her milk; her milk will rear a calf.

Her body and ours are organic wholes, held together for reaction purposes by a nervous system, held together for growing and living purposes by the blood. Into that blood all the cells of the body dip their fingers for what they require; into it they dump what they do not require or what they have made that other parts of the body may require. So it comes about that certain groups of cells are organized to clear the blood of refuse, other groups to deliver to the blood or to the alimentary canal chemical reagents, enzymes, and regulators.

These special groups of cells are called glands—Latin for acorn. Any organ in the body which secretes something the body needs, or excretes waste which otherwise would be injurious to the body, is a gland. I keep moving my elbow; it does not wear out; certain glands secrete elbow oil. Bones, muscles, organs, all contribute to, all benefit by, the scheme of the secretions of glands.

Our body contains literally millions of glands. Some are endlessly duplicated—sweat, oil, and intestinal glands; others are single or in pairs. Some always work; others work only part time. Some function only for a certain period during life and then slink away, like actors who appear during one scene only. Some serve a double function, like the liver and the glands of reproduction. Some secrete definitely known substances; others have no known secretion. Some have a canal or duct by which their secretions are delivered to definite organs; others are ductless.

Our skin is thickset with two kinds of glands which have ducts or canals. About 2,000,000 sweat glands secrete water and so help to regulate our temperature. Fat or sebaceous glands, usually one for each hair, help to protect the body from cold and the hair from becoming brittle.

Lachrymal glands secrete tears through ducts which wash and lubricate the eyes. A duct on the inner corner of the eye drains the dirt-laden tears into the nose, if not secreted too fast; then they spill over the eyelids.

Our alimentary canal is beset with food-digestion glands. Parotids in the cheek, sub-linguals at the base of the tongue, and sub-maxillaries in the lower jaw, "make our mouth water," preparing food for digestion and acting as a ferment to convert starch into sugar. The big glands of food digestion are the gastric glands, pancreas, and liver. The pancreas secretes ferments that digest fats, carbohydrates, and proteins. The liver, largest of our glands, secretes bile, forms urea, and stores glycogen.

The secretions of all these glands are carried by ducts to other organs or systems. They are known as the duct, or *exocrine*, glands. They deal with the upkeep of the individual. On their proper functioning depend in general food digestion and the protection of the body from extremes of temperature and of the eyes from motes. But there is an important difference between the glands of food digestion and the glands which water the eyes, oil the skin, lubricate the joints, and regulate the temperature. Food-digestion glands secrete definite chemical substances, manufactured within the glands themselves.

Some of these chemicals are manufactured in large quantities—hydrochloric acid, for example, by the stomach. Other chemicals are produced in amounts so small that they are only with difficulty discovered by the physiologist; such are the enzymes. These chemicals are prepared by the glands from the nutrient solutions carried to them by the blood. It is their business to pick them out and combine them into such products as in the course of evolution they have become adapted to produce. They must be plentifully supplied with arterial blood.

The primary function of the duct glands, then, is to keep the body fit and to supply it with tools for razing dead bodies so that their debris may be built into living bodies. To that extent they are concerned in growth and the proper functioning of the body mechanism. But the control of growth itself and the determination of the character of the body mechanism depend on other glands—the endocrines— whose nature until recently was not even suspected.

The kidneys are not glands of secretion; they secrete nothing. They are excretory organs. Their function is to filter from the 500 quarts of blood which flows through them every twenty-four hours, poisonous nitrogenous wastes, salts, and enough water to carry them in solution through the ureters to the bladder. The kidneys are indirectly controlled by the vasomotor nerves, more directly by chemical stimuli in the blood itself. Increase of oxygen to the kidneys, for example, decreases urine secretion. Substances such as urea are always filtered out of the blood by a normal kidney, but sugar, chlorides, and sodium are excreted only when the blood carries them in excess. In diseased kidneys the sensitive filtering membrane is damaged, and thus often valuable elements are filtered out from the blood to the detriment of the body.

Abel believes that possibly his false kidney, by which he has filtered out red blood-cells, can be so perfected that the blood of the human body might be forced to pass through it, filtering out such poisons as, for example, corrosive sublimate, which the kidneys themselves cannot remove, and other poisons which because of temporary kidney breakdown cannot be eliminated.

16

> The little fleas which us do tease
> Have other fleas to bite 'em,
> And these in turn have other fleas,
> And so . . . . ad infinitum.

"Flea" is any animal that lives on or within the body of a host and depends on that host for its food. All such are *parasites*. Eccles claims that half of all the animals in the world are parasites.

The most numerous and deadly parasites come from that great half-animal, half-plant underworld known as bacteria. Second only in deadliness are some of the unicellular organisms of the animal world, the Protozoa. More annoying, but of quite a different order in their powers of destruction, are some of the lower members of the Metazoa subkingdom.

To the extent that parasites live on or within us or find a temporary home with us, and to the extent that they are causes of disease and death, they are proper objects of our interest and fit subjects for our attention. Indeed, the claim has been made that *natural* death in man and higher animals is due to parasitic organisms. This probably overstates the case, but it is a fact that micro-organisms enormously influenced organic evolution, that certain forms are constant menaces, and that no part, tissue, or function of our body is germ-proof. The menace is great because of their astounding capacity to multiply, constant because, like the poor, they are always with us. A pin-scratch may be as fatal as a rifle ball; careless handling of milk may plague a city.

The general problem of parasitism is complicated. We shall look only at those parasites which are prone to infest the human body and are likely to cause disease. What are they, how are they carried, how do they enter our body, what damage or disease do they cause, and how may we be rid of them or acquire *immunity?* The answers to even these questions are often interrelated. Malaria, for example, is not a bacterial disease, nor do we "catch" it—it is brought to us by a mosquito. Malaria, as a disease, is not to be understood without reference to its carrier and without a knowledge of the life cycle of the germ which causes malaria. Again, rats are not parasites, yet some of the deadliest scourges of the human race are rat-flea-borne diseases. Why are the rats and fleas immune to plague? And how do they carry germs? The venom of a cobra, the ricin of the castor bean, the toxin of diphtheria germs, are deadly. Are they related substances? Only in their disruption of normal human processes of living and in the similarity of the response our bodies make to such substances.

It is true that no question can be raised regarding any one phase of any human process of living without removing the lid of all of life. The intricacy of life in its simplest forms is profound enough; it is not simplified by the addition of parasites. And yet possibly all living processes in higher organisms are brought about by aggregates of protein molecules

187

which function as micro-organisms. If we only knew more about the protein molecule!

We shall, for keen minds are on its trail, and sooner or later it will yield its secret and life will be new again.

Meanwhile, there are mosquitoes to swat. And with them we may begin to call the roll of our parasitic enemies. Mosquitoes belong to *Hexapoda* (six-footed) insects, the most diversified, the most numerous, and for their size the smartest of all animals. Lice, fleas, ticks, bedbugs, jiggers, mosquitoes, flies—dozens of kinds, millions of each. And a variety for every plant and animal on earth big enough to carry one. They live on us, they live off us. They give us nothing useful. They irritate us. But they do not kill us. We are accustomed to them, "adapted," immune.

That is what immunity means. We are not exempt from fleas or dozens of other parasites. Only immune. We can stand them. The germ of death or disease carried by a parasite is another matter. Immunity may come in many forms.

Insects are the highest animals which infest or bedevil the human body. Lower in the scale is a flatworm, the long, flat *Taenia*, or tapeworm. Its life history is longer and not at all flat. Man gets it from unsalted, uncooked pork. In his alimentary canal it loses most of its anatomy and becomes head and long body of dozens of segments, each for breeding purposes a complete male and female. That is what it is, a series of reproductive units. It needs no sense organs, has none; as it feeds on predigested food it needs no digestive apparatus, has none. Its head is a hook to hang on by and a siphon to suck up food.

Our next lower animal parasitic enemies are the two threadworms—hookworm, trichina. The trichina is well understood and now under control; we hear little of it. The hookworm is well understood; but people will go barefooted.

The trichina lives coiled up in its cyst within a muscle cell—rat, cat, dog, pig, man. There may be 80,000 cysts in one ounce of ham: half males, half females. Eaten by man, the cysts dissolve in the gastric juice, the worms are free. They mate. One female produces 1,000 young. The young break through and settle down in muscle cells—100,000,000 of them in one dead man.

Hookworm continues to claim its millions of victims each year simply because proper precautions are not taken to break the vicious circle of its life cycle. It is another case of Parasites Lost and Parasites Regained, in the words of a Fijian school boy who, according to Dr. Vincent, had heard about hookworms and Milton the same day. Hookworm eggs hatch in warm, moist soil. The tiny worms enter the skin of the bare feet, are carried by the blood to the lungs, where they bore through into the throat, and thence are borne to the alimentary canal, where 500 or more live parasitic lives attached to the wall of the small intestine. Their millions of eggs are returned to the soil to begin other cycles.

Lowest of real animals to infest us are certain unicellular Protozoa. One group, the Sporozoa, is exclusively parasitic; and all are internal, hence often called endoparasites. Some abide in the liver, some in the intestine, some in the muscles, some in the blood of their host. Some are deadly enemies of the human race. Only bacteria are more widely distributed and few germs have more plagued the human race than the Sporozoan Plasmodia which cause malaria. Of the Sarcodina Protozoa, only the endameba is a real parasitic enemy and in the tropics fairly destructive by causing dysentery. A similar but smaller ameba makes its home in our mouth and is always found in pyorrhea (pus-flow) lesions, though it is not yet certain that it causes pyorrhea. Only one genus of Infusoria is parasitic for man, causing diarrhea and dysentery. Of the fourth Protozoan group, the Mastigophora, only the Trypanosomas are parasitic—and cause the deadly sleeping-sickness and allied diseases.

Below the lowest animals and below the lowest plants is that half-plant, half-animal underworld of bacteria. But before we turn to them, let us see how certain germs are carried by animals—flies, fleas, rats, etc. Incidentally, we shall see into the breeding habits of certain germs.

The Black Death of 1348-49 devastated a quarter of Europe, killed 25,000,000 people, and drove Boccaccio outside the walls of Florence, where he whiled away the time writing the *Decameron*. In India, the pest bacillus cost 6,000,000 lives in ten years. Almost all *plague* bacteria are carried by animals, and are transmitted to man by fleas, lice, mosquitoes, or other parasites.

A flea on a dying rat seeks a fresh victim, carrying the rat's plague germs with it. Any man will do. The flea empties its alimentary canal, then bites; the bite irritates the skin, the man scratches it—thereby opening his first line of defense to the enemy! The germs left behind by the flea can now get into the blood. In the new host they begin to multiply. Another flea may carry this tainted blood to another human victim.

More instructive is the propagation of malaria, or ague. When science found out where the mosquito gets malaria and why the astounding clock-like regularity of the paroxysms which wrack the bones with chills and burn the body of the victim with fever, a long stride was made in making this world safe for human beings.

Malaria is caused by three (possibly by four) varieties of Plasmodia of the unicellular Sporozoa. Sporozoa reproduce by spores, hence the name. Ordinarily, one cell or one bacterium divides and becomes two. In reproduction by spores, one divides into many tiny spores, each spore grows to life size, and again divides into spores. Each kind of Plasmodium has its own time rate of reproduction. The ague paroxysm coincides with this reproductive cycle.

The true home of Plasmodia is human red blood-corpuscles. Within, they grow to maturity at the expense of the corpuscle. They then begin to divide and become a mulberry-shaped mass of small, glassy, ameboid spores. This mass

190

rends the corpuscle apart. The spores thus freed attach themselves to other corpuscles and begin a new life cycle.

The rending of the corpuscles releases their toxic wastes into the blood-stream, hence the fever; their destruction of the oxygen-carrying constituent of the blood results in anemia —and pernicious at that, without quinine.

The estivo-autumnal or *quotidian* (daily) Plasmodium completes its life cycle every twenty-four hours. Each cycle releases from six to eight spores or new parasites. It is the most pernicious of all forms of malaria. The *tertian* life cycle is complete in forty-eight hours, at which time it is about twice the size of a normal red blood-corpuscle; from twelve to twenty-four spores are released; the chill occurs every other day. The *quartan* variety breaks from the corpuscle at the end of seventy-two hours, with eight spores and the attendant paroxysm; the attacks are every third day.

In other words, once any one of the three varieties of malaria germs has entered the blood-stream, it propagates itself by spores and without sex, asexually. The existence of its progeny is dependent simply on the supply of red blood-corpuscles. But how does it get into the blood in the first place?

Enter the Anopheles mosquito, of which there are several varieties. They can generally be distinguished from mere mosquitoes by their approach. A mere mosquito on landing humps its back, but holds its body parallel to the surface on which it lights; the Anopheles lands with its head down and body straight out at an acute angle with the surface. The mere mosquito drills with its head for lever; the Anopheles pushes in its siphon with its entire body.

It siphons up the blood of an ague victim. Also minute Plasmodia spores. These are killed in the digestive juice of mere mosquitoes, but begin a sexual life cycle in the Anopheles. In this phase of development the Anopheles is the true, man the intermediate, host of the Plasmodia.

The spores, in the Anopheles, develop into males or

females. The males develop fine thread-like processes. One of these enters a female spore, fertilizes it. The now "married" spore enters the wall of the mosquito stomach, becomes encysted, grows; the mosquito's stomach looks as though covered with warts. The full-grown "wart" now breaks up into spores, each of which produces myriads of minute thread-like bodies. These are carried to all parts of the mosquito's body, even 10,000 in its salivary glands.

The mosquito bites a human victim, discharging saliva and a few thousand thread-like spores. In man's blood they can take care of themselves. They enter an asexual cycle. They soon become incredibly numerous. Assume that the mosquito left only 1,000 spores: by the tenth day they have become 100,000,000; two days later, 1,000,000,000. When 150,-000,000 blood-corpuscles have been invaded, fever begins.

There may be double, even triple, infections—from successive infections of the same type or from infections of two or more types. Quartan fever, for example, may be simple, double, or triple. In severe infections there may be more Plasmodia than there are red blood-cells.

The germs of trench and typhus fevers are carried by "cooties." Typhus fever alone killed 120,000 Serbians during the war—all inoculated by lice. When control measures were inaugurated, the fever disappeared. But true control cannot come to stay until the facts of propagation are known. In 1915 there were 2,500 cases of malaria in an Arkansas town; within three years there were 73: reduction of 97 per cent. Formerly, yellow fever lived in the tropics and now and then visited our Southern ports, with great loss of life. It is almost forgotten now. Controlled by controlling its mosquito carrier. In December, 1918, control measures began in Guayaquil, Ecuador, with 88 cases; they fell by months: 85, 43, 17, 2, 0. None since.

But many kinds of germs need no lower animal agency to help complete their vicious life cycle; mere human social relations suffice. The very manner of our living is sometimes a factor in the presence of germs—and in our susceptibility to their ravages. As Jordan says, tuberculosis is primarily and chiefly a disease of men living in houses and of cattle kept in stables. A tubercular patient may expectorate up to 3,000,000,000 tubercle bacilli in one day; the dried sputum in a cool, dark corner may contain virulent germs for eight months. A few drops of urine may contain up to 500,-000,000 typhoid bacilli.

The typhoid bacillus, for example, before death overtakes its host, passes into the body of another victim, carried by milk, water, food, fingers, filth, flies. If it passes the acid stomach of the new host, it has a clear field ahead until it reaches the lymph-nodes of Peyer in the small intestine. Whether it kills and so dies with its host, or is killed by the leukocytes in the blood, it has already multiplied into an army and has already sent some of its forces out to find new victims. The germs of dysentery, cholera, etc., of the alimentary canal, have similar cycles. But they must all be carried; they no more "pass" from one victim to another without a *carrier* than a letter crosses the sea without a carrier.

Many disease-producing germs which make their homes in our nose, throat, or lungs (germs of tuberculosis, diphtheria, pneumonia, scarlet fever, influenza, measles, whooping-cough, pneumonic plague, etc.), may be carried by the air itself, and generally are sneezed or coughed out to be wafted about until they find new hosts.

During the Spanish War there was a case of typhoid for every seven American troops, a death for every 71; in the World War, there was one death for every 25,000 American troops. In the old pre-antiseptic days, childbed fever mowed down motherhood and in many hospitals regularly killed practically all mothers. Death from childbed fever is now a dark stain on a hospital's reputation. Deaths from typhoid are still too common.

The conquest of germ diseases has only just begun. But the start of that conquest might have been delayed until the sweet by-and-by without the discovery of the germs them-selves under the microscope.

17

In 1683 there lived a curious Dutchman who ground lenses. He scraped some tartar from his teeth, mixed it with water, and examined it under his lens. What he saw was a more astounding sight than that which confronted Balboa, who, from his peak in Darien, saw a lot of water. For ages man had known of the Pacific Ocean and millions of men had sailed its deeps; Leeuwenhoek, the Delft lens-maker, was the first human being to see a bacterium.

And the world promptly forgot him and continued for a century and a half to argue "spontaneous generation" and to exorcise devils as causes of disease. It remained for Louis Pasteur (1822-95) to prove the part bacteria play in decay, putrefaction, fermentation, and many other processes until then hidden from the ken of man. Koch, in 1876, proved the causal relation between the bacillus anthracis and the disease anthrax, and in 1882 invented the "solid culture-media" for the study of bacteria. Pasteur founded a new science—biology; Koch revolutionized man's attitude toward the world and gave the human race its first rational theory of disease.

The naming of bacteria is still haphazard and much con-fusion prevails. But bacteriology is a new science, its inherent difficulties have been great, its progress marvelous beyond conception to the surgeons of Napoleon's armies, who as-sumed that pus was the first and necessary step toward recov-ery from a wound. Some bacteria bear the name of their host, some the name of their discoverer, some the name of the disease they cause. Some bear all the traffic allows—for example, *Granulobacillus saccharo-butyricus mobilis non-liquefaciens.*

All bacteria show a fairly definite character and are either

194

pathogenic (disease-producing), *zymogenic* (ferment-producing), *saprophitic* (decay-producing), or *chromogenic* (color-producing). But the line between bacteria which cause disease and those which do not is far from sharp. Many variable factors determine which bacteria are pathogenic, when they are pathogenic, and for whom.

Bacteria are so small that almost nothing of their anatomy is known but their shape, and that changes according to circumstances. They not only vary during their life cycle, but as individuals; even abnormal and monstrous forms are found.

According to Jordan, all bacteria are inclosed within a cell wall or capsule, which looms up under the microscope like a halo. As this capsule is not cellulose, bacteria are not true plants. Which means nothing, for many sure plants are more like true animals than they are like true plants. It is in the nature of living beings that there can be no sharp line between the lowest plants and animals.

According to outline, three forms of bacteria are recognized: rod-shaped, *bacillus;* corkscrew-shaped, *spirillum;* round-like-a-berry, *coccus.* But these names give no clue to their character; noxious and innoxious bacteria are equally indifferent to how they look under the microscope. The cocci are also called micrococci (small berries). Some cocci divide in one plane and go in pairs like Damon and Pythias, or form chains, and are called streptococci; some divide in two planes and form flat sheets or clusters like a bunch of grapes, and are called staphylococci; some divide in three planes and form cubical bundles, and are called sarcinæ. There are also strepto-bacteria, traveling like chain-gangs. But bacilli and spirilla divide at right angles to their long axes and generally lead detached lives. Up to 1900 there had been identified and named 1,272 genera of bacteria, divided as follows: bacilli, 833; cocci, 343; spirilla, 96.

Because rather sharply differing from both bacilli and cocci, Jordan believes the spirilla group should be put into a class by themselves and called spirochetes (coil-bristle). They are long, spiral, and thread-like; some ten times the length of a red blood-cell. To this group belong the germs of syphilis (treponema pallidum), yellow fever (leptospira icteroides), yaws, infectious jaundice, and relapsing fever.

The average bacterium is about 1/20,000 of an inch long. The influenza bacillus is about half that size; the germ of infantile paralysis is smaller yet. One hundred thousand typhoid bacilli could lie snug in the space of a match; 15,-000,000,000,000 of them to the ounce! A red blood-cell is pretty small, but it is as big as a pea when magnified by the diameters necessary to raise an influenza germ to the size of a needle-point. The smallest visible bacterium is 18/100,-000,000 of an inch in diameter; the ultramicroscopic or *filterable* bacteria (viruses) are one-tenth that size; that is, they are only half the shortest wave-length of any visible light-ray. Under the ultramicroscope, such objects may be seen, but merely as luminous points without difference as to size, shape, or structure. About forty filterable viruses are known to exist, but nothing is known of the germs themselves except that they pass through filters and can be very destructive. Among them are, presumably, the germs of smallpox, dengue fever, trachoma, infantile paralysis, measles, hydrophobia, influenza, and foot-and-mouth disease.

All bacteria have some power of locomotion. The typhoid bacillus can make about a tenth of an inch an hour, or 2,000 times its own length. Some travel faster—so fast that if we could move as fast in proportion to our size, we could run a mile a minute.

Bacteria show amazing vital capacity. They can defy hours of boiling water; their spores can resist a temperature of 212 degrees. Some sulphur bacteria haunt hot springs in water at 190 degrees. Some multiply at freezing point. Typhoid and diphtheria germs will live for days in a temperature of liquid air (284 below zero). Some bacteria have been known to defy liquid hydrogen temperature (464 below zero).

Even more astounding is their capacity to multiply. One becomes two by simple division. The germ of Asiatic cholera can divide every fifteen minutes. Within twenty-four hours one could become 78,700,000,000,000,000,000,000,000,- 000; but the victim is usually dead in less than twelve hours, killed by the toxins of these prodigious workers. In growing and dividing, they have consumed food and liberated carbon dioxide. They are *foreigners* in our system, living at our expense and leaving their toxic garbage for us to eliminate.

The air we breathe and the food we eat are full of bacteria, and our body is covered with them. This is not literally true, but it is true enough to emphasize the question: why are they not always and more promptly fatal? Many factors enter into the case. For example, an entire group of bacteria live on our skin, where they are harmless. A scratch or a pinprick opens the skin. Now they are inside our body, but the only damage may be a boil or a pimple. Boils are usually not contagious and rarely fatal. Sometimes they are. It depends.

The hay bacillus is everywhere; in the air, water, soil; probably some in the dust which my eyelids keep wiping from my eyes. If I am in a weakened or run-down condition, this bacillus may lead to a serious infection in my eye. Ordinarily, nothing happens. The hay bacillus is a parasite, at home wherever it lands; it has established equilibrium with its host. As Jordan says, the less completely adapted the bacterium is to its host, the more virulent the disease. Old diseases decrease in severity, increase in frequency.

Hence the really dangerous pathogenic bacteria as a rule do their damage in short time; they are not adapted to live in their host; they kill. To kill the hand that feeds one is not biologic adaptation. How and why bacteria injure us are again dependent on many factors. But we may recognize two general ways: by specific toxins locally released (toxemia); by invasion of blood-stream or tissue and resultant damage due to general bacterial activity (bacteremia).

Diphtheria and tetanus are good examples of toxemic diseases. They are localized; the toxin liberated is specific and highly poisonous. Syphilis is a good example of a blood-poisoning disease; at first localized, the germs soon enter the blood-stream and from the blood may affect different tissues or organs. Pneumonia and typhoid are tissue diseases primarily, but the bacteria are present in the blood also. Septicemia may be due to other causes than the invasion of the blood by the bacteria of suppuration.

What is toxin—for man or bacterium? In the body of a man or an ape the bacillus of leprosy finds food and raiment; in the body of a dog or a cat, a tomb. An anthrax bacillus will not grow in a solution of corrosive sublimate stronger than one part to 300,000; it will not live if the solution is one to 1,000. As for bacterial poisons, the only general statement that can be made is that they are very poisonous. Tetanus toxin is 16 times more fatal than cobra venom, 120 times more fatal than strychnine. To put it another way, the minimal fatal dose of strychnine is thirty milligrams; of tetanus toxin, one-fourth of a milligram.

Certain plant toxins show resemblance to bacterial toxins. One gram of ricin (from the castor bean), properly diluted, contains lethal doses for one and one-half million guinea-pigs. Ricin agglutinates their red blood-cells; but first there is a period of "incubation" for the ricin, and an antibody (antiricin) is formed. Such chemical behavior and physical action of ricin are strikingly like those of bacteria. But this gives us no clue to the chemical structure of bacterial toxins. They are colloidal, presumably, and in many respects suggest enzymes in their action. In the fact that they do evoke antibodies (antitoxins) lies most of the secret of their control up to the present time.

Which brings us up to immunity. But note, first, that there

are many kinds of immunity—and back of all the same principle: I am either immune or I am not. If I take it or catch it, I am not immune; if I do not take it or catch it, I am immune. But I may go down with it to-morrow! In other words, there are variable factors which will determine my predisposition to infection or my power of resistance against infection: age, hunger, thirst, fatigue, exposure to extremes of heat and cold, are such variable factors.

Even different strains of bacteria vary in their intensity: diphtheria and influenza, for example. There are mild epidemics, there are severe epidemics. Again, certain diseases seem to predispose toward invasion by the germs of other diseases. Acute tuberculosis may follow on the heels of measles; streptococci may invade lungs already occupied by tubercular bacilli. Typhoid fever and pneumonia, diphtheria and scarlet fever, syphilis and gonorrhea, are well known combinations of diseases.

Trypanosoma, the germ of sleeping-sickness, is carried by flies from animal to animal. The disease is almost regularly fatal; it cost Uganda 200,000 human lives, the Congo Basin 500,000. One infected animal sent to the Transvaal started an epidemic among the cattle; 15,000 died.

Why any animals left, then; or any flies? The tsetse fly which carries the trypanosoma is immune, as are the wild animals which live in Central Africa. But let an outsider— dog, horse, man—venture in! Outsiders are not immune; their blood has no answer to sleeping-sickness; they die, unless they can get Bayer's "205."

So it was with Texas fever: the *new* cattle died. So it was when whites introduced such "simple" children's diseases as measles, croup, whooping-cough, to South Sea Islanders and to American Indians. They were not immune. Their bodies had not yet learned the art of compounding anti-toxins to new toxins. They died—"like flies."

Which means that immunity itself is a relative term. We are all susceptible under certain conditions; we all have more or less power of resistance. To some bacteria we are *naturally immune;* to others we are *naturally susceptible.* The problem is to *acquire* immunity. How can we get exemption from disease?

By having smallpox we acquire immunity from smallpox; also by vaccination. Against typhoid, from plague and Asiatic cholera, we acquire immunity by vaccination with dead bacteria—"cultures." With a secretion (or excretion) of living bacteria we acquire immunity from diphtheria. In other words, we become actively immune by incorporating into our body "live virulent bacteria, less virulent bacteria, dead bacteria, bacterial secretions, or bacterial products from broken-down dead bacteria." An anti-bacterial serum is a protective; an antitoxic serum is a curative.

Much is known of the "how" of immunity, almost nothing of the "why." But great advance in the future will come from specific artificial remedies—drugs, *chemotherapy.* The problem is to find a drug that will kill the bug but not the patient —"magic bullets charmed to fly straight to a specific objective, turning aside from anything else in its path."

Quinine is specific death for malaria germs; ipecacuanha for the ameba which causes amebic dysentery. Possibly chaulmoogra oil is a specific cure for leprosy; asphenamin ("606"), for syphilis, relapsing fever, and yaws; atoxyl, for sleeping sickness. The list of specific cures is pitiably small yet. Bacteriology is new, immunology is newer. Only recently have the chemotherapists had real targets to shoot at. The problems which confront them to-day are vastly more important than the puny worlds Alexander exhausted in his conquests.

CHAPTER IV

THE ENDOCRINE GLANDS AND THE CAUSES OF DEATH

1

WHILE life remains in the body, the duct glands furnish the necessary chemicals for heat and energy metabolism and for the preparation of materials for growth and repair. If they fail to supply fuel, the body dies; if they fail to furnish building material, the body stops growing. Let us assume that the duct glands do not fail. It then appears that the body which began as a fertilized ovum develops into a 9-pound infant in 9 months. Why does it not develop into a 90-pound child in 90 months, or a 900-pound prodigy in 900 months? Even if it only kept up its first two years' rate-growth, it would weigh 500 pounds in twenty-four years. It does not grow so big. It stops. Sometimes too soon—it is dwarfed; sometimes not soon enough—it is gigantic, though rarely, if ever, surpassing the nine feet three inches of Machnow, the Russian. But it stops. Why?

Meanwhile the growing body keeps changing in size, shape, proportions. Certain parts or organs appear before others start to appear. For a while the brain grows faster than the

201

motor mechanism; at other times the motor mechanism grows more rapidly. The teeth have their special periods for growth. The infant's thigh bone at birth has 2,000,000 bone-building cells. When that bone is a finished adult product it contains over 150,000,000 bone cells. Why stop at so few? How do the leg bones know when to stop growing longer, the skull bones to stop growing larger? Why does the body grow by fits and starts and finally seem to be complete? What regulates the growth of all these parts and of the body as a whole?

Moore replaced a rat's ovaries with the sex glands from a male; her body and behavior took on decided male characters. By the same operation which converts the unruly bull into a docile ox and the stringy cock into a tender-fleshed capon, the Sistine Chapel in Rome up to 1878 maintained its male sopranos. Why does the boy's voice begin to crack and his face, almost overnight as it were, begin to grow a beard where there was no sign of one? Is sex also, like growth and individuality, a whim of "heredity," or are our sex, individual traits, and physical growth under the control of definite regulators? Fifty years from now we shall begin to know the details, but enough is now known of the ductless glands and their secretions to open up not only a new chapter of life, but new accounts with life. They regulate sex, rate of growth of tissues and organs, and consequently physical traits.

The secretions of the ductless glands are discharged direct into the blood, hence they are also called glands of internal secretion, or *endocrines (endon,* within; *krino,* I separate). There are commonly said to be seven endocrines proper: thyroid, parathyroid, and thymus, in the neck; pituitary and pineal, in the center of the head; adrenals and spleen, in the abdomen. But it is not yet proved that the thymus, pineal, and spleen are true glands. The liver, pancreas, and sex glands also function as endocrines.

Endocrine secretions are chemical in nature and are usually called *hormones* (exciters). They are also called autacoid substances: from *acos,* a remedy—they act like drugs. They are drugs, some of them of astounding potency. In fact, no man-made drugs are so powerful as some we make in our own drug-store glands.

Mere regulation is not, of course, confined to the secretions of glands. For example, the chief regulator of the respiratory system is carbon dioxide, given off by every cell of our body; thus liberated, it functions as a hormone or "exciter." But, as Abel puts it, the hormones actually known are definite and specifically acting indispensable chemical products which modify development and growth of other organs, especially during embryonic life, and the entire metabolism, including that of the nervous system, during adult life. Then, too, there is a collective operation of the endocrines, as yet not definitely known, but summarized by Barker as follows:

More and more we are forced to realize that the general form and the external appearance of the human body depends to a large extent upon their functioning. Our stature, the kinds of faces we have, the length of our arms and legs, the shape of the pelvis, the color and consistency of our integument, the quantity and regional location of our fat, the amount and distribution of hair on our bodies, the tonicity of our muscles, the sound of the voice and the size of the larynx, the emotions to which our "extérieur" gives expression—all are to a certain extent conditioned by the productivity of our hormonopoietic glands. We are, in a sense, the beneficiaries and the victims of the chemical correlations of our endocrine organs.

In short, as the discovery of enzymes and antibodies gave a new insight into the problem of the nature of living processes, the discovery of the hormones opens up anew the whole conception of heredity. We can now say that men are alike because they inherit the same kind of blood and similar sets of glands to secrete hormones for the blood to carry; but that men differ because they do not meet the same physical and chemical conditions during life and as a consequence do not develop the same catalyzers, the same immunity agents, or the same regulating agents.

Or we can say, with Loeb, that the organism itself molds itself into an organic whole; in the case of the human ovum, into a human being, because the genus *Homo* and species *sapiens* inhere in the specific protein of the human ovum; but that the traits of individuality or "Mendelian characters" are determined by the enzymes regulating metabolism and the hormones in control of growth and so of personality.

2

The endocrine gland best understood is the *thyroid* (shield-like) astride our Adam's apple. It varies individually and with age. It is relatively largest in fetal life. At birth its weight in proportion to the entire body is as 1 to 300, by the third week as 1 to 1,160, and in the adult as 1 to 1,800. It is generally larger in women than in men. Why this is so is not yet known.

The thyroid usually consists of two equally developed lobes two inches long, an inch and a quarter broad. They vary greatly; one lobe may be much larger than the other, or may be quite absent. Generally the two lobes are connected by an isthmus; this also varies in position or may be absent. There may be accessory thyroids down the trachea as far as the heart.

Only in higher fishes does the thyroid become a ductless gland, take on new functions, and start a new career. In man, a duct is sometimes found in the isthmus—vestige of a condition found in lowest fishes, echo of millions of years ago. It is prone to trouble.

Frogs' eggs develop into fish-like tadpoles. Tadpoles lose their tails and gills, develop true lungs, and become frogs. Remove the tadpole's thyroid: it never becomes a frog; it remains a tadpole for life. Feed a tadpole with thyroid: it becomes frog in a hurry, the fish stage of its existence being reduced from a year to two weeks; but the frog is only as big as a fly. Feeding thyroid to tadpoles evidently produces two results: it hastens metamorphosis but retards growth.

Children with deficient thyroids, through removal, atrophy, or injury, become heavy-featured, gibbering, idiotic dwarfs known as *cretins;* they do not metamorphose into normal adults. Their skin is dry and hairless; their sex glands are under-developed; their pubic hair and puberty develop late or not at all; their temperature is subnormal; they are pot-bellied because their pelvis remains small, their limbs short and thick. The corresponding adult condition is known as *myxedema:* white, hairless, and thick, dry, rough skin; obesity; lowered temperature and metabolism; pulse slow and weak; mind dull.

These appalling results in both children and adults have been corrected by feeding thyroid extract. The changes thus produced have been little short of miraculous. Cretins have increased in stature several inches in one year. The first myxedema patient to be treated died in 1920 after twenty-nine years of good health due to thyroid feeding.

Enlargement of the thyroid from whatsoever cause is called *goiter*, or Derbyshire neck. But an over-developed or over-active thyroid produces a definite disease known as toxic or exopthalmic goiter, or Graves' disease. This is characterized by increased metabolism and blood pressure, rapid pulse, lax and moist skin, nervousness, and protruding eyeballs—hence the name, "exopthalmic." The remedy is still in the hands of the surgeon. The cause and significance of change in the thyroid in toxic goiter and the cause of endemic goiter are not yet understood. Nor is it understood why women are more prone to toxic goiter than men, the disproportion in some localities being as high as fifteen to one.

It is believed that the activating principle of the thyroid hormone is *thyroxin*, isolated by Kendall in 1918. Thyroxin is a crystalline compound of three molecules of iodine fixed in a protein derivative: tri-iodo-tri-hydro-oxyindole propionic acid, or 65 per cent of iodine.

Only the thyroid secretes thyroxin, and apparently it is the iodine in thyroxin that tells the story. Iodine is found in many seaweeds; is three times more abundant in codfish than in human beings; is found in traces in milk and in drinking water; and gets its name from its violet (iodes) color!

Possibly no life exists without iodine. Certainly normal human life is impossible without one one-hundredth of a grain of thyroxin a day. Three and a half grains of thyroxin are all that stands between intelligence and imbecility. But, there are, of course, dozens of causes of subnormal mentality other than hypothyroidism.

No limit of function can yet be assigned to any one endocrine, because they are parts of an organic whole and function as parts of living individuals. So with the thyroid: much is known, its whole story is far from known. But from what is known Hoskins characterizes it as a regulator of energy discharge to aid in adapting the animal to its environment. To Carlson it is a specific necessity for the development of the reproductive mechanism in males and for the lunar cycle in adult females. Both views are founded in facts and are not in conflict.

3

Closely associated with the thyroid are two other endocrines which develop in the epithelium of an embryonic branchial cleft or gill-arch. Of these the parathyroids are so closely associated in post-natal life in some animals that it is impossible to remove the thyroids without removing the parathyroids also. They were only discovered in 1880.

They are about as big as peas and are paired, generally two on each side and near the thyroids. They also vary in number, size, and position; they may extend far down the trachea. Their function is not yet understood, nor is it yet known if they are glands of internal secretion. It is known that death follows their removal, generally in from twelve to forty-eight hours. Sometimes recovery seems assured, but death has only been postponed—and not beyond fourteen days. Death is accompanied by *tetany*—acute muscular convulsions, and not to be confounded with tetanus, or "lockjaw." In some cases the hair and nails fall off, the teeth become loose and shed, and cataract of the eye develops. Hence it is inferred that they have to do with calcium metabolism. It is claimed that tetany may be cured by parathyroid feeding, but Carlson maintains that true tetany has not yet been cured by this method. Improvement may result from transplanting parathyroid from other animals, but when all the parathyroids are removed tetany and death follow. Parathyroid function is a condition of life.

What is tetany?

Infantile tetany is called "fits"; it is thought to be due to defective parathyroids. The calcium metabolism is upset: bad bone growth, the teeth do not calcify. The phosphate metabolism also seems to be upset: not enough phosphates are excreted. Also a tendency to acidosis in the blood, probably due to defective carbohydrate metabolism. A substance called methylguanidin appears in the urine and blood; it is bad poison. Guanidin is also found in decomposing horseflesh, in culture of the anthrax bacillus, etc.

Guanidin increases neuromuscular excitability: fits, cramps, tetany spasms. A strychnine salt also does it. The motor responses to stimuli are no longer co-ordinated, but become convulsive—"tetanized." That is why the lockjaw germ is called the bacillus of tetanus. With it at work releasing its specific toxin, muscles of jaws and other skeletal muscles "lock." Spasms follow the slightest stimulus. Possibly methylguanidin breaks down the resistance of the synapses of the neuromotor system—as strychnine and tetanus toxin are supposed to.

We seem to be far from the parathyroids. It is not known

if they secrete a hormone or if they are glands, but whatever they are they are vital structures, and certain death—and death with certain accompaniments—follows their removal. But Collip has recently reported that he has prepared an extract from animal parathyroids, which he calls *parathyrin*. With this he claims to control tetany in dogs, and to have treated a child in desperate condition with successful results.

No one knows yet what constitutes a normal human parathyroid. There is even more doubt as to what is a normal *thymus*, or whether it is a gland, or what happens when it is removed. It lies just under the upper end of the breast bone, is well developed in the fetus, better developed at the age of two, largest at puberty. It then begins to lose its character and becomes connective tissue, lymphatic tissue, and fat. But this change is delayed by castration. Hence it is assumed to hold back the development of the sex glands until puberty. Post-mortem examination of 400 idiots showed no thymus in 75 per cent. Its removal in young animals retards growth but hastens sexual development; the sex glands remain weak, the body flabby and dwarfed.

Riddle claims that the thymus lost its value for man and mammals when their ancestors began to incubate their eggs within their body and ceased laying them, as do birds and reptiles, with albumen and shells. That was the original function of the thymus. Pigeons whose thymus has been removed lay eggs without shells; but if fed thymus, will lay normal eggs with shells. If your hens' eggs have too little albumen or a soft shell, feed your chickens dried thymus of an ox. And thank the thymus because its secretions made it possible for our reptilian ancestor to invent an egg that could evolve into a human ovum.

4

The *adrenals*, or suprarenals, get their name from their position just above the kidneys. Normally they are of the size and shape of a large bean. But they vary: one—or, in rare cases, both—may be absent; there may be accessory adrenals varying in size from a pin head to a large pea. Removal of one adrenal produces no known result. Removal of both is always fatal, often within a few hours. When death does not follow their removal it is because accessory adrenals are present and can function.

The adrenal in some fishes is two separate organs. In the human embryo it begins as two; these unite to form one body with two distinct parts: an outside *cortex*, or bark, and a *medulla*, or core, completely inclosed by the cortex. The cortex arises from the middle germ-layer and is derived from the Wolffian body, which also assists in the development of the urogenital system. The medulla is part of the outer germ-layer and is derived from the same embryonic tissue as is the autonomic nervous system; *it is largely composed of nerve-like tissue.* Its importance is possibly second only to that of the brain. No other organ in the body is so well supplied with blood.

Removal of the cortex is always followed by profound prostration, loss of appetite, apathy, labored respiration, weak and irregular heart, paralysis, and, within a few hours or days, death. Its secretion has not yet been isolated; it is not certain whether it is a secreting or a detoxicating organ. It is a vital organ. It appears to stimulate sex-gland growth and bring on sexual maturity. Its over-activity, as, for example, when involved in a tumor, makes for precocious sexual development. When it is infected, as it sometimes is in tuberculosis, a disease results called "Addison's," from its discoverer in 1855. This is the only disease definitely known to be caused by insufficient adrenal cortex. It is as yet incurable and ends in death. Nor has the attempt to overcome cortical deficiency, due to disease or removal, yet met with success. Addison's disease is accompanied by great muscular weakness, nervous depression, digestive irritability, and such

increase in pigmentation of the skin that a white skin looks
like bronze.

The *medulla* of the adrenals is possibly more important
than the cortex. As it cannot be removed without injury to
the cortex, it is not yet certain that it is a vital organ as the
cortex is known to be. *Adrenin,* the hormone of the medulla,
was the first endocrine secretion to be isolated. Its derivative was discovered by Abel in 1897 and named "epinephrin"; its pure form was isolated in 1901 by both Takamine
and Aldrich. By 1908 it was so well understood that it was
artifically produced from a coal-tar derivative. It is now a
drug on the market and sold as epinephrin or adrenalin.
Abel describes it as a di-hydroxymethyl-aminoethylol benzine
or an "aromatic amino alcohol." Here is its formula:

$$C_6H_3(OH)_2COCH_2Cl + NH_2CH_3 \rightarrow C_6H_3(OH)_2.COCH_3.$$
$$NHCH_3.HCl.$$

And here is a curious fact. This remarkable drug is found
in man in a gland of internal secretion. The principle of this
drug is the constituent of a gland of external secretion in the
skin of a toad. That fact was unknown to the New England
colonists, but Toad Ointment was known. Abel quotes the
recipe:

Good-sized live toads, 4 in number; put into boiling water and
cook very soft; then take them out and boil the water down to
half pint, and add fresh churned, unsalted butter, 1 pound, and
simmer together; at the last add tincture of arnica 2 ounces.

What was Toad Ointment good for? Sprains and rheuma-
tism! The Chinese still treat or "cure" dropsy with toad-
skin preparations, as did Europe up to 1775, when it was
supplanted by digitalis. But if the colonists had persevered
they might have isolated from their toads, as did Abel, a
crystal composed of $C_{18}H_{24}O_4$ and called *bufagin (bufo,
toad)* with the property of a powerful heart stimulant and
thereby good for dropsy. But they could not have derived
epinephrin from their toads because they did not have the

right kind of toads. Epinephrin is found in the skin glands of external secretion of an Upper Amazon toad. The secretion of these skin glands smeared on arrows makes a fine poison for the natives, so powerful that in a few moments it will kill a deer or a jaguar. The skin of that Amazon toad contains both epinephrin and bufagin, both powerful drugs, acting fatally on the heart and blood vessels. Imagine what happens to the animal that eats that toad!

Which brings us back to adrenin, a powerful drug, a powerful cardio-vascular stimulant. Normally our blood contains about eight milligrams of it, which means that the proportion of adrenin to arterial blood is one part to a billion. Administered as one part in twenty million, it acts on the uterus and is a useful drug in hemorrhages following delivery. It influences some tissues when diluted to one part in 100,000,-000. It depresses the intestinal canal when diluted to one part in 330,000,000! What such dilution means has been worked out in terms of street sprinklers each of 625 gallons capacity. A procession of such sprinklers twenty miles long and 200 to the mile would hold just enough water to dilute one ounce of adrenin down to one dose. Large doses are fatal.

Adrenin is a drug, one of the most potent our body concocts. Yet adrenal feeding leads to no known or proved results. The administration of the drug adrenalin does lead to profound results. Our body blood contains this drug. Whether it is made by or excreted by the adrenals is still an open question, but that adrenin has specific action on the vascular system, the nervous system, the blood, the alimentary canal, and on sugar mobilization, there is no doubt. Nor is there any doubt that when administered as a drug it increases the action of local anesthetics by constricting the blood vessels, thus preventing local loss of the anesthetic. And as this reduces the amount of anesthetic required, it also reduces the amount of toxin danger from the anesthetic. It checks hemorrhages. It allays the spasms of acute bronchial asthma. It also stimulates weak hearts and fortifies the hearts of the old and infirm against the shock of operation.

In short, adrenalin exerts an influence upon all smooth muscle enervated by fibers of the autonomic nervous system. That makes its responsibility enormous, its influence on human destiny second to none.

What, then, is the nature of this tiny but potent capsule tucked away in the depths of the abdominal cavity, nestling above the great excretory organs of the blood? Recall the potency of a toad's bufagin to control the heart, the potency of a toad's epinephrin to kill a strong animal. Try to picture a molecule of human adrenin from the above formula. Realize the close association of the fundamental vital processes with the autonomic system. Is the human adrenal a "brain" which takes charge of us when we are confronted by emergencies which mean life or death? It may be thought of in that way.

5

In crises our body goes on a "war footing"—as our country did a few years ago. Piano manufacturers began to make airplanes. Artists turned from painting corset advertisements to camouflaging battleships. Our sugar rations were cut that the fighters might have enough. The entire plant of the nation turned from peaceful pursuits to speed up the fuel for the engines of war. Life had become a dog-fight.

Ever try to take a bone from a dog? Or observe a cat when a dog suddenly appears? Or a mother when some one injures her child? How do you feel when you are "horror-stricken," "sick with disgust," "paralyzed with fear," "crazy with pain," or so mad you "choke?" Tongue cleaving to the roof of the mouth, "cold-sweat," pupils of the eyes dilated, pounding heart, hurried breathing, hair on end, muscles of face and especially of the lips trembling and twitching: such are among the obvious *symptoms* of pain, of horror, of fear, etc.

We recognize many emotional states and are subject to them in varying intensity: pain, anger, fear, rage, horror, sorrow, anxiety, grief, terror, disgust. An insulting word may literally alter our entire nature. We *feel* these states; we observe the results in others. What is not so obvious is that the body itself often undergoes profound physiological change.

The mechanism by which our natures can be suddenly altered is to be found in the middle or sympathetic division of the autonomic nervous system and—according to the theory—the secretion of the medulla of the adrenal gland. The way these two work together and the striking, sudden, and far-reaching consequences of their actions, form the basis for Cannon's claim in 1914 that adrenin is nature's reply to the crises, the unexpected do-or-die emergencies of living animals. Emotional behavior gets its kick from adrenin. With adrenin cowards may fight for their lives, brave men may surpass themselves, and all of us can run as we never ran before; or shed tears of sorrow over the loss of friends.

There are three divisions of the autonomic nervous system. The upper, or *cranial,* is concerned with the joys and sorrows of life. Its nerves conserve the body, building up reserves and fortifying the body for times of crises. By narrowing the pupils they shield the eye from too much light. By slowing the heartbeat they give the heart muscles longer periods for rest. By causing the mouth to water they set the juice flowing and supply muscular tone for the alimentary canal's ceaseless movements. The lower, or *sacral,* division covers the emptying mechanisms of large intestine and urogenital system; relief and comfort acts.

Between cranial and sacral is the *sympathetic* division— enormously important. It dilates the pupils of the eyes, hurries up heartbeat, stands hairs on end by causing each smooth hair-muscle to contract, opens sweat glands (pouring out excess heat), stops movements in stomach and intestine, releases sugar (the best fighting fuel) from the liver; and releases adrenin. *The medulla of the adrenal, alone of all the*

213

endocrine glands, is connected with the autonomic nervous system.

Here is the point. Adrenin itself, injected into the blood, will dilate pupils, stand hairs on end, constrict blood vessels, stop the vegetative activities in alimentary canal, and release sugar from the liver. Remove the liver from the body, keep it alive artificially: adrenin will cause it to release sugar.

The real business of the adrenal glands, according to Cannon's theory, is emergency function. When we must fight or run for our lives, our body has no time to fool with a mouth watering for its appetite or several yards of alimentary canal activity. The test tubes for chemical action, and the fires to keep these actions going, must be neglected for the moment. Their energy must be made available for action in the big striped muscles of the motor fighting-or-fleeing mechanism.

When a joy is so strong or a sorrow or a disgust so deep that it breaks over the threshold of the cranial division and enters the sympathetic, we lose our appetite: no saliva, no gastric or pancreatic juice, no movement in the intestine. Even an empty stomach stops growling and holds its peace when war is on.

And war is on when any of life's instinctive acts with emotional trimmings are thwarted. Anger. The body is prepared to fight. All its life long life has had to know how to kill, how to avoid death. It has had to learn to count on its muscles and its nerves when the test comes. Adrenin is supposed to be the answer.

According to Cannon's theory, adrenin bucks us up. It speeds up the heartbeat. Draws blood from spleen, kidneys, intestines, and other inhibited organs of the abdomen—thus also reducing their size. Drives blood to the skeletal muscles, brain, and lungs. Relaxes the smooth muscles of the tiny air sacs in the lungs, thus facilitating the exchange of carbon dioxide waste for the greater oxygen required in great effort. Orders the liver to give the blood more sugar, the optimum source of muscle energy. Drives fatigue from the muscles.

Contracts the blood vessels of the skin and makes the blood coagulate more quickly, so lessening our liability of bleeding to death in case of wound. Adrenin wins battles and makes men brave; lack of it may make them cowards.

It has been urged against Cannon's hypothesis that it is not yet conclusively proved. What is proved is that without adrenals—or accessory adrenals—no man lives; with adrenin far-reaching changes occur which, combined, transform the vegetation body into a fighting machine. Nor is there any doubt as to what our emotions do to us. The rôle that Cannon ascribes to the adrenals is reasonable and plausible; it has proved to be a working hypothesis in biology.

6

The *pituitary* gland is about as big as the tip of the little finger, hangs from the base of the brain by a hollow stem (hence also called the *hypophysis cerebri*), and is housed in a pocket of the sphenoid bone called the Turk's saddle. It is as near the center of the head as it can get; hence operation on the pituitary is enormously difficult. But if the patient —dog or man—does not die from brain injury, removal of the pituitary itself is not fatal. It is not a vital organ, but a normal pituitary is essential to normal life.

The gland has two lobes, each of different embryonic origin, and probably different in function. The *anterior* lobe is much the larger and is an ectoderm structure, arising as a fold of the lining of the mouth. Its structure is that of a gland and it has a rich blood supply. It does not remain constant in size. It seems to be associated with rate of growth and sexual development. Its removal is followed by many symptoms, but which are due to its removal, which to injuries to the brain, is uncertain. A substance called *tethelin* prepared from this lobe has been used experimentally and otherwise, but no chemical individual has yet been isolated. It is claimed, but not proved, that tethelin hurries sexual maturity in the young and promotes sex activity in adults.

The *posterior* lobe arises from the floor of the third ventricle of the brain and is largely nerve tissue. For a dozen years its active principle was known to science and used as an extract called *pituitrin* by physicians and surgeons, especially as a rival to ergot in obstetrics. Used in overdoses or at the wrong stage of childbirth, it caused several deaths, because it can so act on the uterus as to tear it open.

Abel is convinced that the posterior lobe has only one hormone and not four, as had been claimed by German chemists. From it he has only recently isolated a pure tartrate which he characterizes as "extraordinarily potent" and endowed with several different and distinct properties. It is a thousand times more powerful than any hitherto known stimulant for non-skeletal muscle tissue—a thousand times more powerful than the "extract" pituitrin which, wrongly used, could tear a uterus asunder!

Recall the twenty-mile procession of street sprinklers required to reduce an ounce of epinephrin to a test dose: to reduce an equal amount of Abel's pituitary hormone would require not twenty miles of sprinklers, but 5,000 miles! The actual test was made on a virgin guinea-pig's uterus; it contracted when suspended in a solution of one part hormone to 18,750,000,000 parts water. Such facts, as Hoskins says, make endocrinology kin to astronomy.

This hormone acts on the entire cardio-vascular apparatus. By restricting the small blood vessels it causes prolonged rise of blood pressure. It acts upon the respiration, causing a rhythmic increase of breathing up to a certain degree of rapidity, then a gradual decrease again to a temporary stoppage of breathing.

When injected daily it has proved a remarkable remedy in the disease known as *diabetes insipidus,* not to be confounded with sugar or mellitus diabetes. In the latter the kidneys eliminate sugar that belongs to the blood and is needed by the body. In insipidus, it is claimed the kidneys leave so much sugar in the blood that the body gets fat. But the danger in diabetes insipidus is the excessive and uncontrollable elimination of water by the kidneys and a consequent incessant thirst.

"Joe," the fat boy of *Pickwick Papers*, had a fat chest, flabby muscles, and sexual infantilism. To-day "Joe" would be diagnosed as *dystrophia adiposogenitalis*. The anterior lobe of his pituitary was probably diseased and consequently under-functioned.

Too much activity in the anterior lobe in early life is believed but not proved to lead to gigantism, in later life to acromegaly. There seems to be no doubt that the pituitary gland is closely related to growth, especially in connective tissue, cartilage and bone, and sex-gland activity. But where abnormal growth occurs it is rarely possible to say whether it results from specific activity—too much or too little—in the gland, or from the pressure of a tumor on or in the gland or on the floor of the third ventricle of the brain. Other glands than the pituitary may be involved when the pituitary itself is abnormal. Whether the pituitary was the primary or the secondary cause of the upset in response to growth stimuli is not yet known.

Abnormal adult growth changes known as acromegaly are characteristic and unmistakable: enlarged bones of the head, hands, and feet, general lassitude, pains in the muscles, lack of interest, and depressed sex activity often leading to impotence or amenorrhea.

The famous Irish giant Magrath had a pituitary as big as a hen's egg. His hands resembled shoulders of mutton, his lower jaw was a massive appendage to a huge face. A diseased pituitary in a normal adult caused the face to grow massive and ugly, with bulging masses about the eyes, the nose huge, the lips thick; the chest huge and barrel-shaped; the hands and feet of enormous size. A dwarf of twenty years with an under-developed pituitary had the bones of a child a few weeks old. Another dwarf of mature years and so tiny as to have been "served" in a pie at the Duke of Buckingham's table in honor of the Queen of Charles I, began a second period of growth. Some alteration in the pituitary, possibly.

That the pituitary is concerned in sex growth is inferred from the fact that it becomes enlarged following castration; as it also does during pregnancy when the ovaries temporarily change their function. It is suggestive also that at that time the hands sometimes enlarge and the face changes.

Perhaps no structure, in proportion to its size, is more interesting or of less importance than our *pineal* gland. Of the size of a grain of wheat, it lies high up in the base of the brain behind and above the pituitary. It reaches full development at the seventh year, then begins to atrophy, and in adults has become connective tissue and "brain sand": minute grains of phosphate and carbonate of lime. This "sand" is often found elsewhere in the brain, even in fetal life.

Descartes held that the pineal is the seat of the soul. He was long on philosophy, but short on comparative anatomy. Yet possibly he was nearer the truth than he realized. Millions of years ago the pineal was a third eye and looked straight up to heaven. Extinct reptiles have a hole in the skull for this pineal eye. The sphenodon, an almost extinct New Zealand reptile, is the only living animal with a pineal organ that resembles a true eye. Most lizards have a pineal organ, and, above, a hole in the roof of the skull. The hole is covered by a scale; the organ, therefore, cannot function as a true eye, it may serve as an organ for sensing lights and shadows. Except the lowest fishes, all vertebrates have a relic of this "eye." In Man the "relic" has a vestige of the optic nerve.

No pineal hormone has yet been discovered, nor is it yet certain that it is a gland. Nothing certain is known of its function, nor is it certain that it has any importance beyond pre-adolescence, if it has any then. From the fact that tumors of the pineal are often associated with precocious mental and sexual development, it is inferred that its business is to promote early physical growth and retard sexual development. But this is only inference—the tumor may also have involved the mid-brain.

7

To Lavoisier's dictum: "Life is a chemical function," we might add, "and ceases to function without sugar." At any rate, we eat more sugar than we should, because our body finds sugar where we little suspect it. Sugar is the finest fuel our blood can find to keep life on the move. When anything happens to our sugar refinery, sugar storage, or sugar delivery, we suffer from one of several more or less fatal diseases.

The regulator of sugar metabolism is a group of secreting organs known as the *islands of Langerhans,* in the "sweetbreads" or *pancreas,* and which act as a gland of internal secretion. Its hormone, *insulin,* is delivered direct to the blood. Pancreatic juice, an important digestive fluid, is delivered by the duct of Wirsung to the alimentary canal.

Diabetes (from the Greek "to go through") follows when the islands of Langerhans stop functioning. The isolation of insulin, chiefly due to Banting and McLeod, ends a search of many long years and closes one of the most interesting chapters in the new science of endocrines. There is a remedy for diabetes mellitus, but no cure. Life can be prolonged "indefinitely"; but insulin feeding alone will not prevail without control of diet.

It is significant that of the more than a million sufferers from diabetes in this country 90 per cent are overweight; and that of those over fifty years of age there are twenty fat for every thin diabetic sufferer. From which we infer that the human pancreas as regulator of sugar metabolism tends to break down when we take on more fat than we require. We take on fat when we eat more sugars and fats than we use up.

The pancreas is a very vital organ. Its removal, or the removal of seven-eighths of it, is followed by a condition like that of diabetes: increased urine, abnormal thirst and hunger, death. Its hormone, delivered to the blood, regulates the output of glycogen from the liver, and is necessary for the building of glycogen and the oxidation of sugar by the body tissues. This is the route:

The portal blood carries glucose to the liver. The liver converts glucose into glycogen (animal starch). The liver itself is not an endocrine gland, although it does deliver sugar to the blood direct. It stores up no hormones, but it reeks with extracts. It stores vitamins; it destroys fat; it stores glycogen. It is a vital organ. Nothing takes its place or can do its refining. All its processes depend upon its own liver cells. How it converts sugar into animal starch for storage purposes and how it reconverts it into sugar when the secretion from the islands of Langerhans tells it to do so, are not known. It does. If the islands stop sending messages, the liver gives up all its sugar to the blood, but the body cells cannot store or burn it and so it is filtered by the kidneys from the blood and passed on to the bladder.

The spleen has no duct; it has no secretions. It is not a gland. Just what it is no one knows. Its functions are not specific, nor does its removal seem to impair health, growth, or longevity. In the fetus it is probably an incubator for red blood-cells; after birth it seems to be an incinerator of red blood-cells. They work so hard carrying oxygen they wear themselves out in from ten to fifteen days. Perhaps 10 per cent of all red blood-cells are destroyed each day. It is possible that an "enlarged" spleen destroys red cells faster than it should; it may therefore be responsible for chronic anemia. It does produce a chemical catalyzer; its enzymes convert nucleins into uric acid.

The secretions of the stomach and small intestine—gastrin

and secretin—are drugs to be used on the spot. They are dangerous drugs if used elsewhere in or on the body. Stomach and intestine may produce hormones. May. If they do, they presumably regulate the pancreas, gastric glands, etc.

Neither lymph nor lymph "gland" has any endocrine function. Nor has the blood. A quart of my blood may tide you over until you can make enough to supply your loss. But my blood is my blood; it is in dynamic equilibrium, constantly changing to meet the specific requirements of the particular families of cells on its route in my body.

Kidneys, if veal or sheep, are good to eat. They are good as food. But "extract of kidney" is as good to repair a faulty kidney, or to treat uremia or nephritis, as powdered glass is to restore a watch crystal. The kidney is not a gland, it secretes nothing. It is a filter or excretory organ.

Other "extracts" are doped out to meet the demand. Brains for dementia præcox, tetanus, epilepsy, etc. Such treatment, says Carlson, is "less rational than the principles and practices of Mrs. Eddy. Perhaps we could make for greater progress if the manufacturers [of dried brains] could be induced to use the brains of horses instead of asses and sheep for their raw material, and the finished product was taken by the doctor instead of being given to the patient."

Dried lungs, tonsils, retina, iris, nasal mucous membrane, and such can be had in the drug stores; "cures" for tuberculosis, tonsilitis, etc. Rubbish. The few hormones that are really known are so powerful, so useful, so wonderful, that they have encouraged imitators. The result is a new crowd of quacks, ready to "feed" anybody anything that sounds like something and is therefore presumably a remedy.

8

Gonads is Greek for seeds. As the organs or glands of reproduction of both sexes produce seeds, it is a convenient and polite word for testes and ovaries. But the newspapers in referring to gonad operations, rejuvenescence, etc., always speak of "glands." Only the context makes it certain that the "glands" referred to are not the parotid or thyroid or some other equally "respectable" gland.

This reluctance—which Robinson characterizes as "shame-faced, prudish, and squeamish"—to face the facts necessary to solve some of the simple but vital problems of everyday life is almost a chronic psychosis, with signs now and then of a tendency to sanity.

Psychology has diagnosed the "impurity complex" and shown us what is back of the blatant prude who advertises his or her "purity." It has also shown that the purity of the ignorant, when purchased at the price of a stifled natural curiosity, is not a safe and sane "purity." The study of biology has begun to break down this impurity complex and the unholy, unnatural doctrine begun by early Christian monks that the sex impulse is man's sign of degradation and the source of his most devilish energy. Nature knows better.

Sex is a primary biologic function of all life above the lowest. Its characters and qualities have an ancient lineage. Its impulse is as real as is the force which makes the tides to ebb and flow. It has profoundly influenced structure and behavior. It is a fundamental element of all higher life; its external characters a neat advertising dodge of Nature by which she sells her wares and thereby insures her family.

To sex we owe more than poetry; we owe the song of birds, all vocal music and the voice itself, the plumage that comes to supreme glory in the bird of paradise, the mane of the lion, the tresses of women, the blush of the maiden, the beard of men, and all higher forms of life in plant and animal world. It is woven into every fabric of human life and lays its finger on every custom. To the debit side of the sex account we must charge many silly stupidities and some of the foulest injustices which go to make the thing we call human culture the amazing and variegated mosaic that it is.

We are more enlightened than we were, but we have not

yet reached the stage where the mere mention of sex will not provoke some one to respond with a reproach or an insult. Whole blocks on Main Street assume that "sex knowledge" is of questionable propriety, or, at best, to be kept dark in "doctor-books"; or regard it as the banal possession of the frankly shameless. As a result, most pseudo-scientific "sex" literature slops over into the emotions and lets facts alone, or presents facts under disguises. Much of it has no biologic background or anything of the laws of life which govern man no less than every living thing. It is fear (sometimes called "reverence") that makes us "let sex alone." It is mock modesty and foolish shame, masquerading under the name "decency," that compels museums to clothe marble Fauns and plaster Joves and bronze Cupids with plaster-of-Paris fig leaves, often awry or nicked at the corner.

Back of much of this confusion and nonsense is the paradox which culminated in Puritanism: Marriage is a divine institution and the god of Love is a saint, but sex is shameful and Cupid is a carnal beast.

Man is "high," "animals" are "low"—without minds and of course can have no "souls." We have. Ours is a "divine" parentage, our bodies "sacred." Hence art, from Phidian sculpture to sophomoric poem, tends to the greater glory of Man: men and women more like gods and goddesses; gods and goddesses glorified men and women.

And so it came about that the commonest thing in nature next to keeping alive became invested with the sanctity of heaven. Love begins with a capital "L" because it is sacred. So it is. Without it the world of man stops. There would be no more fishes in the sea if the males did not like the females. Love is fine. Put it on a pedestal, magnify it, glorify it, deify it. But why leave Cupid on the pedestal? To worship him blindly is on a par with any other fetishism, and quite as intelligent. Take him down and dust him off, repair his broken ears, mend his battered nose, refeather his

arrows and restring his bow. Why not have a look at him?
What is he made of?

9

Certain glands are essential to life. Their removal is followed by death. Not so the gonads proper. They may be
removed, in fact are constantly being removed—especially
those of women—in the operating rooms. What happens?
The patient lives. The gonads are not necessary for individual life, only for that of the race or species.

Physical differences between men and women are *sexual*.
There are *primary* and *secondary* differences. The secondary characters begin to assume definite form in both sexes
at the beginning of puberty. These characters are by-
products of the male and female gonads.

The gonads are like true duct glands in that they discharge
their secretion through ducts, but this secretion, unlike that
of other duct glands, is not discharged into and consumed
by the parent body. The gonads have an additional function: they secrete a hormone which regulates the appearance
and growth of the secondary characters and supplies the
impulse back of sex behavior. In this they are like true
endocrines, which deliver their regulating secretions direct
to the blood stream. Thus the gonads are also glands of
internal secretion.

For ages it has been known that boys or girls deprived of
their gonads before puberty develop into "womanly" men or
"manly" women and throughout life retain an infantile type
of body. Eunuchs ("guardians of the couch," created for
religious and social ends), develop neither the voice nor the
beard of men; in women similarly altered the mammary
glands remain undeveloped, their bodies do not become so
feminine.

Experiments on chickens show that when the ovaries are
completely removed from a young hen, she begins to take

on the secondary sexual characters of the male: she develops comb, wattles, and spurs; her plumage becomes more brilliant; she grows larger; she takes on the typical behavior of the rooster. This can only mean that the ovary itself, by its own internal secretion taken up into the blood stream, has power to modify the body in the direction of the female sex. It has been inferred that secondary male characters were potentially present in the hen, but were inhibited by the ovaries.

Moore implanted a piece of ovary in a young male guinea-pig. His body was modified; his teats came to resemble those of a pregnant female. His behavior showed no sign of acquired feminine instincts. Another investigator reports "timid, shy, and mothering-the-young" behavior of a guinea-pig thus altered. But all investigators agree that the male gonad transplanted into an altered young female leads to change in both body and behavior. She becomes aggressive, quarrelsome, and behaves like a typical male toward other males and toward females in general. Her physical modification is equally profound.

Cattle breeders have long known that the female of bisexual twins is generally sterile and tends toward the male in physical characters. Such sterile females are called *freemartins*. Lillie investigated. The twins, it seems, develop independently in the two horns of the cow's uterus, but join below in the outer fetal envelope. Through this they exchange blood. The precocious hormone of the fetal male sterilizes the fetal female ovary! It seems so extraordinary as to be almost incredible.

But there is no doubt about sterile freemartins, nor about the fact of their intercommunicating arterial blood stream in fetal development. Lillie's conclusions mean that the male fetus secretes a specific gonad hormone before its gonads are really formed; this male hormone sterilizes the female gonad.

The fact that both pancreas and thyroid hormones are

known to be secreted in intrauterine life lends weight to the inference that the sex hormones themselves are produced by the primitive germ cells. That there is no exchange of gonad hormones between the human fetus and its mother seems evident from the fact that the developing male fetus does not influence the sex life of the mother.

In other words, while the nature of the sex impulse is the same in the two sexes, the sex hormones themselves are not the same. But they are not antagonistic. "Maleness" can be produced in females; "femaleness" in males. The male hormone in a young spayed female modifies both her behavior and her body. The female hormone in a castrated young male body modifies only the body.

The male fetus does not modify its mother: she is still in possession of her own gonads. The male fetus modifies the behavior and sterilizes the gonads of its twin female fetus. Human twins, if "identical," are always of the same sex; if not identical there is no exchange of blood, for each has its own fetal membranes.

10

The adult female gonads in mammals contain ova in varying stages of ripening and interstitial stroma or cells. Both seem to have an identical origin and both pass through similar changes in development.

The ova or germ-cells develop in Graafian follicles. When ripe they burst through the wall of the ovary. The ovum escapes. The ruptured follicle reassembles and enlarges for about a week, filling the rent in the ovarian wall. Then it breaks up and is absorbed before the next follicle matures. But if the ovum is fertilized, the follicle continues to develop for three months and then persists until the end of pregnancy. The ruptured and changing follicle is called the *corpus luteum* (yellow body) because of its color after the escape of the ovum. Corpora lutea are supposed to produce a hormone. The ovary does produce hormones, how or where is not well understood; nor, in fact, has the ovary itself parted with half of its mysteries.

Removal of the ovary or its absence or atrophy in the young is followed by an arrest of secondary sexual characters. The primary sexual characters, including the breasts, remain in an infantile condition. The lunar cycle does not appear. The body tends toward fat. Removal in the adult leads to atrophy of the primary sexual characters, the suppression of all sex functions, and of most sex behavior.

The ovary can be transplanted from one part of the body to another; it long continues to function as an endocrine gland, no femininity is lost, nor does the lunar cycle cease. When transplanted from one body to another it may form blood connections, but it eventually degenerates. But as long as a piece of it remains alive in its new hostess her sex life, including lunar cycle, continues "normal."

For transplantation purposes a bit is as good as the entire ovary. Where, then, does its hormone come from? It produces one: Carlson thinks probably several. None has yet been isolated or can be detected in the human blood. But Allen and Doisy claim to have isolated a mammalian ovary hormone which resembles the long-desired "love potion" of romance and literature. "Female animals treated with it take the initiative in courtship, even at an early age." Injected into young animals, they "become mature before they normally would."

This hormone is an "extract of the contents" of the Graafian follicles. Why not? It is all plausible. Nothing seems more certain than that the sex impulse and all secondary sexual characters in all mammalian females are dependent upon the normal functioning of the ovaries. The physiological and anatomical changes in the Graafian follicles during the life cycle are both profound and significant. As they are the source of the ova, it is reasonable to suppose that they carry the control of sex impulse or behavior and the acquired secondary characters.

When the follicle erupts and discharges the ovum, it becomes the corpus luteum. When the corpus luteum is destroyed, pregnancy ends and ovulation is resumed. Hence the inference that the corpus luteum is responsible for uterine changes leading to the implantation of the embryo and for the early growth of the fetus. When corpora lutea are fed to hens, they lay no eggs; hence the inference that during pregnancy they inhibit the ripening of the Graafian follicle and so prevent ovulation and menstruation and restrain the sex impulse. They influence the mammary glands, but the development of these during pregnancy is believed to be due to hormones from the fetus to the maternal blood. The mammæ themselves are not known to have any endocrine function. Their removal does not prevent child-bearing or have any other effect than "psychic and cosmetic," according to Carlson. But removal of the ovary is removal of feminine nature.

No mammals below Primates have anything approaching the specific lunar cycle of a woman's life between puberty and the menopause. While slight menstrual hemorrhage occurs in many species of Primates, it is essentially a human process regulated by the normal and mature ovum, but its function is not yet understood nor is there agreement as to just what takes place or why there is such wide range of individual variation. The *climacteric* is reached when no more Graafian follicles mature.

Disordered sex life—except the menopause—in woman may be due to other than ovarian deficiencies: other endocrines may be involved, perhaps the adrenals or the pituitary. It is not certain that *ovarian extracts* are anything but extracts and so of possible value only through suggestion. Nor can *luteal extracts* check human ovulation; the corpus luteum can. Nor is it at all certain that any ovarian extracts on the market contain any hormone. It is certain that the normal ovary, through its hormones, functions for all secondary female characters and has the specific sex functions for such distant organs as uterus, placenta, and mammæ.

The functions of personal incubation assumed by one-half of the race ages ago necessitated an elaborate internal mechanism. For its perfect functioning, elaborate and complicated controls were necessary. It follows, and is biologically inevitable, that the sex life of the female of the human species is far more complex than is that of the male. But it is biologically conceivable that in a no great distant future reproduction in the human species can be radically altered. Under such controlled breeding, the ovaries of only physically sound individuals would be used and to the limit of their two hundred ova; these would be fertilized artificially and developed in man-made incubators. Such control of human life seems quite attainable; much more so than the synthesis of life in any form.

11

The male gonads contain spermatogonia. These develop into germ-cells and fertilize the ovum. This involves two factors: the ovum is stimulated to develop; the male inheritance is afforded a vehicle. The gonad performs this function through external secretions. But as the spermatogonia themselves are cells early set aside in embryonic development and are not products of chemical change as are the secretions of other duct glands, the gonads in their reproductive functions are not comparable to other glands. They, as the ovaries, are arsenals where ammunition for life is cultivated.

Between the cell clusters where spermatogonia develop are other groups of cells, the *interstitial cells of Leydig*. These cells appear in the embryo before the spermatogonia cells. Under the X-rays they are not affected; the sperm-cells are. When the gonad does not descend, or in one transplanted into another body, the germ-cells atrophy; the Leydig cells are unaffected or may increase in size. Thus they show greater power of resistance than the germ-cells; they are embryologically older.

Absence, atrophy, or extirpation of the gonads in the young male prevents the appearance of the secondary sexual characters—beard, change in the larynx and character of skeleton—and checks development of the reproductive mechanism. It also delays the final ossification of the heads of the long bones and the sutures of the skull. It lowers the rate of metabolism, increases the tendency to take on fat, and lowers vasomotor irritability. It perhaps leads to changes in the endocrine system, enlarging the adrenal cortex and the pituitary, diminishing thyroid growth, checking thymus involution. It changes behavior: less bold, less pugnacious, more infantile; it shuts off the sex impulse. In the adult, loss of gonads stops the sex impulse and tends to atrophy of the reproductive mechanism, to obesity and lowered metabolism.

Nothing else. Life is not shortened, nor mental or physical efficiency impaired. Hence, as Carlson points out, "growing old" is not to be charged to gonad dysfunction, but to damage by age to all the tissues of the body. Gonad removal leads only to loss of structure and function specific for sex life.

Curiously, evidence seems to indicate that gonadectomy in the two sexes leads to opposite changes in the adrenals: in males, to an increase of 15 per cent; in females, to a decrease of 20 per cent. The net result is to increase the resemblance between the two sexes.

The spermatogonia cells are simply future germs. This throws the responsibility for the regulation of the development of sex mechanism and function on the interstitial cells. Moore has recently furnished new proof of this. In *cryptorchic* individuals (the gonads remain within the abdominal cavity) there may or there may not be spermatogonia; if not, the individual is, of course, sterile, but if the Leydig cells are present, the individual is male in structure, function, and behavior.

When the *vas deferens* or excretory duct of the gonad is ligatured, the spermatogonia are said, but not proved, to atrophy; the germ-cells cannot, of course, be discharged and consequently the individual is sterile. But as long as the Leydig cells are intact, sex life is unimpaired. This is the basis of the famous operation of Steinach, and is based on two assumptions: that ligation of the *vas deferens* increases Leydig cell growth; that it causes the spermatogonia apparatus to atrophy. Neither of these assumptions is yet proved; in fact, Oslund asserts that both assumptions are contrary to fact, that vasectomy produces no testicular changes and "cannot be looked upon as a method of causing rejuvenescence."

When gonads are transplanted into other male bodies, the individual maintains sex life as long as enough Leydig cells remain alive. This was Steinach's first method of "rejuvenation": "a biological futility, a catering by the surgeon to the elements of sex degeneracy," says Carlson. And adds: if the transplant be from goat or monkey, "the surgeon is the monkey, the patient is the goat."

Grafts of goats or monkeys are not yet known to become vascularized, nor is it known that the Leydig cells survive up to two years. It is known that the sperm-cells do not survive transplanting. It is not settled how long a gonad will live after removal: "most glands die in a few hours." At most, the graft can only temporarily restore the sex impulse; any true "rejuvenescence" of mind or body can only come from suggestion.

Suggestion likewise, thinks Carlson, is all that backs the whole tribe of "genital" extracts on the market and which are guaranteed "cures" for everything from growing pains to melancholia, including goiter, scurvy, cholera, anemia, delirium tremens, and syphilis.

The adrenal cortex and Leydig cells have a common embryonic origin, but they come to have quite different functions. No gland can play the rôle of the Leydig cells; if they are lost, sex life is lost. The only compensation possible is in the direction of general metabolism.

In both sexes, gonad hormones are specific regulators of sex characters up to puberty; the hormones that sustain sex life during maturity are possibly quite different from those which determined development. They are the catalyzers of development; they must vary with the stage or degree of development.

12

The race of bisexual animals depends on the coming together of male and female. Moths find their mates by their olfactory antennæ; fishes, by color and behavior; frogs, by voice and touch; birds, by voice and sight; mammals, by scent. Man is a mammal, but he has traded his scent organ for a nose and he kills his odor with soaps or artificial scents. He discovers his mate, as do birds, by voice and sight. Either sex, deprived of the gonads, has no need for secondary characters; nor do they appear unless the gonads function as endocrine or "puberty" glands. That is the business of the hormones of the gonads: so to catalyze developing structure that the two sexes already determined in prenatal development will not look or sound alike, but will look and sound good to each other. Secondary sex characters, therefore, are additional devices of nature for making each sex easily recognized by and more attractive to the opposite sex. Hence the "instinctive" repugnance of normal men for "manly" women; of normal women for "womanly" men.

Puberty means sexual maturity; the individual is ready to assume the next stage in normal development: parentage. Modern life departs from the normal; it pays no attention to the facts of puberty. The age of marriage tends to become more and more remote from sex maturity; the education of the youth proceeds as though there were no such thing as puberty.

In normal life in girls, as in the females of all mammals, the milk glands at puberty take on rapid growth. The most noticeable changes in the boy are the appearance of hair on the face and a startling change in the growth of the cartilages and vocal cords of the larynx. The voice at first breaks; by the time it becomes normal again it has, as a rule, dropped one full octave. Meanwhile the boy outgrows his collars faster than he does his hats. In both sexes hair appears on the pubes.

While early growth depends on the amount and nature of the food and on general hygienic conditions, puberty as a rule appears earliest in individuals of short stature. Thus, it comes earlier among Italians than Scandinavians, the difference agreeing with the relative statures of the two peoples.

Girls of European descent grow faster than boys between the ages of ten and fifteen. Between eleven and fourteen the girls are actually taller; between twelve and fifteen, heavier. At fifteen the rate of the girl's growth begins to diminish. The skeleton begins to mature, for both sexes, at puberty. The girl's pelvic girdle undergoes a marked change in width. She also becomes more plump.

Between the fourteenth and eighteenth years for girls, and between the fifteenth and twentieth years for boys, a new impulse enters life. This impulse, only vaguely present before, is now the impelling force. For this reason: puberty means more than mere physical change, it means sex *maturity*; it is a result as well as an event. Besides the physical changes which increase the demands for food-energy, the whole organism is involved in maturity.

The boy or girl is now preoccupied with a new order of internal affairs. This necessarily involves the entire nervous mechanism—not in its structure, but in the nature of the situations to which it must now adjust the individual. The second great crisis in life is at hand. It is a different individual, the world itself is different. Up till now the primordial instinct of self-preservation has had only one main drive: food-hunger; to this is now added the drive of mate-hunger. It enters the race fresh and will have its say. The body itself, under both direct and indirect influence of the sex mechanism, is stirred to its depths. The inhibitory centers in the spinal cord are lowered; the susceptibility of the brain is increased through the vasomotor nerves.

The outcome of the conflict is determined by many factors. In animal life and the majority of the human race, the result is courtship and mating. We generally solve the problem satisfactorily, but promiscuity and certain unbiologic and unsocial habits, with sex complexes leading to neuroses, seem to be increasing.

But the real point in all this is that the gonads normally do function as endocrine glands. As a consequence the two sexes do differ, in bodily structure, in behavior, in organic necessity. As Ellis puts it: "A man is a man to his very thumbs, and a woman is a woman down to her little toes." Specialization in bodies is older than civilization, and there has always been a real difference between men and women beyond that of the primary sex organs. Which prompts Keith to remark: "No legislation can blot out structural differences that have taken geological epochs to produce." But substitution of gonads can. In fact, Riddle cites two cases of female birds that laid eggs and were in all respects true females; they ceased to be females, became males in form and function, and fathered young. No surgical operation involved: only destruction of female organs due to tuberculosis; male organs replaced them, followed by male behavior. What all this signifies is not yet known. But this much, at least: sexual characters depend on sex hormones; complete sex-transformation in adults is possible.

Shorn of her locks and dressed in man's costume, woman is still woman. Yet how many times she has passed for a man—as a sailor, a soldier, a coal-miner! Her femininity tends to disappear beneath the male's make-up. The two sexes differ in degree rather than in kind.

The assumption that women are not as "adult" as men has no basis in fact. Yet we keep hearing about the "infantile" character of woman! Her body does more nearly resemble the infant's than does the male's, but this only states half the truth. In all that is essentially "human," her body is more human than man's. The adult male may be less infantile than the adult female; he is also less essentially "human."

The typical female skull is so delicate and smooth that sex can be postulated nineteen times out of twenty. It has none of the asperities, ridges, and prominences which mark the skull of the male. The bones of her face, especially of the jaws, are much more "human" than are the corresponding bones in man's jaws.

The weight of the skull compared with the weight of the long bones shows this interesting progression: greatest proportionate weight of skull, children first, women next; then short men, tall men, apes. In weight of skull compared with that of thigh bones, the advantage again is with woman.

Our pelvic girdle is in some respects more "human" than the skull itself. It is the distinguishing sex trait in the skeleton. To the trained observer there is no mistaking the pelvic girdle of a female for that of a male. A moment's reflection will show why this should be so. In man, the pelvis supports the abdominal viscera and continues the support of the upright body from the legs. To perform these two functions it became modified in two directions: broader, by expansion of the iliac crests; more compact and substantial, by a greater, broader sacrum. The sacrum is the key of the pelvic arch; it carries the backbone, and incidentally the entire upper part of the body. Woman's pelvis has traveled further than man's in this regard. Her breadth across iliac crests is proportionately greater than the depth from pubic symphysis to top of sacrum. Her sacrum also is more distinctively human in its great breadth.

The two bones which form the basin of the pelvis—of which the iliac crests are easily felt beneath the skin at the sides of our abdomen—meet in front to form the pubic symphysis. The joint of the symphysis is made by a strong ligament which yields under pressure. In the male pelvis the ligament is narrow; in the female, wide. The slope of the pubic bones below the joint is also greater in the female, an additional factor in enlarging the outlet of her pelvis.

Can our pelvic girdle become more "human"? The upper rim might become better adjusted to support the body, but a girdle so narrowed as to prevent childbirth stops variation in that direction. This seems to set a limit to the size of the human brain at birth. In most still-born deliveries the head is too large to pass the bony outlet of the pelvis. We may assume that the limit of brain size at birth has been reached.

Man's pelvis is long, narrow, strong; woman's, broad, shallow, delicate, roomy. Her thighs are relatively greater. Her carriage differs from man's because the heads of her thigh bones are farther apart. As she transfers her body from one thigh to the other in walking, she must make a greater effort. Her pelvis is a compromise between an arch to support viscera and an outlet to make childbirth possible.

Women among so-called savages are notoriously as strong as men, although there is always a division of labor between the sexes. The most splendid human bodies I have ever seen were those of black women working under extremely primitive conditions in gold and emerald mines in South America. Their backs, shoulders, and arms spoke of great strength, but there were no bulging muscles. Even apart from their breasts, their bodies were unmistakably "feminine."

The luxuriant head hair of women of European descent is not a mark of sex: it is the barber that makes—or made—the difference. Chinese and Indians were proud of their hair and had as much of it as their spouses. Head hair is a race and culture and not a sex factor.

Sex differences are strongly marked in brain size among man and apes. The male gorilla's brain is 18 per cent larger than the female's; the orang's, 14 per cent; the chimpanzee's, 8 per cent; man's, 12 per cent. But the disparity is due to general disproportion in size between the two sexes. Structurally the brains of the two sexes are the same, and as compared to weight of body are heavier in women than in men. If a relatively large brain is a "human" trait, the brain of the child stands highest, woman next.

More males are born than females; in the so-called white races, about 105 males for every 100 females. Yet woman's longevity counter-balances the disproportion; at the age of fifty, unless migrations or wars upset the calculation, we may expect to find as many women as men.

Differences between the two sexes, yes. The male specializes in the direction of brute strength and the courage that goes with it; the female retains her youthfulness in body in general and especially in face and neck. With age some women begin to appear neutral, halfway between man and woman. But the vicious element in such phrases as "Woman's proper work" and "Woman's true sphere" is the assumption implied of lack of capacity. To assume that her capacity for intelligent behavior or human adjustments is less than man's is biologically and physiologically absurd.

Comte's idea is better biology and sound psychology: "Between two beings so complex and so diverse as man and woman, the whole of life is not too long for them to know one another well and to learn to love one another worthily."

The endocrines are new to science; some have only recently been discovered; the function of some only recently suspected; not one is yet perfectly understood. Yet their astounding importance, and the claims quacks make that gland "extracts" are cure-alls and gonad operations a Fountain of Youth, conspire to whet the appetite for facts faster than the laboratories can sift them out. Hence new crops of quacks who dispense pills or elixirs or their services with a knife or a ligature; and a raft of literature which, as Hoskins says, "for its vagaries, fantastic exuberance, and wholesale marvel-mongering, is without a peer in the history of modern science."

Little is yet known of endocrine co-operation, or what takes place in some when others fail. No gland or other organ functions for or by itself, or lives a life of independence; the entire body mechanism makes up the organism. The business of the glands is the business of the body as a going concern, to keep it fit and enable it to function, as infant, as youth, as adult, as senility overtakes it.

Carlson thinks the following endocrine teamwork probable: the gonads cannot function if the thyroid and possibly the pituitary and adrenal cortex are subnormal; removal of thyroid and probably of gonads stimulates the pituitary; thyroid extract seems to stimulate the adrenals and the pituitary, as it does the heart, liver, and kidneys; removal of the thyroid stimulates the parathyroids—at least in tadpoles; tumor of the adrenals induces gonad precocity; removal of the gonads retards atrophy of the thymus and leads to change in pituitary and adrenal cortex.

It seems certain that removal of the thyroid is followed by cretinism in children, myxedema in adults; of the parathyroids, by death; of the pancreas, by death; of the adrenals, by death; of the pituitary, by infantilism in children, by impotence in adults; of the thymus, by sexual precocity; of the gonads, by sex infantilism in children, by atrophy of secondary sex characters in adults; of the pineal, by no known endocrine effect.

Most of each endocrine may be removed from an animal without apparent loss of function of its internal secretion; the inference is that no endocrine normally works to its full capacity. A normal thyroid stores up enough to last several weeks; the adrenin reserve only suffices for a few hours. But in general almost nothing is known of the storage capacity or rate of production of hormones. It is known that symptoms may not appear after removal of the thyroid for weeks or months. Removal of the pancreas is followed by symptoms within ten hours; of the parathyroids and adrenal cortex, almost at once.

Post-mortems prove these connections: thyroid with cretinism and myxedema; adrenals with Addison's disease and death; pituitary with infantilism; pancreas with diabetes.

Known positive results from large endocrines or excessive endocrine secretions are few; it is not yet proved that large glands yield large results. It is only inference that excessive thyroid secretion causes toxic goiter; of the anterior lobe of the pituitary, gigantism; of the adrenal medulla and the thyroids, excess pep; of the adrenal cortex, the pineal and pituitary, sex precocity; of the gonads, excessive sex urge; of the thyroid, diabetes. Results claimed for excessive thymus and pineal activity are not yet proved. As their loss produces no known effect, what could necessarily result from their increased function?

Can endocrine disorders be "cured" through the nerves of endocrine secretion? The pineal, the posterior lobe of the pituitary, and the medulla of the adrenals are themselves modified nerve cells. But, except the medulla, neither the cutting of all the nerves to all the endocrines nor artificial stimulation shows any effect on the body or change in the glands themselves. The nerves to the endocrines seemingly have little or nothing to do with their secretions. But most quacks feed their patients "gland extracts." Few hormones are yet known. Apart from insulin, adrenalin, pituitrin, and thyroxin, the quacks themselves know nothing further of any of the various extracts they often feed for unknown diseases. With "diet and rest," extracts are as potent as the bread pills of old.

The endocrines are part of the body, and so subject to heredity, tumors, lesions, tuberculosis and other infections, especially to faulty metabolism. The influence of the thyroid and pancreas on general metabolism and growth is fundamental. They must, therefore, influence all the body, including all the glands. The thyroid normally functions only if there is enough iodine in the food. If in doubt, take cod-liver oil or eat sea grass.

15

The endocrine glands are intrinsic parts of the body, in intimate touch with living processes. Muscular activity starts the sweat glands, the muscles are fed with sugar, the adrenals pour their secretion into the blood to neutralize the toxins of fatigue, and so on.

Arrest of development or over-stimulation of the endocrines brings about change which may be harmful or of benefit to the body. Giants, fat women, cretins, men and women under-sexed and over-sexed, imply variation in the structure and functioning of these glands. Apparently some individuals are better fitted for the work of life than others; still others are so well fitted that they overdo it. No two human beings are exactly alike; they do not and cannot act alike. We should hesitate before passing harsh moral judgments upon activities due to inherited or acquired physical structure.

Possibly several generations must pass before the real and definite function of the endocrines is fully understood. Possibly new drugs will replace the old; pills compounded on formulæ learned in nature's laboratory, elixirs for all the ills of body and mind we are now heir to. The fact that the emotions are expressions of states under control of the glands and closely bound up with the sympathetic nervous system opens up an enormous field for speculative possibilities. Russell thinks it will be possible to make people hot-headed or timid, strongly or weakly sexed, and so on, as may be desired. In case of war the timid souls will simply be injected with certain glandular extracts or synthesized regulators!

There is another angle. Almost nothing has yet been done on the racial anatomy of the endocrines. Are shape and size of head, face, nose, eyes, teeth, lips, length of limbs, and stature, character and shape of hair, due to the activity of the endocrines? Keith thinks this possible and suggests that whites are what they are because they have more thyroid, adrenal, pituitary, and gonad hormones than other races, and that inherited condition of glands points a mechanism through which heredity controls development and established type variations. Racial character—such as emotional reactions, intellectual capacity, and personality in general—would thus vary likewise, and for the same reason.

This compounding of elixirs for all ills from endocrines, and the solution of the problem of race and individual variability by reference to variation in glandular mechanism and functioning, take us too far from reality, too far into possibilities. We of to-day are going concerns and our interest in the past is only in the light it can shed on what we are and can do to-day. And that is a personal question—for this reason:

No two human beings are alike. Every human being continues throughout life to change. The question, What is good for the human machine as a going concern? is, therefore, always personal and individual; it all depends. Some want to go fast, others prefer to go slow. One may see *ideal* life only in the chest of Hercules; another, in the wings on the feet of Mercury. But most humans are born right; there is nothing the matter with our inheritance.

There is a normal rate of growth and of growing old. Too much or too little upsets the normal rate. With nothing to chew on, normal development of jaws, teeth, muscles and glands of mastication need not be expected. Without work or play, normal development of the bones and muscles of the motor mechanism is not to be expected. "Exercises" and "physical culture" are too often taken as pills and drugs: controls, but not cures.

Glued to a chair with head tied to an account book or a last makes for less than the normal work designed by nature for heart and lungs. By and by lungs and heart lose their original capacity for work, as do muscles which are never extended.

Man has inherited a body of a certain type which functions best under certain conditions of food, work, rest, sleep, etc. These conditions also are part of each individual's inheritance and consequently must vary with individuals. Sauce for the goose is not necessarily sauce for the gander. It is true that some Jack Sprats can eat no fat, their wives can eat no lean.

The real question, then, for adults, is personal. Is my machine capable of giving the service I shall require to carry me where I want to go? Many are ready enough to answer, No. But they are not willing to distinguish between hunger and appetite or count calories instead of cost; and they will walk a mile for a cigarette, but not a foot for health's sake.

But every child is entitled, in civilization as in savagery, to the full development of its normal inheritance. Civilization has taken curious, often monstrous, bents; and even now in many places does not hesitate to deny children the free exercise of their human birthright to develop sound minds in sound bodies.

16

"How can a man be born when he is old?" asked Nico-demus. And answered his question with another, "Can he enter a second time into his mother's womb and be born?"

Life does grow old and young again, but nature knows of no such rebirth as puzzled the brain of Nicodemus and has become entangled in the folk-customs of so many peoples. Growing old and growing young again are age changes, both, in Child's words, "merely one aspect of *Werden und Vergehen*, the Becoming and Passing-away which make up the history of the universe."

What is it that grows old and young again? "Life" grows old. What is "life"? We have certain criteria—none too good—for living beings; and certain criteria for death. But life itself, can it be defined or described? Is it a thing or an action, a process or a function? There are living beings and processes or functions of living. But life cannot be restricted by this or that process or function, nor described as this or that chemical compound; nor as any one certain or particular form. Life is something more than process or function, compound or form.

Life is a result of action in something. The "something" is a physical body of protoplasm. The "action" is change, many and complex and dynamic. Dynamic changes and physical body are inseparable; they influence and condition each other.

Man himself is such a physico-chemical system of dynamic changes. What disturbs this system disturbs the being; the being is the system. If the disturbance is so great that the being cannot readjust itself, the system breaks down, the being dies.

Probably we shall never know just how life itself began. If we could concoct a reaction-complex capable of living, we might not know just when life begins. The complex structure and the dynamic process known in living beings are always bound by a bond which, broken, ends life.

Hence life is unlike any machine made by man. In machines, dynamic processes take place in complex structures, but we can always distinguish between process and structure. Nor can the machine function until the structure is completed. But the living being always functions and has been functioning since life began. The structure determined function, function determined structure. In other words, life constructs its own machine by living.

Living means changing. Living processes depend on change. The body during growth adds to itself certain chemical compounds which are physiologically stable; that is, they are of such a nature that they can be built into the body. The energy used up during the building or growth period is furnished by the oxidation of less stable compounds.

The growing child is a rapidly changing being. We age fastest during childhood. The rate of metabolism is then highest. In old age it slows down. In starvation, new compounds are not synthesized as fast as old compounds are broken down. But starvation only ends in death after many weeks because the most vital functions are carried on in the most active organs. Because of their activity they are fed, first by stored fuel or fats, next by muscle. When this fuel is exhausted, death soon follows.

Thus, growing and growing-old are simply two aspects of the same complex dynamic activity. Both are phases of production and progress. We shall know how to grow young when we know how to increase the rate of metabolism or vital change, and how to change the cells of the body so that an increase in rate of metabolism is possible.

The nature of the *rejuvenescence* that hinges on the internal secretions of the sex glands is not part of the problem raised by Nicodemus. A man "renewing his youth" is one thing; Life growing young again is quite a different thing.

Life resides only in living beings; the way they are born

again when old is one phase of evolution. The process is called reproduction, of which there are many methods. Have they all something in common? Or is there some unique quality in reproduction in man and higher animals not found in the lowest animals? Whether there is or not, the fate of the individual organisms concerned is different. Those that reproduce by division do not die; at any rate, as Weismann said, there is no "corpse." Death does overtake those that reproduce bisexually. But reproduction in man is bisexual. Man, as individual, dies; he cannot be born again when he is old, or young. The life that is in him can grow young again; but only by a process known as reproduction. That is the nature of reproduction.

Rebirth, then, as that word is commonly understood, is biologically inconceivable. It is possible that to-day complex chemical substances are in process of becoming of the nature of protoplasm in which *living* reactions take place, and which, could we observe them, would be recognized as living beings. But the laws of chance are against it and all our conceptions of evolution are against it. A possible "rebirth" is quite as improbable.

All that is known of the facts of evolution and all theories as to the mechanism of evolution favor the idea that every man and every being alive to-day have been alive since life was evolved. It is even more certain that every man and every organism alive to-day began life as part of an adult or "old" organism. But as man and all organisms begin their individual existence as young organisms, it follows that something, somewhere, somehow, has renewed its youth, has become young again.

Call this "something" life. Life itself has grown old during evolution. The life that is in man and in all living beings is old, millions of years old; it grows young through reproduction.

There are only two great kinds of reproduction: without sex or *agamic* (no wife), and with sex or *gametic* (wife).

In agamic reproduction, a new individual arises from part or parts of the body which have come to lie beyond the physiologic limit of size; they are physiologically isolated parts of the body. In gametic reproduction, as in man, the germs of life are also isolated—so far as the parent individual is concerned, "dead and shed," Child says. But by adult life they are also already highly specialized and have already completed their growth.

Weismann assumed that the germ-cells are *young* and that they are *special* only in the sense that they are set aside at once in embryonic development for the purpose of reproduction; hence the doctrine of the "continuity of the germ-plasm." He also assumed that nothing could influence these cells; hence there could be no transmission of a character acquired by the body of the individual carrying these cells.

But germ-cells in bisexual reproduction are in no sense "young"; they are no more "special" than any other group of cells of the body. Only after the embryo has begun to build its body are the cells resulting from cell divisions set aside to become the store of future germ-cells.

Ovum and sperm are *old* cells, especially the sperm. They are as differentiated as almost any cells of the body. They have ceased to grow; they have a low rate of metabolism; but the dynamic substratum present in both is old protoplasm, grown old during the long years of evolution. As a result it has become stable, highly individualized. Otherwise there could have been no evolution of such structural permanence and complexity as we find in man and higher animals.

Hence evolution is not chiefly change in form, but change in the dynamic reaction system of protoplasm. As individual man develops and grows old, so evolution itself represents a change from a less stable to a more stable condition in the dynamic reaction system.

The protoplasm of the germ has also evolved. As a result of that evolution, it has reached such a stage of differentiation that it can no longer react alone, as it does in lower organ-

246

isms. Only by marriage of ovum and sperm is the carrier of life brought back to pre-embryonic conditions. Fertilization is the only *rejuvenescence* known to man and higher animals.

By fertilization the old protoplasm of the ovum is reconstituted, reduced, rejuvenated. The fertilized ovum is younger than ovum and sperm were before they united in fertilization. It begins life anew; and as a parasite. Having escaped from the old individual, it is no longer subject to the inhibitions of the old. Not until it begins its post-natal existence will it be subject to the inhibitions of human society.

The fertilized human ovum is possibly less an "individual" than a protozoon, but that ovum is protoplasm which has been evolved to the point that within it is potentially present the foundation of the structure and form of an adult man or woman. That ovum can do what the growing child does: so transform food materials that it can build some into new protoplasm and incorporate the new within its body; it can oxidize other food materials to set free the energy it uses in building its body. This transformation of food materials is metabolism, change, the foundation of the function of life.

Life itself, then, is change in protoplasm, itself a dynamic entity. Change or reaction is determined by its physicochemical constitution and by its relation to the external world. *Adaptations* are thus seen as simply special features of this relation. The mechanism by which life renews its youth is such an adaptation.

I agree with Child that it is impossible to conceive of evolution and of so-called "adaptations" without assuming that "acquired characters" can be inherited. But often, as Child points out, tens of thousands of generations may have been necessary for such inheritance to become appreciable.

Without such adaptation there would be no such living beings as man and higher animals. There might be something else "just as good," for, as Russell says, we have only our own word for it that man is superior to the ameba; we can have no idea what the ameba would think of the proposition.

Nor need it necessarily disturb our self-esteem to realize that only our own conditioned human eyes see man as a "finished product" of evolution. Pearl aptly argues that Omnipotence could have made a much better machine than the human body—"that is, if he had first learned the trick of making a self-regulating and self-reproducing machine. Each part of the human body is only just good enough to get by—workmanship like that of an average man. If evolution happens to be furnished with fine materials it has no objection to using them, but is equally ready to use shoddy if it will hold together long enough to get the machine by the reproductive period." Which is another way of saying that evolution's main concern is the continuation of life rather than of this or that kind of living beings.

But this does not necessarily mean that senility and death are the inevitable ends of human existence, either as individuals or as race.

17

Man and other warm-blooded animals are killed by freezing or by boiling, or by cutting off their air or food supply. Death comes also in other ways: foreign substances are taken in, or get into the body, which cannot be eliminated or combated; or vital parts of the body are injured by mechanical or other means. In other words, we die when the conditions necessary for life have been so changed that life becomes impossible.

We are specific mechanisms in which certain physico-chemical changes occur in a certain routine order. We live as long as the mechanism is in good repair and the changes take place. Mechanism and changes are one. They only seem two when life is looked at from different angles. Together, they represent life: they balance; they are in equilibrium; they are adjusted; they harmonize. Normally they go through life together, always preserving this harmony. Cut off a leg: the blood does not stop circulating; it readjusts itself to the changed condition. If it cannot readjust, what is left of the machine stops.

Anything which necessitates serious readjustment is pathologic. The body is diseased when under conditions to which it is not adjusted. There are almost as many diseases as there are cells in the body; certainly many more than there are tissues or organs. Disease in any cell, cell-group, tissue, organ, or system, is felt everywhere. The noise of a toothache may be faint by the time it reaches the toe, but the toe is none the less interested. A gallstone may be of particular concern only to the liver, but the liver's concern is the body's concern.

Life is played to a certain tune; it need not be a monkeywrench to set its chords jangling. An undigested bean will do, or a bean in the windpipe; or any one of a thousand things. But despite the nicety of the balances and co-ordinations which make for normal health, the body's capacity for readjustment is remarkable. It is not *we* who fight for life, but our living bodies. They hang on to life in spite of much we do to discourage them.

This fighting power is part of our inheritance. We cannot grow a new limb, much less a new head or a new trunk, as some animals can. We can store fuel fat as no lower animal can; and experience, as no other animal can. It is not to be charged to our inheritance if we fill our experience-loft with rubbish. We can make repairs; in some tissues, very extensive repairs. We can make antibodies.

These antibodies illustrate the vast numbers and the enormous complexity of the processes that go on under our skin, and the fine adjustments that must always be going on to keep the body tuned up for the business of life.

Something seems to happen when the body faces civilization. There is probably not a single adult in this country with a body in perfect tune: what the life-insurance companies would call "Class AA risk."

Of 1,000 employees examined by one motor company, just 1,000 were imperfect. Of a group of hundreds of thousands examined, 10 per cent had "slight defects," the other 90 per cent had "defects not so slight." Nearly 40 per cent of the white school children of Washington have defects—teeth, vision, hearing, etc.—which can be located without removing their clothes. Over 45 per cent of Pennsylvania's youth were not physically fit to be sent overseas to be shot at.

This means two things.

More get past Cultural Selection than Natural Selection; the openings in the sieve are larger, the nature of the struggle is different. Runts which grow to Roosevelts and Steinmetzes in civilization die early in nature. Runts which become nothing but charges on society also survive in Cultural Selection. In other words, individuals with inherited or postnatal defects live because society supplies that which their bodies lack to maintain a balance on life. A freak in nature does not live long; in civilization, it makes good money.

Millions of minor defects are due to bad food-digestion. We inherit omnivorous teeth and thirty feet of alimentary canal made for every kind of food but cooked and predigested. Also, powerful muscles hung to strong bones, leveraged for work. The body was built on the theory that these muscles would be worked. The very work the muscles are supposed to do is part of the process of living. The flow of lymph and the circulation of the blood in general depend on a mechanism built to function best when the motor apparatus is in motion. That is why we have bones and muscles, and that is why we have blood and lymph.

One bad tooth in an ancient skull or among savages is an anomaly. A perfect set in an adult American is a far greater anomaly. Toothache means that the cavity is almost in to the nerve. That means almost in to the entire body. Our body is a double sack, each sealed up tight. Whatever breaks through the wall of either sack (skin or alimentary canal) is a *foreign* body and *potential* death.

Apart from congenital influence, most defects originate in the mouth or alimentary canal. Children are not born with defective gums, bad tooth germs, narrow palate, stunted jaws, adenoid growths, or diseased tonsils. Our inheritance is usually all right; we do not use it according to directions. The newborn comes with a full set of tools for building a full-grown, sound, healthy, defectless body; too often it is treated as a cunning little toy to a doting household for six years or so, and is thereafter chiefly of interest to the statistician collecting Defects or Defectives.

Metabolism is adjustment for the functions of life. We inherit an adjustment machinery adapted for a certain kind of active life, but before it is of age we have taught it a "civilization" that was never contemplated by the designer of the machine. Civilization is kept busy keeping the machine in repair.

One good defect deserves another. Defects lead to other defects. Many bodies are kept so busy repairing leaks in the lungs, or picking cinders out of the fuel, or keeping foreigners out of the blood, that they have no time for the main business of life: giving their owner a lifelong joy-ride.

18

Weismann held that death is an "advantageous adaptation." For what? To whom? Looks like nonsense. Osler said that man is as old as his arteries. There was enough truth in this to make it take. It means even less to say that man is as old as his endocrine glands. Arteries and glands are as old as the man.

Metchnikoff held that because of "disharmonies" in the body, the phagocytes devoted too much time to eating pigment in hair and too little to the bacterial flora of our digestive tract. Result: fermentation, poison, death. His theory beat the gland-treatment theory into the drug stores, but sour milk is losing ground as a cure for old age.

Puberty is a period, but a kind of sex life begins at birth; for many, real sexual maturity never comes. So it is with adults; some are more adult in body and mind at fifteen than others at thirty-five; some hurry through to senility before body and mind have become fully adult. Normal old age is physiological; it is no more a disease than adolescence, and should be as agreeable. In pathologic old age, senility is premature and is a disease. The seat of the disease may be anywhere or may be due to bacterial infection.

In *natural* death, we die by inches. But while there is only one path by which we may enter the world, as Pearl points out in his remarkable book on Death, there are many that lead to the River Styx. Death does not strike at random, but in an orderly way; and there are many ways of dying. We die when an essential part of our body breaks down.

From an analysis of the mortality tables of England and Wales, the United States, and São Paulo, Brazil, Pearl found that over half the deaths in all three countries are due to faulty wind and food canals. While both canals are inside the body, they come in contact with air, food, and water from the outside. The skin also is exposed to the world, but it is armorplate against foreign invasion. Wind and food canals have no such protecting layer of pavement cells as has the skin. Outer skin and lining of wind and food canals constitute the body's first line of defense against invasion of bacteria.

The next chief cause of death is the circulatory system; the blood is the body's second line of defense. When the first fails to check the enemy, the way to the blood is open. Hence the great part played by the circulatory system as the second great cause of death. As Pearl says, we should live much longer if our lungs were as good as our heart.

The death rates show certain important age and sex fluctuations. Early infancy deaths are heavy. There is then a sharp drop until the 10-15-year period, when the rate begins to rise to the 20-25-year period. Thereafter the rate rises slowly until the 50-55-year period, when it begins to rise again rapidly.

The death rate from failure of circulatory system rises steadily from maturity until the eighty-fifth year, when it slows down. But between the fifth and thirty-fifth years this rate is higher in females than in males, presumably because the changes accompanying puberty are graver. Up to the sixty-fifth year deaths from breakdown of the sex apparatus are also much greater in females.

The chief cause of death among males during the first year is from the food canal; after that, to the sixtieth year, the respiratory system; after the sixtieth year, the circulatory system.

Nearly 60 per cent of the deaths were from organs derived from the endoderm or inner germ-layer—the layer that originally was outside the body. In the developing embryo that layer comes to be folded within the body and lines the food canal and accessory organs of digestion. It is an old-fashioned, out-of-date relic of antediluvian ectoderm. As a lining for the food canal it is our weakest spot.

Our strongest spots are the skin cover of our body and our nervous system. Both are derived from the ectoderm or outer germ-layer. Deaths from structures derived from this layer make up only about 10 per cent of the total. Almost no germs get through a healthy skin. The cells of skin and nerves have differentiated most from their primitive structure.

The remaining 30 per cent of deaths are from the mesoderm or middle germ-layer, circulatory and urogenital systems and muscles. The breakdown of the female reproductive organs is also a heavy factor in infant mortality.

While mortality due to breakdown in ectoderm organs is about the same for the two sexes, female mortality from mesoderm is as great as from endoderm breakdown twenty years before it is in males.

Death comes, then, according to Pearl, because our bodies are made up of systems specialized in structure and function. In becoming specialized, their cells have become so differentiated that they have lost the power of indefinite and independent existence. Thus the cells lining our lungs can be nourished only if the cells of the food tract and the blood keep on the job. Some systems are better made than others. The brain outwears the heart, the heart outwears the lungs.

The striking agreement as to the causes of death which Pearl finds in such dissimilar countries as England, the United States, and São Paulo, force him to conclude that innate constitutional factors, along with environmental factors, largely determine rates of human mortality. In certain diseases, of course, environment is the important factor.

The causes of death, Pearl finds, are in the following descending order: respiratory system; digestive system; circulatory system and blood; nervous system and sense organs; kidneys and related excretory organs; sex organs; skeletal and muscular system; skin; endocrine organs. Or, arranged proportionately according to embryonic germ-layer origin: endoderm diseases 5.2 and mesoderm diseases 3.8 times those of ectoderm origin.

We may be as old as our arteries—and so no good for digging a sewer; but we are also as young as our brains— and so, good where brains are needed. But when any vital system breaks down, the machine stops and we are dead.

19

Medical authorities believe they could add thirteen years to life if given full control in cases where death could reasonably be prevented. A better life insurance is to pick parents who will live to be eighty; they will give you a twenty-year better hope of longevity than parents who will die under sixty. They are the best life insurance.

Why not? Each group of animals has its normal span of life. Also man. Human beings vary; most of their specific characters are inherited. Longevity is a specific character, longevity also is inherited.

Those who live to great age as a rule are children of parents who lived to great age. If one cannot choose both parents who will live to old age, it is better to choose a long-lived father than a long-lived mother. Four per cent more children lived to be eighty where the father, but not the mother, lived to be eighty, than where the opposite condition prevailed.

Karl Pearson concluded from a study of the life span of brothers that environment is not the important factor in longevity; also, that from one-half to three-fourths of deaths are *predetermined at birth by inheritance factors*. This conclusion has never been advertised by health resorts or elixir manufacturers.

Death rates and life spans are but two phases of the problem of longevity. If environment—including health resorts, elixirs, poverty, and bacteria—is not the factor in death rates, it cannot be the factor in the life span.

From one-half to three-fourths of the death rate is selection: death comes when one has used up one's inherited capacity for life. Adults of sound body are more likely to leave offspring than those of weak; their children are more likely to survive. Weaklings may survive to maturity, their children are less likely to survive.

Hence the high infant death rate in the first two years; the unfit are weeded out. Natural Selection is still at work; it has always been at work. This rate is especially high among children of unsound parents. Hygiene and prevention lower the rate during these two dangerous years—prolonging lives to succumb at a later but early stage.

A banana fly of ninety days is as old as a man of ninety

years. Twenty-four hours after emerging from the pupa stage, the female fly lays eggs. These in one day become larvæ, pupæ three days later, adults five days later; ten days to a generation. Pearl tested the life-span inheritance theory on these flies. More females than males survived—as in man. The only fly that lived to be eighty-one days old was a female. Long-lived parents bred offspring that lived long. Pearson was right: duration of life is an inherited character.

How about germs of diphtheria, tuberculosis, etc.? Loeb tested this on flies, with the surprising result that those kept free from bacteria were possibly shorter-lived than germ-laden flies, certainly no longer. The experiments indicated "that higher organisms must die from internal causes even if all chances of infection and all accidents are excluded."

We are never without bacteria; we could not live without them; there is no habitable spot on earth free of them. Of humans who have reached the thirty-fifth year, 95 per cent have been infected at one time or another with the bacillus of tuberculosis; in less than one in ten does it become active.

Death rates in the poverty lanes of Paris and London do not tally. In Paris the excess death rate in the poorest as against the richest quarter is 104 per cent; in London, only 30. The lowest death rate in London is not in the richest quarter. The real influence of poverty on death rates could only be determined by transposing the inhabitants of the two groups and comparing rates. The "poor" of Paris and London are not necessarily *biologically* poor.

It is the pace that kills. "General Sherman," the giant redwood, was killed at the age of 2,171 years. He was a seedling in 271 B. C. He never knew what hurry meant. Nor did the tortoise that lived 350 years. The faster we live, the sooner we live life up. Rate of living is a factor in longevity. Slonacker tested this on rats. He put four in squirrel cages and let them race. The average life span of the marathoners was 29.5 months; one lived thirty-four months and ran 5,447 miles. Three other rats were reared in squirrel cages, but were not permitted to race; their average span was 48.3 months.

Loeb tried flies. Cold makes flies sluggish; those at cold temperature lived longer than those at high. At 86 degrees, his flies lived 21 days; at 68 degrees, 54 days; at 60 degrees, 124 days. From which he inferred that if we could keep our blood temperature at about 45 degrees, we might hope to live about 1,900 years. But life would be at a low level!

Unfortunately, our early ancestors left no trustworthy vital statistics. But from trustworthy inferential data there is reason to believe, as we might expect on purely biologic grounds, that longevity is on the increase. At least, life expectancy has improved during the last 2,000 years. Of 100 Romans born in Egypt in the days of the Empire, only 9 could expect to live 68 years. Of 100 English alive at 10, 39 live to be 68. Women especially had less expectancy of life in Roman days than now—they were in luck to be alive at 25. But a Roman of 78 years was a better risk than an American of the same age; a Roman had to be very hardy to live beyond 70. In America, many weaklings are carried up to 60; beyond that age their expectancy rapidly diminishes.

From which we conclude that modern environment is better for man, or that man is fitter for modern environment.

20

Life goes on: only individuals die. Some individuals apparently are also endowed with immortality—such are the Protozoa or one-cell organisms. Nearly all Metazoa or many-cell organisms die—their endowment is mortal.

Man also is a Metazoon. All men die. Must they die? Until recently this would have been a foolish question. It cannot yet be answered, but experiments now going on for twenty-five years give us food for thought.

Since boys have been boys it has been known that the

snake's tail does not die until the sun goes down. For ages it has been well known that many animals have the power to grow certain missing parts. A fish-worm cut in two grows into two worms—the head grows a tail, the tail a head. Cut a crab's eye from its stack, it grows another eye just as good. Cut a leg from a crayfish, it grows another leg. Cut a finger off the human hand; no finger grows on. But our hair keeps on growing; it may grow even after the last heartbeat. Cut a nerve fiber of a finger; the fiber "dies" from the point where cut to the end of the finger and so paralyzes that end of the finger. But the live end begins to grow again and finally reaches the end of the finger. Even though the finger had been mangled, the nerve finds its way, if it has to go around bone and muscle. At the end of its journey it stops growing; the finger is no longer paralyzed.

In 1907 Leo Loeb informed the world that he was growing frog nerve in a glass jar. Biologists began to grow pieces of tissue from other animals in glass jars. Wilson chopped up a sponge and squeezed the pieces through close-woven cloth to separate its cells. He "cultivated" one cell; it grew into a whole sponge. Carrel cultivates all sorts of adult tissue in glass jars; even cancer cells. He has cancer cells that have outlived several hosts. He cut a piece from the embryo of a chick; after nine years it was still alive and growing. He cut muscle cells from a chick embryo's heart; they grow and beat.

That opened the coffin again. Tissues cut from living bodies, it was thought, should not grow, they should die! They are not *germ*-cells, they are only body or *soma*-cells. Soma cells were not supposed to be endowed with immortality. Yet under cultivation they live, they multiply, they grow. In a jar.

Soma cells also are potentially immortal!

Then why do they die? Why is our saliva full of dead cells and the skin of our body covered with dead cells? Why is the body that was living now dead?

258

What is death? No one yet knows. No one knows what life is. We only know the living from the dead. We know more about the causes of death than we did. But are we checking disease, postponing death? Can we renew our youth? Are we about to make death merely an accident? Can we synthesize life? Man by nature is not too modest, nor by training without hope or the habit of stretching his imagination. Our answer, then, is, "Yes, why not?" And a pleasant time is had by all. Molasses catches more flies than vinegar.

Such important functions of our body as heartbeat, breathing, digestion, and absorption are beyond the control of our wills; they have their own centers or systems of control. We do not even yet know where all these centers and systems of control are located.

When we know just what takes place when a sweet becomes a sour, or how a cell converts sugar into glycogen, or why a heart beats in a certain solution and stops dead if the acidity of that solution is increased by one billionth part, we can begin to talk about prolonging life.

Not one single process that goes on in any one cell of our body has yet been completely analyzed. When some of the processes of life have been even fairly well analyzed, it will be possible to speak of the artificial synthesis of life.

Nevertheless, there is every reason to believe that we may look forward to a greatly increased control over evolutionary processes. Why not? Think of the already enormously increased ability to control growth in living organisms. This control has only come with an understanding of the nature of the stuff of organisms in which energy is transformed, and of the relation of organisms to the external world. With wider understanding will come wider control. But progress must be slow, because, as Child warns us, we deal with internal conditions which are the result of millions of years of alternating change.

It is all so new. There are to-day a half-dozen flourishing

259

sciences devoted to the study of life where a few years ago there was not one. For the first time in human history man has trained his new-found instruments of precision on newly conceived problems. He can at last ask questions about himself and about life in general. Direct questioning has replaced vague and childish speculation. Problems have been formulated and solved. And every problem solved has opened wider vistas—and more problems. But no problem was ever solved by propaganda. Nor is disease checked by mere optimism—though digestion can be checked by a bill collector and a mouse's heartbeat increased from 175 to 600 per minute by a mouse trap.

The death rate is declining; it has been declining for centuries. Men born to-day can expect longer life than men born twenty, fifty, five hundred, or five thousand years ago. Why this is so is not at all well understood. The decline in death rate in modern times is as true of "backward" countries as it is of Germany, England, the United States. The drop is also as true of the non-preventable diseases as of those which are supposed to be subject to control.

The part that health officers, etc., play in this decline is uncertain. War has been increasingly waged against tuberculosis for nearly a century; the tuberculosis rate has dropped less than that for diphtheria, croup, typhoid, and dysentery.

The cause of many diseases is yet unknown, of others only partially surmised. Man responds to his environment, as does all life; but he is changing his environment, in places at an extraordinarily rapid rate. What is the result or what will be the result of these changes is not yet known, nor can it be predicted with any degree of certainty.

We hand public health, as we do government, over to a power which we expect thereafter to run of its own accord. But neither ever gets very far ahead of the load it is supposed to carry. Meanwhile, for every one that knows what to eat and why, there are a hundred who eat for their tongue's sake and let it go at that, not knowing that a double chin may be a misdemeanor or that arteries and nerves may be as easily choked in fat as a cat with butter. Many use their body as a clothes horse and are only concerned with the parts that show.

Startling facts come from physiological laboratories. They force us to revise our conceptions of life and death, of youth and old age. All protoplasm is potentially immortal. Man is protoplasm. Hence . . . But Man is highly complex protoplasm—*an organism of infinite complexity,* of tissues and organs and systems greatly differentiated, some more, some less. This mass of protoplasm functions, lives, because these parts work together for a common end. They are marvelously balanced. Upset the balance: disease; if the balance cannot be restored, the machine is broken. A few minor parts may be restored; a few may be dispensed with. The machine breaks when a vital part breaks. It never runs again.

Isolate the liver or one brain cell and study it a lifetime: liver as function and cell as behavior are as meaningless and as lifeless as a last year's bird nest. The parts of the human body are meaningless in and by themselves. Put some cells in a glass jar and watch them grow. Where does this land us? Those cells are immortal—in "proper medium."

Each of the billions of cells in the human body must also be kept in proper medium. Those cells themselves are the medium. On their own shoulders rests the burden of keeping that medium proper; they and they alone can right the machine, they and they alone know the levers. If they cannot reverse, there comes a crash. The machine is broken.

Nothing yet has come from the laboratory to give us hope that the crash is not inevitable. All vital processes are reversible; they must be. To live is to keep making compensations: changes, backward and forward. Simple organisms have it in themselves to make these compensations; they have their dynamic equilibrium in their own hands, as it were.

Man does not: it is the price he pays for hands. Hands wear out. Even brain cells. We cannot grow new hands

261

or new brains. They grow up together, though of different heritage, the brain being far more ancient, hence more enduring. They live together: a pin-prick on the finger may be the death of the brain.

The break may come from within, or from without, or from any one of a vast number of causes. Three out, all out. So in the game of life. The number of our outs—or innings—is set in our inheritance and buried from sight in the complex mechanism which is ours for a while. We can burn it up or jolly it along. But beyond a certain point there seems to come a limit to its mileage. The machine wears out because it is that kind of a machine. It dies because sooner or later the Marksman of Death strikes a vital spot.

Pearson in his *Chances of Death* pictures a Bridge of Life across which is a trickle of humanity. They are under the fire of the five Marksmen, one for each Age. They fire with different weapons, speeds, and degrees of precision. The first Marksman concentrates a deadly fire upon Infancy—before as well as after birth; "beating down young lives with the bones of their ancestors." The second Marksman aims a machine-gun at Childhood; his fire is concentrated, the loss is less appalling. The third shoots at Youth with a bow and arrow; there is no great loss. The fourth fires slowly at Maturity with a blunderbuss; his hits are scattered. The fifth Marksman of Death is a sharpshooter; no one can escape the Death of Senility.

CHAPTER V

THE INTEGRATING ORGAN AND MECHANISM OF ADJUSTMENT

1

OF all the 'ologies I studied in school, the one that gave me the least light on man and myself was *psychology*—excepting, possibly, mineralogy. It worried me: I wanted to learn about my own and man's *psyche,* and did not. I assumed it was because the course was over my head. It was.

For this reason. To the old psychology heads were like crystals. By gazing into them, called "introspection," the *mind* could be seen and studied. Crystal-gazing never did call itself a science; mind-gazing did, but is now also only a cult. The introspectors could not agree as to what they saw. But that they were looking at "mind" they had no doubt. Their logic was simple and convincing: mind is not matter, the body is matter; mind and body, therefore, are separate and distinct entities. They turned the body over to sawbones and kept "mind" for themselves and went on arguing about what they saw in it.

"I see red," says one. "Is it pure?" asks another; "is it perception, sensation, connotation, or ideation; or is it a conception, or the imagination? Is it as content, awareness, or as ego? If as ego, can you time it; if as awareness, can you weigh it?" This is all nonsense, of course; but not more so than the *psychology* I studied in school.

The net result of *introspection* was a Noah's Ark of stalls each labeled for an occupant, a "content of the mind." It was not unlike the shaved-head phrenology charts with allotted areas for *bumps* of amativeness, adhesiveness, philoprogenitiveness, and other *faculties*. Phrenology broke down before the fact that my bump of "amativeness" may be due to a thick skull, water beneath the skull, or the fact that with no *bump* at all I am very amative.

The old psychology went the same way. *Mind* was found to be neither a "secretion of the brain" as bile is of the liver, nor any thing or process apart from a living body. It was next discovered that the brain itself is simply a part of the central nervous system, the body's integrating organ or mechanism of adjustment. That this mechanism is born primed for many primitive naked-and-unashamed activities, but is unlearned in modern ways and learns only by experience, was the next step in the downfall of the old psychology.

With the realization that some individuals have no mind at all, individual behavior began to be a problem. With the realization that the outstanding fact of evolution is individual variation, and that the significant fact of the genus *Homo* is individual behavior, and that stereotyped behavior in an individual is a sign of abnormality and if vicious lands him in a padded cell, the old science of mind-gazing lost its pep and the gazers began to try to find out what happens to human beings and why. And that is a real problem, from the complete solution of which we are yet miles and years.

To solve a problem is to know its laws. To know the laws is to be able to make predictions. For example: I can predict the behavior of a pint of ethyl-alcohol under many physical and chemical changes so accurately that you can expect

264

your pint of C_2H_5OH to behave the same way under the same conditions. That is *science*. I cannot predict your behavior when you drink that pint of alcohol—the personal equation is too big.

Sciences are *exact* to the extent that the personal equation is eliminated. The personal equation can never be eliminated in predicting human behavior.

General predictions, yes. Cats are cats, dogs are dogs, pigs are pigs. No two alike, but enough alike for practical purposes. Can you predict any certain tomcat's behavior an hour hence? You cannot even predict next week's weather. A three-year-old child contains more elements than the weather and is driven by more forces. Can you predict its behavior? The particular behavior of any one human being under any one certain condition may depend on an infinitesimal amount of a hormone yet unknown to science. Give up? No; look into hormones, into individual inheritance, into millions of reflexes many of which may be put out of action by the wink of an eye. What is the nature of hormones, what is it that is inherited, how are reflexes conditioned and acquired, how are they put out of action, why can a wink be so devastating?

Man both makes and outlaws his own laws. He cuts off his nose to spite his face; dies to live and makes a martyr of himself in the name of custom; scarifies his face and body, deforms his head, waist, and feet, and wears sackcloth and ashes, patent-leather shoes, and plug hats in the name of fashion; and consigns to hell his infants' souls in the name of the Saviour he implores to save his own soul.

The vagaries of human behavior seem as countless as the sands of the sea; but the sands can be classified and described. Human behavior also, though the problem is more complex and shifting. That man makes an ass of himself and elects himself a saint only adds zest to the study of human behavior. Man is not only the most curious thing in the world, but the most interesting, not only to live with, but as an object of observation.

The old psychology died hard; it has not been easy to give up *mental faculties*. But in surrendering mind to philosophy we have gained living human beings; in abandoning the search for some magic power to transform human nature we have discovered how to transmute "imps into angels by the alchemy of smiles."

Not that we are born imps, but helpless infants with a specific nature called human and a definite equipment for learning human and inhuman behavior. This inheritance makes up the raw materials of the new psychology. What is its nature, how is it modified by nurture? These two problems resolved, the new psychology can begin to formulate the laws and principles which govern human reactions, in individuals, in groups, in nations. When that time comes—and it will— it will be possible so to organize human affairs and human society that the innate love for life can find satisfaction in loyalty to ideals and service to humanity.

2

Everything cuts up or behaves: electrons, atoms, ions, molecules, water, gunpowder, living beings, everything. We can know things only by their *behavior*. Living things have their own modes or ways of behavior; there are certain criteria of livingness. Among these criteria is growth in a complex dynamic protoplasmic mechanism. Such a mechanism cannot grow without energy. This energy comes primarily from the sun; the earth itself is the source of the protoplasm.

The living organism thereby called to life came at last to be born of woman. From the beginning of its individual existence as a fertilized ovum until senile decay and death exhaust its inherited potentialities and complete its living cycle, it never stops *growing*, although it does stop growing larger. This growth or change of body during the life cycle

266

is one aspect of human life: *genetic* behavior or morphology.

During life certain vital processes take place in glands and organs of digestion, circulation, respiration, etc., whereby the growth of the body is regulated and the individual is maintained in health. This is *visceral* behavior.

The third aspect of behavior includes the responses whereby the individual is adjusted to the outside world. These responses are generally made with the motor mechanism of the body and involve locomotion or speech, and hence are called *somatic* behavior, or psychology.

But note that all forms of behavior of all living things have a common origin, spring from a common root, and obey the same fundamental laws of life. Hence every phase of human behavior is but part of the problem of life in general —and every problem of life involves all of life and the environment of life. The uniqueness of life is the way living beings respond to vital stimuli, thereby so adjusting themselves that they continue their existence as living beings. Therein lies the uniqueness of life. To say, with Herbert Spencer, that life corresponds with environment is, as Herrick points out, to advance life no further than a self-registering thermometer. The thermometer reacts to an outside stimulus; the stimulus is an *impinging energy*. But life not only wars against disintegrating agents, "it captures the attacking forces, appropriates their base of supplies, and compels the hostile phalanx actually to turn about and fight the battles of the triumphant organism."

Why this unique behavior of living things? It is their *nature;* that kind of behavior is inherent in living protoplasm. Because of its nature, it adjusts itself to its environment. It eats, it excretes; it derives energy from food, it is driven by energies which impinge upon its body. Some of that energy is dissipated in heat and in energy-consuming activities inside its body; some of that energy is stored within its body; some of that energy is expended in waiting for or going after more energy. These are all *vital* processes and consume energy for *vital* adjustments.

"Vital" is a useful word and cloaks much that is yet inscrutable. But the energy with which you hold this book is but the energy of your impinging environment so combined with the energy within you—orginally won from nature by plants—and so transformed in you into such a high potential current that it can be made to do such work as human machines are by their nature and training impelled to do.

Living impulses, vital adjustments; the call to live, the response to the call; the living being as an individual; the reactions of the individual living human being: these matters are now our concern. But again let it be said that any *psycho-analysis* which neglects the facts of genetic and visceral behavior will never discover the materials with which to synthesize a human being. Human psychology is rooted in living human protoplasm and can be explained only in terms of its antecedent history.

3

The pyschology of bacteria is not well known because they have only recently been discovered. But the lowest-lived bacteria known to the microscope make distinctions that baffle the biochemists who study them. They have an astounding capacity to transform energy and they are sensitive to extraordinarily minute stimuli. Their behavior can only be described in physico-chemical terms.

Some bacteria produce light. Do they burn luciferin? Do they use the enzyme *luciferase* as catalyzer? Fireflies do, and have special organs for its manufacture. These organs are controlled by nerves and respond to certain stimuli; and they all light up at once! Firefly behavior can be talked about in psychologic terms, but such terms tell us nothing of the life-light of the light-producing bacteria that cause decaying wood and flesh to glow. The *psyche* of bacteria is physics.

Animals are fond of sugar. There are hundreds of sugars; some are so much alike that man cannot tell which is which. Bacteria can. They can detect a thousandth part of 1 per cent of certain sugars; they prove it by their behavior. Are they on speaking terms with atoms? At any rate, their reactions are more refined than those of the sugar chemist's reagents. And yet bacteria are so low that science has not yet decided that they are real *cells*. But they are *alive;* they respond to stimuli and run the gamut of adjustment behavior on which life depends.

Animal adjustment generally involves locomotion. Low forms flow, because life is fluid. The *solidity* of bones, horns, teeth, hair, etc., is due to dead mineral matter between living cells, as is the "wood" of trees. White blood-cells *flow* through membrane. Certain Protozoa that live on moldy wood can flow through cotton mesh so fine as to strain the food from their body. Once through, the streams of protoplasm unite again into a single body which behaves as though it had not been strained. By such streaming movements amebæ and white blood-cells ingest food particles by flowing around them.

A worm has been seen under the microscope to swim through the protoplasm of a frog's muscle, the protoplasm closing behind the worm. At one point the frog's muscle had been injured—it was "dead"; the worm could not swim through that, it went around it as though it were a stone.

Because of this fluidity, living protoplasm can respond. Without fluidity, muscles could make no response. Cutting a nerve *paralyzes* a muscle but does not kill it, though disuse will cause it to waste away. Every living muscle-cell can respond to stimulus.

The microscopic cilia lining our windpipe move in definite rhythmic sequence, wave after wave, like a field of waving grain. A speck of dust excites them to move; the larger the speck, the faster they move. Cilia are ancient structures, the sole motor mechanism of many micro-organisms. Could we get as much work out of our motor apparatus as the little paramecium does with its cilia, we could lift 1,500 pounds. Cilia cut from a frog's throat keep right on moving; they will work a weight uphill.

Bacteria, amebæ, white blood-cells, muscle-cells, ciliated cells, are all types of behavior, samples of life's adjustments to livable conditions. Every living cell and every living organism, from yeast to man, has its own reaction system, its own type of behavior; its own *psyche*—if you like that word.

4

Washburn's *Animal Mind*, second edition, lists 841 titles consulted in the preparation of her book. That was eight years ago. The next edition will probably list a thousand titles; shall we know more then about the "mind" of animals?

Can the mind be seen? Why not. We "see" metabolism, and know much of the processes of chemical exchange between living organisms and their environment. We call these exchanges physiological processes; and while there are many that are only partly understood, and many that are as yet only partially guessed at, no one speaks of physiological processes with furrowed brow, unless, indeed, the process at the time is functioning badly. But "mind" suggests mysteries, vague realms in which souls converse with souls and *psychic* phenomena defy every known or conceivable law of matter and energy.

Mind is not *matter;* neither is the attraction of the positive half of the magnet for molecules of potassium and sodium, *matter.* But the attraction of an anode for potassium and iron filings is a relation between matter. Certain elements are attracted by an anode, some are repelled; a youth is attracted by a maiden. There the matter is; it is open to investigation. The "matter" may be a wisp of hair or a downcast eye.

Mind is like life: it is known only by the company it keeps,

living organisms; they are real. There are criteria for livingness. They often fail. An organism may show no signs
of life: as an opossum, or a grain of wheat. Is it alive?
Only by applying certain stimuli can we tell. If it makes no
response, it is dead. "Certain stimuli": what? Stimuli known
to be harmful to opossum or vital for wheat germs.

The live grain germinates under proper stimuli. Its behavior can be observed and described in terms of energy and
matter, and in its behavior will be found no contradiction to
the laws of physics and chemistry. That germinating grain
shows behavior; it has no mind, of course? Plant physiolo-
gists are not so certain; some are quite certain that if an
ameba has a "mind," a grain of wheat has.

Has the ameba a mind? But, first, what is mind: consciousness? reason? intelligence? intellectual faculties? Or
all these combined? I may think I know what is on my mind
and what my mind is. How can I know your mind? I look
at a picture: I know what I see; I know the emotions, memories, etc., the picture rouses in me. I cannot know what that
picture is to you except by your behavior: words, actions, etc.
Even then I must interpret your behavior in terms of my
own experience. There may be nothing in my experience
which gives me a clue to your behavior.

When Washburn says that we know that *consciousness*—
"as evidence of mind"—resides in ourselves, that it undoubtedly exists in animals with structures resembling ours, and
that "beyond this point, for all we know, it may exist in
simpler and simpler forms until we reach the very lowest of
living beings," I do not see that she has moved either forward
or backward. To say even that mind is a quality of livingness, a sign of life—as is oxidation a sign of metabolism—
is probably quite as futile. To say that one ameba engulf-
ing another is a sign of hunger, a spitfire cat with an arched
back and slashing tail a sign of anger, a dog with a can tied
to its tail yelping down the street a sign of fear, and a strutting

cock a sign of amorousness, is to anthropomorphize animal behavior.

Mental states, yes; we have names for dozens of them. I know how I feel when I am kicked and I have names for my feelings. I do not know how a kicked dog feels. I can judge only by his behavior. He might wag his tail and appear to like it. I could then only understand his behavior by knowing his history: the kick might be an invitation to a fox-hunt.

Mind, like life itself, is quantitative. I stretch my arms, a button pops off my vest. I decide to change my tailor, or reduce, or have the button sewed on in the morning, or sew it on myself. I do nothing. Another button pops. Now what?

The ameba has no buttons to worry about. Sound and sight of buttons never enter its mind. The stimuli which beat upon it from the time it is pried or kicked loose from another ameba until it loses its own identity by dividing into two amebæ are not such as beat upon the near-by frog that is now calling its mate.

We cannot know how the world looks to the ameba. But we can put questions to it: what do you think of red ink— do you like it, can you digest it, do you want more? How does it feel to be turned loose in a drop of water, with nothing to stand on or hang to? Such questions are put to amebæ and to other living creatures. These questions are in terms of physical and chemical change in environment. By their behavior under changed conditions inferences are drawn as to their mind.

But the ameba's mind must be of a different quantity from ours. We "smell" and "taste" food. Can it distinguish brickdust from protoplasmic dust by smell and taste? It can make the distinction—and does, without visible structure of taste or olfactory organs.

By its behavior we know that the ameba distinguishes and that in certain ways it makes finer discriminations than we do. Whatever its *senses,* we can only say they are appropriate to its needs.

272

When Jennings says that the ameba "reacts to all classes of stimuli to which higher animals react," he simply bears testimony to an inherent criterion of living organisms: a certain kind of reaction system. By that system they maintain a certain dynamic equilibrium and thereby adjust themselves to stimuli destructive of and favorable to life. If that system fails, they lose their minds—as does a drop of water when an electric current passes through it.

In other words, it is time to give the mind a rest. The loose use of the word has probably done more to befog thinking than any other word, except possibly "unconscious." It means so much it means nothing. By using it in connection with animal behavior it implies some transcendental mystery in living organisms. There is much ignorance among human beings as to the nature of human beings—so much, in fact, that it borders on the mysterious; but the mystery of a sand dune, of a snow crystal, of a flash of lightning, and of an ameba's response to a lump of sugar or a bull's to a red rag, is all of the same order. To identify *mind* with *protoplasm* or with *nervous action* is to talk about a hole in the ether or disembodied spirits. This is not a static world, and matter will cut up as long as the sun shines. When matter is as complex and has had as much experience as has the stuff of which we are made, it seems inevitable that it should have a vast capacity to vary its behavior in response to the situation in which it finds itself. It can do this because it is irritable. When it can no longer get excited about certain things, it is finished *as protoplasm*. If you still insist on *mind*, call it a manifestation of the kind of excitability that inheres in all dynamically active protein compounds called living beings.

Meanwhile, we shall do well to recognize, with Herrick, that the real problems of human psychology are still over our head and that the problems of animal psychology are proportionately difficult as their sensori-motor organization differs from ours. "The popular dramatization of animal life and imputation to them of human thoughts and feelings may have a certain justification for literary or pedagogic purposes, the same as other fairy stories. But let it not be forgotten that this is fiction for children, not science nor the foundation of science."

5

The microscope reveals no nerves in the ameba. But the ameba has curiosity: it explores its world, even though that world is less than a drop of water. The ameba is an individual, as was Socrates, or as you and I are. Socrates was condemned to death for corrupting the morals of the youth! He had irritated some of the best minds.

All life is irritable. This irritability inheres in every living cell of every living body. Because of that quality the ameba is excited to explore its world and man his. That quality leads to the ego in the individual and to culture in the human race.

The enemies of Socrates were so excited that they put him to death. Hunger can so excite an ameba that it commits cannibalism. Moisture and heat so excite a grain of wheat that it sprouts; if it does not respond to sprouting stimuli, it is dead. An ameba beyond the stage of excitability is dead.

Irritability is in the nature of living things, regardless of size and shape, whether plant or animal, one-celled or many-celled, and of every cell in every living body. Because of this irritability, life responds. An ameba responds to hunger by pursuit and capture. These actions are responses, reactions. My response to fried chicken may be a smile, mouth water, and activity in the mastication mechanism. My response to fried chicken half an hour later may be a sickly grin; I do not want to think of food. The ameba acts the same way after a hearty meal.

Without excitability there could be no response to physical or chemical change in environment. Any change in the environment which causes excitation is a stimulus. Environment is a big word and covers all outdoors and all our insides, including toothache and an idle thought; the kind and degree of change which serves as stimulus depend on the organism. Man's is infinitely complex because he can store experience and vary or delay reactions and because he can respond with words as well as with more overt action.

A baby cries in the next room; my response to that stimulus may be words, or a bottle, or any one of many possible responses. The response I make will depend on a lifetime's accumulation of stimuli and reactions.

Our brain itself and our wonderful special sense organs are rooted in the nature of living things to maintain their dynamic equilibrium by appropriate reactions to vital stimuli. When we cannot do this, we are dead as a door nail.

Nails react to chemical and physical change, but their reactions are because of the elements in them and not because they are nails. Iron may enter the ameba's soul; its reaction is not that of elements to elements, but as a complex reaction-system. With that it can respond by appropriate action to such stimuli as would leave the nail unchanged for a million years, or flee from an acid that would dissolve the nail in a few moments. The nail is *irritable;* but there is no sign of organization in its responses. Nor can it reproduce itself, nor perform the functions of metabolism, nor go in out of the rain. It cannot adjust itself to its environment; life can, because it has an adjusting mechanism.

Living protoplasm has the power of adjustment. Our nervous system is our visible mechanism of adjustment. It is new in life, as are skeleton and intestine; but new only as a new contrivance for doing something that has been done throughout life. The automobile is a new contrivance for getting about, but living organisms got about before there were automobiles—or legs, or wings, or fins; and adjusted themselves to their environment before there were nerves or intestines.

275

The microscope shows no behavior mechanism in an egg-cell. But a pin-prick in the membrane of that cell causes it to vary its behavior: it dies. That same pin-prick in another egg-cell may start it on a road which ends with a frog. Is this "behavior" or "metabolism," psychology or physiology? Once it would have been called black magic, and Loeb, the man who did it, would have been hanged—or made high priest.

To-day the man who describes one ameba chasing another calls himself a psychologist; the man who describes what happens to the ameba that is caught calls himself a physiologist. Yet chase and digestion are two aspects of the same problem: why protoplasm and man go to war. In other words the fundamental difference between physiology and psychology is precisely *nil*.

In chase and digestion the ameba reacted, behaved. It moved: it has power of locomotion. Its movements were *purposive*. It persisted. It tried and tried again. And does other tricks which are black magic unless we assume that the lowly ameba is in all essential respects organized for life. It is the inherent character of excitability that comes at last to be expressed in nerves. Nerves are late in life, excitability began with life.

A flea bites an elephant's tail. The flea-bite is a *stimulus*. The stimulus excites—what? The tail? No; the elephant. The elephant is annoyed and decides to lash its tail to shake the flea off. The fact that the stimulus led to action implies more than mere irritability. The stimulus was transmitted across many feet of elephant body. That implies a *conduction* system.

The ameba is not so large. The space a stimulus must traverse across its body is measured with a microscope. But the stimulus is conducted across its body as it is the length of the elephant's body. Protoplasm is so organized that an exciting stimulus can be transmitted throughout its body. It responds as an individual and thereby adjusts itself to its environment.

It is the excitation-conduction system of living organisms which makes adjustment possible. That system began with the lowest form of life, it is as old as life itself. It grew more complex as the organism became more complex. It led finally to special organs for receiving stimuli, special wires for conducting stimuli, and special motor machinery for reactions according to the needs of the organism as a whole for adjustment.

Excitation, as Child points out, is the great energy-liberating process; it leads to faster living. In conduction, excitation passes from one region to another. The dynamic change in the excited region is the exciting factor in the adjoining region. But both excitation and conduction are not only independent of specific forms of life, but also of the nature of the stimulus or external factor. Which means that the nervous system is to be thought of in more than mere terms of structure.

In fact, apart from teeth and bones, there is little or nothing in the human body that has meaning as mere structure—or as mere function. Structure and function are inseparable in living organisms.

For more than 3,500 years anatomists studied blood vessels and blood—and knew next to nothing or worse than nothing about the marvelous river of blood which ceaselessly bathes the myriads of living cells of the living body. Because it does bathe these cells, carrying to them what every living cell must have (nourishment and oxygen) and relieving them of what every living cell must be rid of (refuse), the enormously complex bodies of Man and animals above the humblest are possible. The blood stream made *integration* possible in complex bodies—such complex structures could function as a unit; the blood made for a degree and a kind of individuality in a complex organism otherwise impossible.

Now note: the blood transports chemical substances. But

that is not enough. My feet may be ever so bountifully supplied with blood and my transportation system may be doing its work perfectly. But suppose I have stepped on a tack or want to tell my feet to get a move on: how can my foot tell me about the tack or how can I tell my feet to move faster? Here is where the nervous system comes in as copartner with the blood as an integrating mechanism.

The blood carries matter; what do the nerves carry—electrons, charges of electricity? Possibly. At any rate, all living protoplasm is irritable and presumably electrically sensitive. Whatever it is that nerves carry, there is no doubt as to results: physiological influences, excitatory or inhibitory, are transmitted. With nerves, quick action at a distance is possible; a complex mechanism is knit into one going concern. The nervous system is the great integrating and coordinating organ. By specializing in conduction it makes possible quick action in distant members, widely scattered regions, multifarious organs, and diverse tissues; the entire organism can thereby adjust as an individual.

There is nothing simple about our nervous system, nor even of any one of its billions of component cells, but as long as we keep in mind its nature we can make progress in understanding it—and that is a long step toward understanding pa, ma, and the baby.

6

A ray of sunlight through a hole in an awning strikes me on the brow; I do not sense it. A moment later the same ray strikes me in the eye; now I sense it. It is a decided stimulus. I respond, become dynamically active. I move my chair; hundreds of muscles are involved in the adjusting reaction. Yet if that had been a ray of tropic sun, I might have felt it on my brow as heat; and responded with appropriate movements. My response in one case was called out by a stimulus to an organ (my eye), in the other by a stimulus to a region (my skin); but in both responses my adjustment was made with reference to a new relation between myself and my environment.

A light ray falling on any part of an ameba's body is sensed; the animal as a whole makes appropriate response.

There is a difference. I was stimulated by the light ray only as light or only as heat. By light only when the ray fell on an organ specialized for light: that is, for ether vibrations of certain length. The ameba felt the ray as vibration, but whether as heat or as light we do not know. What is certain is that its entire outer surface is sensitive to ether vibrations. Its whole outer surface, therefore, may be said to be receptive. Through its "skin" it receives stimuli from the outside world. Its entire exterior surface is its *receptor* of stimuli.

Both ameba and man responded to the ether-wave stimulus. This implies two additional processes. First, some means of communication whereby the stimulus was transmitted from exterior (skin or eye) to the body within. In man, the means of communication was a nerve; the nerve was the *conductor*. There are no *nerves* in the ameba; yet the message was transmitted. The response in both animals was movement—adjustment. This was effected in man by certain body movements; also in the ameba. In man, the movements took place through the mechanism of muscles and bones, activity in glands, etc. This mechanism cannot be discovered in the ameba, but by some means the body responded; the message was carried out. The means in both animals was the *effector*.

From ameba to man is a long jump in evolution. What evolved: what is back of man's complex nervous system and his many complexes of behavior? Evidently some sort of system as old as life itself and inherent in every living being. This system implies excitability and transmission in general, and in particular, *receptor, conductor, effector*. Through a system of this pattern man and every living being make adjustments to environment.

Through evolution this system of adjustment has developed into certain mechanisms and methods. Man's responses are not ameba's, nor elephant's, nor gorilla's; the environment to which he must make adjustment is his own, his responses are his own.

Two important points as to the nature of the nervous system can now be seen in bold relief:

First, in spite of structural complexity the nervous system of man and higher animals can be conceived of in terms of conductors of messages from receptors to effectors. The three make up the *reflex arc*. The arc itself is not seen as structure in low organisms—but they react as though the arc were present. In other words, the reflex arc is something new as visible structure in evolution; the dynamic action performed by the reflex arc inheres in ameba, hen's egg, muscle cell, every living thing.

Second, the receptors in man's earliest ancestors were on the external surface. Where else should we expect to find them? Life adjusts to externals; it must be so organized that it can keep in touch with externals. Man's receptors are on or in his skin, or begin their embryological development, as does his entire nervous system, from the outer germ-layer. Temperature and tactile receptors are pure skin structures, and as compared with such special sense organs as eye, ear, and nose, are in some respects more primitive than those of any other warm-blooded animal. But all receptors are so located as to be exposed to the action of environment change.

As the entire outer surface of the ameba is sensitive, so man's entire outer germ-layer is potentially nervous. But the nervous system itself as it exists in man is simply the final product of the evolution of the excitability-transmission relation of living protoplasm. Its complexity in man—especially of brain cortex—is a measure of his capacity to escape the limitations of behavior set by the reflex arc. He can refer his reactions to a higher court. But even reactions

280

in this higher court are based fundamentally on reflex arc units. The reflex arc is the basis of all human behavior.

While the conception of a reflex arc in which response follows stimulus as does the ringing of a bell the pushing of a button, is valuable, it must be understood that the simple reflex is a "convenient abstraction," as Herrick calls it. It is no master key to unlock the secrets of the brain. In actual fact, "each *reflex center* is usually a region where more or less complex compounding of simple reflexes is effected, where a single afferent impulse is distributed to all the muscles necessary for the complex motor response, where antagonistic impulses meet and struggle for possession of a final common path, or some other correlation of higher order is effected."

All this does not, of course, diminish the value of the concept of the arc as the mechanism for immediate response in unit behavior. This unit, says Herrick, involves the following processes: stimulus (some physical agent impinging upon excitable protoplasm); excitation (effect of the stimulus upon some receptive apparatus); afferent transmission to a center of correlation; central adjustment (whereby the afferent impulse is transferred to an efferent pathway); efferent transmission (to some specific peripheral or end organ of response); response (in some specific effector—muscle, gland, etc.).

The possible permutations of reflex arcs which form the bases of human behavior reach staggering figures, unnumbered billions. Therein rests man's capacity to learn to do *new things,* to react to situations not predetermined by his inherited structure.

7

Living beings as transformers of energy give us the clue to the second great step in evolution and an insight into the nature of nerves; and thereby a better understanding of the life of man.

The transformation of energy is a dynamic process. It implies motion, movement. Movement implies force, power. Living beings are power plants generating energy for home consumption. They must be, because living beings must have something to live on, raw materials to be built into living bodies. These materials exist outside the body. They must be captured from the outer environment and brought within the body cavity. Within, they are inspected; what can be used is used; the refuse is then ejected. These physiological processes are purely material (chemical) exchange. Life trades with the world of environment and in death balances the account.

This material relation of living beings to environment is only possible because life is dynamically related to environment. Living beings are so constituted that environment so acts on them that they react. The more complicated the organism, the higher the rate of dynamic action.

This is beautifully illustrated in the respiration rate in the human brain. The cortex or gray matter is the region of highest activity; it consumes twice the oxygen and liberates one and one-half times the carbon dioxide the white matter of the brain does. Measured by oxygen consumed and carbon dioxide produced, the dynamic activity of the cerebrum is greater than that of the cerebellum. And so on, down through the various regions of the brain to spinal cord, which has the lowest rate of all.

Material exchange in one-celled organisms is effected through the exterior surface. This naturally limits the size of the organism, both for growth or material relations to environment and for change or dynamic relations. Hence the energy requirement of living organisms varies according to surface area rather than to volume of body. A dog transforms more energy relatively than an elephant; a baby needs more energy relatively than its father.

Why "naturally"? Because, as we have already seen, any increase in size causes volume to increase faster than surface.

282

The combined surface area of one billion amebæ is six hundred thousand times greater than that of one ameba with a volume equal to that of the billion individuals. Using Huxley's metaphor, our fictitious one-billion-amebæ-sized ameba has increased its population (volume) six hundred thousand times faster than it has increased its import and export facilities (surface area).

Life cannot do business under such conditions. In the course of evolution the processes we call "living" began to occur in exceedingly small bits of protoplasm; these small bits (cells, protozoa, etc.) have remained the physico-chemical units of all living processes and of all living beings.

The second great step in organic evolution occurred when these units were impelled by certain natural forces to pool their interests and thus form larger and larger co-operative organisms.

Now for the behavior, or dynamic relation, of the organism as a transformer of energy. A raindrop on my hand may be as effective a stimulus as a cloudburst to drive me to cover. But a slight stimulus is effective only over part of an ameba. The stimulus may be so slight that it "dies out" before it is transmitted across the ameba's body. There is no special conducting path in the ameba.

I may shout and shout in my room: no one in the office below hears me, although the man in the next room may be annoyed and the man in the room beyond excited. My voice, through a speaking tube or telephone wire, is conducted to the office below, or halfway round the world.

For stimulus to carry across the body of an ameba, it must be of a certain intensity. The greater the distance across its body, the more intense must be the stimulus to traverse that distance. In other words, without definite paths of conduction it must be assumed that in low organisms every stimulus is conducted with a loss or *decrement* and that stimuli of varying quantity provoke reactions of varying quantity.

Nerves, then, are primarily *conductors*, paths along which

impulses are transmitted. They do it at a speed of about 400 feet a second. The nature of the impulse they conduct is not known. Nerves can be artificially stimulated by mechanical, thermal, chemical, and electrical means. The impulse itself must be some form of energy. The conduction is probably electrical in nature, but presumably not like that of an electric current.

Nerve fiber in man and highly organized animals conducts impulses on the *all-or-none* principle. A fly lands on an elephant's tail. That landing is not an *adequate* stimulus; it does not pass the *threshold*. But if the fly bites the tail, the stimulus is adequate; it passes the lowest limit (threshold) which will bring about a reaction. The impulse, being sufficient to pass the threshold, is delivered as a maximal excitation and without decrement, regardless of the strength or intensity of the stimulus.

We may, then, think of life as having moved from a one-cell hive into a mansion of countless cells because the outside world of environment excited life to wider activity. It could make the move only through specialization in the excitation-response mechanism. With man, that mechanism reached such perfection with all-or-none conduction and all-or-none muscle engines that one pistol shot could fire all civilization, as one small spark can fire a whole magazine of powder.

8

Reflex action requires no reflection; if it did, we should have no time to *reflect*. Yet they are from the same word, "to bend back." In reflection, we turn the memory pages of a misspent career or whatever it is we are reflecting about. In reflexes, life itself knows how to act; we may or may not be conscious of the act.

I am writing. From time to time my eyelids snap shut; I am not conscious of it, nor is the blinking due to conscious effort. My eyes blink as fast as dust or dryness stimulates certain nerves to close the lids. The stimulus removed, other muscles open the lids.

If the stimulus is a cinder, mere winking might not remove it; the lids may be drawn tighter. Meanwhile I become conscious: pain has come as a stimulus. I react now. But my effort to overcome reflex effort may not suffice: I may have to use strong finger muscles to overcome the pull of less strong eyelid muscles.

The eye-blink was a *reflex* action. It started with excitation in my eye due to an external stimulus. That excitation was conducted by a nerve to the central nervous system; from central by another nerve to eyelid muscles: they contracted. The structure or mechanism involved—receptor (eye), conductor (nerve), effector (muscle)—is a reflex arc; the action involved in a reflex act. On the other hand, my behavior in removing the cinder—perhaps involving a mirror, cotton, match, or a journey to a physician—was a general reaction and far from simple.

The arc in the eye-blink functioned as a unit; the reflex act performed a definite service of biologic value. And work of arc and result of act both transpire without my knowing or heeding. Only when the arc fails to work, or when the act fails to remove the cause of excitation, does consciousness take charge.

The reflex arc, then, is an instinctive mechanism to translate impulse into action. It is the simplest unit of reaction; the reflex act the simplest *adapted* or *purposive unit-response* to an external excitation. Arc and act made higher organisms possible. Through them order and unity are preserved in highly complex forms. With the appearance of brain and spinal cord as central adjustor for these many arcs, the evolution of monkeys and man was well on the way.

Why does the eye blink—at a shadow even? Why does an invisible speck of dust close the eye? Or a speck of pepper set the lachrymal glands to secreting? Or a sudden strange noise touch off the whole body, including rate of heartbeat, change in composition of the blood, activity in a thousand glands?

What happens, how the excitation is conducted to the effector muscle of eyelid, lachrymal gland, etc., is generally fairly clear. How the stimulus *excites* is still a profound secret. How does the message get on the wire?

At any rate, it does. And it is also in the nature of the wires to central that messages marked: "Answer urgent" are given precedence. Herein is the biologic value of the reflexes. The newborn babe does not have to think about food, much less have to learn to close its windpipe when swallowing: it does not even have to learn to suck—and that is a very complex process.

Reflexes are *inherited* types of action; they go with the birthright. Some function before the doctor can say, "It's a boy!"; some appear only after some hours; some, only after weeks. The grasping reflex is so well developed at birth that a normal child can support its body by grasping a broom handle. In a baby born without a brain this reflex persisted till its death at the eighteenth day. The babe can close its eyes from birth. The blink-reflex appears in the third month. It can shed tears in the fourth month.

Some reflexes are simple, such as the eye-blink; some, complex—many muscles or glands respond, as in tickling; some spread—different parts of or the whole body responds; some, periodic—the reaction is repeated, trembling, coughing, hiccoughing, sneezing, swallowing.

When we are keyed up our reflexes are quick and intense—*tonic*. A "nervous" person jumps at anything. A brainless frog injected with a strychnine solution is very sensitive to reflex stimuli: the slamming of a door sets it jumping! Mental effort to inhibit pain intensifies the agony of human beings suffering cramps caused by strychnine or tetanus poisoning. It is like trying to go to sleep: the harder we *try*, the wider awake we are.

Reflex action may be conditioned and habits of reaction

developed to work like reflexes; otherwise our newborns would have a hard row to hoe. If we had to depend on our inherited reflexes and instinctive types of behavior, we should never be as clever as the bees and ants nor have as much intelligence as a *capuchin* monkey.

Man's inherited reflex action repertoire is just enough to keep him on the floor. A chick and a colt inherit a better set than that. Ours are of enormous importance and save us time, effort, energy. But what counts most in human behavior is the manner in which they are "conditioned" and what kind of habits are built upon and around them. They arose in response to certain organic needs; too often they are conditioned in ignorance, superstition, selfishness, or vice; or in the lap of luxury as sources of amusement and family pride—equally useless for society.

9

Living protoplasm is excitable; with nerves, it is more easily excitable; with brains, it need not get excited and so can find time to go a-fishing. The nature of nerves, then, is to make us nervous. Therein is the real difference between man and tree: with nerves, the tree would be the higher life.

The baby is a "bundle of nerves"—and gets on mother's. And grows along at the usual rate, knowing nothing of nerves. Then, without a second's warning, comes a day when the youngster cries out, "GOT THE TOOTHACHE!"

That means that the nerve back of that "toothache" is exposed to the world. That is why it cries out: exposure to the world is not the way nerves were brought up. Nerves are not accustomed to exposure, nor adapted to contact with outdoor environment. They are inside performers: they carry messages from somewhere within the body to something within the body. The "somewhere" may be a cell or group of cells on or anywhere within the body, but normally not in the nerve itself.

No tooth "aches." When certain cells became enamel, others dentine, and others cementum, and united to build a tooth, they traded feeling for form and surrendered most of their excitable heritage to become almost solid ivory. That is why the nerve inside the tooth gets so sore when the tooth gives it the air, so to speak.

It is the nature of nerves to be extraordinarily sensitive to and remarkably efficient conductors of excitation. Hence the whole mechanism of *end-receptors:* shock absorbers; they break the news to the nerves, gently but firmly. It is the nerves' business to send the news to the proper organ for response. If the news is startling or in code, it will be carried to the higher brain center for consideration or decoding.

I go along a dusty pike in my bare feet. I cut my foot on a bit of glass. It does not hurt much; and if I am on my way to the swimming hole, I do not mind it. Who told me my foot was cut, or that it was not a tack I had stepped on? Perhaps a mile of nerve fibre and millions of nerve cells were involved in carrying messages before I finished with that cut.

We have big nerves and little nerves, long ones and short ones, as we have muscles of varying length and size. The units are cells: in muscles, bound into sheaves; in nerves, bound into cables—trunk lines of communication. There the general resemblance ends. Nerve cells are called *neurons* —and when inflamed spell *neuritis.* But they are true cells; they have a nucleus in a mass of cytoplasm and grow and in general behave like ordinary cells. But they are unique in their astounding capacity to vary: in size and shape, especially in their outgrowths—"infinitely complicated and bewilderingly complex," Child calls them. Some are as complex in architecture as elm trees, and are called *dendrons;* also called *afferent* because they carry messages *toward* central.

Other outgrowths of neurons are called *axons* (axis); their branches are fewer and shorter; they are more slender and more uniform than dendrons, and may be three feet or more in length. For example, connection between the cortex of the brain and muscle in the calf of the leg may be made by two neurons: an upper motor neuron which extends to the lower end of the spinal cord, a lower or peripheral motor neuron of the sciatic nerve which ends in a muscle of the calf. Axons are also called *efferent:* they carry messages *from* central to glands, muscles, etc. Generally a neuron has only one axon; it may have several dendrons.

A telephone wire can transmit messages either way. Living protoplasm was organized on that plan. But with neuron conduction paths impulses are carried only one way. The axon appeared first; it is more highly polarized than the dendron, grows faster, is more sensitive. The dendron is more primitive, and perhaps plays a part in the nutrition processes of the parent neuron and hence is a less efficient conductor of messages.

Each neuron is a distinct entity and is *visibly* connected with no other neuron. The branches of an axon generally interlace into the branches of a dendron of another neuron. But between is a gap: the famous *synapse* (tying-together), the junction between two neurons.

The synapse is something of a puzzler, but of great importance. If it were perfectly understood we should have a much clearer idea than we have now of many perplexing problems in human behavior.

Nerve fibre—and muscle cells—conduct impulses without decrement, on the *all-or-none* law. At the synapse the impulse is slowed up or even blocked; or it may be speeded up. In any event, something happens. Slight resistance is apparently lessened by repeated excitation—hence the ease of action in habit formations. As though a path were worn smooth with frequent usage. Why? What is the synapse?

There is no synapse in the nervous system of a jellyfish, nor true neurons; simply a *nerve net.* Harvey cut a doughnut-shaped ring from the disk of a jellyfish, entrapping a nerve impulse. That impulse traveled around that ring for eleven days; 457 miles! No decrement, no slowing up of impulse. Apparently it might be traveling yet had not the muscle become fatigued and had not the impulse been interfered with by regenerating tissue. Further, in that nerve net impulses travel either way.

In higher animals, a *synaptic system* with highly specialized neurons having numerous and intricate endings has replaced the nerve net. It is a more efficient system in that it is more modifiable. It provides "an anatomical mechanism for correlation and co-ordinations of the most intricate patterns, and for the modification of the directions taken by nervous impulses arising from transient fluctuations in the relative permeability of the different junctions" (Herrick).

The synapse, then, is a barrier, presumably a living semipervious membrane through which ions, *bearers of impulses*, can pass and in one direction only; the physico-chemical nature of the ions or conducting substance may be thereby altered.

Synapses have been compared to the valves in the veins which prevent the blood from flowing backward, but the comparison suggests nothing of the rôle played by the synapse as a modifiable tissue making for impressionable and plastic behavior.

With the arrangement of neurons and their processes as found in higher animals, the complicated patterns of sense organs, nerves, correlation centers, and response organs of reflex and instinctive behavior were possible. With the plasticity of the synaptic tissue, the kinds of memory and association which make for intelligent behavior were possible.

When that "tooth" begins to "ache" the nerve that carries the ache impulse to central is not to be hushed up on a stopache order from central. It is central's business to have a look at that tooth. As it is the nature of nerves to be nervous, it is the business of brains to attend to nerves—and to see to it that they are not exposed to stimuli for which they are not adapted.

Any one nerve carries impulses toward or away from a nerve center, not both ways; it is either afferent or efferent. And when it is overloaded or stimulated above normal intensity, it carries a message of pain in addition. Therein lies the biologic function of pain.

10

The world into which we are born is not a world of walls, pictures, floor, rugs, chairs, bed, or even of bath, mother, and milk. It is a world of matter and energy, of things hot or cold, soft or hard, sharp or round, sweet or sour, of various physical and chemical stimuli, of various kinds of physical energy, vibrations in the ether and in material media.

The world into which we are born is a small world, but it is a world of stimuli.

Some made us afraid, some made us angry, some made us smile. What happened when the nurse declared, "It's the homeliest brat I ever saw"? Much, if the mother heard it; to us, just born, nothing. The remark was a stimulus, but created no sensation in us: it was not an *adequate* stimulus. If the nurse had bawled that remark in our ear, we should have heard it—for we were born with ears attuned to the human voice. And it would have frightened us, not because of its sentiment, but because of its noise. A loud noise would have been a real stimulus: sound-waves of such length as to disturb our inherited equilibrium. We reacted to such rude noises. They were adequate stimuli.

The world of our environment keeps beating in upon us as stimuli: pressures, chemical substances, sound-waves, light-waves. How we interpret these stimuli, what they mean to us, these make up our world. To no two human beings can the world seem the same; nor be the same on any given two days or moments to the same individual. Under different circumstances, the Count of Monte Cristo would have traded his cave for a gallon of gasoline.

Orion's light-waves have been stimuli for men's eyes for ages. To one age Orion was just "stars," to another age these same light-waves are a library of astronomy, physics, and chemistry. A hickory tree is a dozen different things to a dozen different men; a dozen years later each man has a different notion of the tree. Same tree.

A bloodhound picks up a scent and is off like a shot and tracks his man across fields and through forest. The stimulus that hound picked up means nothing to man. He may root his nose all over the lot, but he can never smell the truffles the hog's nose finds beneath the soil.

This outside world of stimulus, then, is real to us only in so far as stimuli reach us and as we interpret the stimuli. To other animals there are other worlds than ours. It must be so. Two men in an airplane see two worlds: how must the world they see look to an eagle, a lark, a bat, a butterfly? The world is so different to some animals that their behavior can be explained in no terms of known sense of seeing, hearing, smelling, or tasting.

Man's tongue cannot distinguish sodium, ammonium, lithium, and potassium chlorides—they all taste salt; but the earthworm can, and reacts differently to each.

Cut an earthworm in two. The tail end squirms as though in great pain. Not a squirm from the other end; it crawls away as unconcerned as you please. Knife is one kind of stimulus to head end, something else to the other end.

A marked male moth was set free a mile and a half from a caged female. The male was on the cage the next morning. Our smell stimuli come in the form of gas or vapor. Some animals seem to smell *vibrations*. Ants especially sense stimuli far beyond human reach.

The white rat can hear a *noise*, but not a *tone;* a tuning fork is no stimulus to its ear. Sound-waves are stimuli to such as are tuned in.

292

A shadow is an adequate stimulus to a starfish. Cut out its eyespots, the shadow is still an adequate stimulus. Other marine forms without eyes respond to shadows. "Sensibility to difference," Loeb called it. Even the ameba senses changes in intensity of light. Blinded frogs can distinguish red from blue light through their skin. Yet Watson found that rabbits and rats cannot distinguish *red* from *darkness*.

Possibly all animals below man are color-blind. When the bull sees *red*, he sees heat. Radiant heat and light, after all, only differ in wave-length; both are ether vibrations. Certain animals evidently sense certain vibrations in their skin which are not stimuli to the skin of higher animals. Bees are color-blind, but they can see ultra-violet light rays invisible to human eyes.

Space relations come to us as certain light-wave stimuli and we use our stereoscopic vision to determine these relations. Yet animals without stereoscopic vision and with practically immobile eyes give evidence of infallible judgment in estimating distance.

How do they do it? We know our world as it reaches us, as sensation. We know what our sense organs sense; the range of vibration that is stimulus for eye and for ear; the range of chemical change that serves as stimulus to tongue, etc. We know our environment in so far as it serves as stimulus. Each kind of animal and plant *knows* its world in the same manner. And for each of us the world is what we sense it. For many there are no rainbows, sunsets, or Orions, except in picture books.

Think again of the child at birth. To how few things is it receptive! In almost literal truth, it has no "sense" at all. And yet a normal newborn has all the sense organs or *receptors of sensations* it will ever have. They are the analyzers of stimuli from the world outside the body; the *windows of the mind*, Herrick calls them. Each can be penetrated by or is receptive to only certain kinds and ranges of external energies. External ear, refracting media of the eye, etc., are merely devices which modify, strengthen, or concentrate, and so make more effective the action of the stimulus. Rarely is it the fault of the sense organs themselves if "having eyes they see not, having ears they hear not"; nor if, with the whole world as stimulus, they never get beyond the vegetable plane of existence.

11

Nerves conduct impulses. An impulse is a push. What is it that pushes? Pushes what?

I look up: I see stars. I get a crack over the head: I see "stars." Same stars? With an eye open I see light. I close both eyes and press my thumb on one eye: I see light. Remove both eyes and stimulate either optic nerve with electricity: I see light. Those who have had an eye removed on the operating table report "blinding light."

What do we *see* with, then? Obviously, not with the eyes. Even mechanical pressure on the optic nerve, when the eyes are removed, produces a sensation of light. We do not "see" with that nerve; it merely conducts the stimulus, the impulse—no matter who or what pushed. It must be that we see with the brain. We do: we also "hear" with the brain. And if our optic nerve were attached to our ear, stimulus of ear would be received by the brain as light.

It follows that the impulse which is carried by the optic nerve may start outside or on any part of the nerve itself, but once on the nerve the impulse is carried to the brain and there registers as light, the intensity depending on the intensity of the impulse or stimulus. We say the light is seen by the eye because the brain projects the sensation to its point of origin. Pain in the stump of a leg is often "felt" in a foot that has been amputated.

There may have been neither stars nor light in sight when I received the crack on the head; the sight center in the brain was stimulated: I saw "stars." The optic nerve never carries sound impulses. No matter what the impulse that is put on it, the brain "sees" the impulse as light.

The eye is the outer end-organ of the optic nerve. The retina is the receptive part; it is part of the brain itself—the *seeing brain.* The eye is the most highly specialized of all sense organs. It is called a *special* sense organ because specialized to receive certain stimuli which, carried to the brain, arouse a special sense, the sensation of sight.

TABLE OF ETHER WAVE VIBRATIONS [1]

Wave length	Number of vibrations per second	Receptor	Sensation
00 to .1 mm. (electric waves)	0 to 3,000 billion	None	None
.1 mm. to .0004 mm.	3,000 billion to 800,000 billion	Skin	Radiant heat
.0008 mm. to .0004 mm.	400,000 billion to 800,000 billion	Retina	Light and color
.0004 mm. to .000059 mm. (ultra-violet-rays)	800,000 billion to 5,100,000 billion	None	None
.0000008 mm. to .00000005 mm. (X-rays)	400,000,000 billion to 6,000,000,000 billion	None	None

[1] From *Neurology,* by C. Judson Herrick, 1922, by permission of the author and the publishers, W. B. Saunders Company.

The eye itself is the receiving apparatus for certain kinds of physical energy—ether-waves; but it can receive ether-waves of certain lengths only. Thus, by reference to the foregoing table, it will be seen that of all the countless ether-waves that impinge upon our retina our eyes respond only to those with a rate of vibration of from 400,000,000,000,000 to 800,000,000,000,000 per second, one octave of the ten contained in the solar spectrum. These light-waves travel at a velocity of 186,000 miles a second and vary from 1/30,000 to 1/60,000 of an inch in length. Within this range the human eye can distinguish up to 230 pure spectral tints and up to 600,000 degrees of purity and intensity.

Ether-waves vibrating faster than 800,000,000,000,000 per second are called ultra-violet rays and are beyond human vision. X-rays are the ether-waves shorter than the ultra-violet. They are less than a quarter of a millionth of an inch long and vibrate at a rate from 400,000,000,000,000,-000 to 6,000,000,000,000,000,000 per second. Their penetrating power is also astounding; neither flesh nor bone stops them, nor thin sheets of zinc, iron, or lead. The existence of the three octaves of the ultra-violet series and the X-rays series would have remained unknown to man had they not been discovered by indirect means in physical laboratories.

Above the octave visible to the human eye are the six octaves of the infra-red. Of this series the human skin is receptive to waves of from 3,000,000,000,000 to 400,000,-000,000,000 as radiant heat; as it is also to the octave which stimulates the eye as light. Thus, ether-waves of the same energy may be received by the eye as light, by the skin as heat. The physical stimulus is identical; and presumably the nerve impulses from skin and eye to brain are identical. The discrimination is made in the brain. Optic nerve impulses register *light;* warm-spot impulses register *heat.*

Beyond the infra-red octaves of the solar spectrum are the long, slow electric, or *Hertzian,* waves; they never stimulate the eye, only the ear when transformed by a Marconi into waves in material media. Hertz's discovery made the radio possible.

So also the human ear has its limitations as receptor for sound-waves or vibrations in material media. The normal ear is a *special sense* organ for vibrations of about ten octaves, from forty feet to one-half inch in length, and from 30 to 30,000 per second. Within this range about 11,000 different pitches can be discriminated. Exceptional individuals are sensitive to vibrations as slow as 12, as fast as 50,000, per second. Vibrations ranging from mere contact up to 1,552 per second are received by the skin and sensed as touch or pressure. Compared to light-waves, sound-waves travel at a snail's pace, only 1,100 feet a second.

The anatomy of the internal ear is quite as complicated as is that of the eye, though not so well understood. But presumably an essential part of the hearing organ is a tiny membrane in the inner ear which contains about 20,000 exceedingly minute short fibres of varying length. These, it is thought, vibrate in response to wave-lengths transmitted within through the ear drum and the complicated mechanism of the middle ear.

Just as pressure on the eyes may be transmitted as light, so disturbance within the auditory apparatus registers on the auditory nerve as sound. Disturbed blood pressure inside the ears gives rise to such noises as ringing, roaring, rushing, etc.

Both eyes and ears are specialized as to kind and amount of stimulus they receive; they have *selective excitability* and so lower the *threshold* of excitability for specific stimuli and heighten it for all other stimuli. The sound of a ticking watch can be carried through teeth and bones to the auditory nerve; but the ear will carry a tick so faint that it will not reach that nerve through teeth and bone.

Our eyes see more and our ears hear more than a gorilla's not because ours are better receptors or are excited by different stimuli, but because our experience differs from the gorilla's; the difference is in the mind's eye and ear.

We do see with the eyes and hear with the ears; such is the nature of these receptors. Only it must be understood that the eye is a photo-receptor, the ear a sound and position receptor; our *sensations* of sight and of sound are dependent on brain cortex, where they rise to consciousness. In dreams we see sights and hear sounds—in the brain cortex only; the receptors or end-organs of sights and sounds may have received no stimuli.

When an end-organ is discovered in man's body adapted for stimuli such as can be transmitted by a nerve and which can be produced by "conscious thought" in another's brain, then—and not until then—will it be time to investigate *thought transference* and *mental telepathy*. "Spirits" may communicate with "spirits"; but allowing myself a maximum of "psychic" power—whatever that means—I can conceive of no voice without mechanism, nor noise without friction. Science may never see with its eye the hydrogen-ion involved in nerve conduction, nor know how atoms or ether waves excite living protoplasm, but it cannot get excited about something it cannot even conceive. When Sir Oliver Lodge talks with "spirits," he does it outside a physical laboratory and as a misguided enthusiast, and not as a physicist. To talk of or to ghosts is to talk of or to a ghost story. Neither X-rays nor Hertzian waves transcend any known laws of physics. Thought-transference and disembodied spirits transcend all the known laws of physics, nature, and common sense.

12

Taste and smell organs are the other two of our four *special* senses. Eyes and ears are *somatic* receptors and receive physical stimuli, ether or mechanical waves. Taste and smell organs are *visceral* receptors and are stimulated by chemicals in solution; hence they are called *chemical receptors*. Smell is also a somatic receptor, and as the stimuli for smell come from outside the body, the organ of smell, together with the organs for hearing and vision, is also called *exteroceptor*, to distinguish from *proprioceptors* and *interoceptors* within the body.

But bear in mind that "special sense" organs are not pri-

marily *organs of special senses;* they are special receptors
to receive certain stimuli from the environment. Through
adequate response to such stimuli we make the adjustments
necessary to maintain life. The adjustments are made only
after the central nervous system has analyzed the stimuli.
Thus, to use Herrick's figure, the odor of ethyl-alcohol may
lead to action in the great somatic effector, the motor mechanism, to get the alcohol; the odor of that alcohol in the mouth
may lead to swallowing it. The first odor was an exterocep-
tive stimulus and led to a distance or *somatic* reaction; the
odor in the mouth was an interoceptive stimulus and led to
a *visceral* reaction. The discriminating mechanism was the
central nervous system.

We have a sense of taste; the organ of taste is the tongue.
Is it? Most of the tongue cannot taste anything. Nor can
any of it *taste* honey from molasses, black coffee from quinine, clam juice from beef broth, or an apple from an onion.
It can *feel* fine distinctions; it is a better *touch* than taste receptor. *Taste buds* only receive stimuli: sweet, on the tip
of the tongue; sour, at the sides; salty, at the tip and sides;
bitter, at the root. Only these four qualities: sweet, sour,
salty, bitter. The fine discriminations we make in our mouth
are with the aid of our olfactory organ in the nose and with
our tongue as a *tactile* organ. Tea and wine "tasters" are
tea and wine *smellers.* But there is enormous individual
variation in the distribution of the taste buds; they may also
be found in the soft palate, the epiglottis, even in the larynx.

The *bitter* receptor is a thousand times more delicate than
the salty—because there are more bitter poisons than salty
ones? Why, then, should the bitter buds be at the root of the
tongue?

Taste *buds* are receptors for chemical stimuli. The sweet
buds are excited by sugar; also by chloroform, lead acetate,
and other things no more chemically related to sugar than
a rabbit. There is sugar in a rabbit, none in lead acetate.
When the sweet bud is excited, it *tastes* sweet; the bud seems

to taste atoms or ions. Even the sugar in the blood may be *tasted* by victims of diabetes, as may the bitterness of bile by the victims of jaundice.

A catfish can taste almost all over its body—it has taste buds scattered around in its skin. Do things taste *sweet, sour,* etc., to a catfish?

We smell with our *olfactory receptor,* the lining of one of the seven small cavities in our nose. The stimuli are received on microscopic hairs bathed in liquid and must enter into its solution. Man, it is said, has "lost the sense of smell." At any rate, our smell sense is miles behind a dog's and probably not as keen as a shark's. Yet the human nose easily picks up the scent of an almost inconceivably small amount of an alcohol derivative which smells like garlic and is called mercaptan.

How small is "almost inconceivably"? It requires a thimbleful of air to fill the cavity of the smell receptor. One 460-billionth of a gram of mercaptan evaporated in a thimble of air sniffed up our nose smells like garlic. What is the nature of that stimulus? In that almost inconceivably small fraction of a gram of vapor there are 200,000,000,000 molecules.

Life smelled before there were noses. The skin of the humble sea anemone is peppered all over with olfactory receptors. No doubt the ameba smells and tastes. It must have chemical receptors. It must distinguish useful from noxious molecules. It may know how atoms taste and smell. It is certain that a world of environment acts on both animals and plants without tongue or nose. Yet they are *sensitive:* they respond to stimuli. Human beings deprived of the four special senses manage to live and to experience *sensations;* sensations arise in the cortex of the brain.

Of all our special senses, smell sensation dies out quickest. The first whiff is the best—or the worst if it is that kind of an odor. If it is, and dangerous, move; in a few moments it can no longer be smelled. The *odor* may last, the smell sensation passes. But not the memory: some of childhood's vividest memories are mixed up with the smell of dust, burning brush, etc.

While a certain patch inside our nose and certain buds on our tongue and in our mouth are *specialized* for certain chemical stimuli, our skin and the mucous membrane of our lips, mouth, and alimentary canal can *taste* acids, mustard, and all *irritating* substances. In other words, certain parts of our body are sensitive to certain chemical stimuli; they are less sensitive than the specialized end-organs for chemical stimuli. For example, ethyl-alcohol in dilution strong enough to be smelled must be 24,000 times as strong to be tasted, and 80,000 times as strong before it excites the mucous membrane of the mouth.

In speaking of certain *vestigial* structures of our body, reference was made to Jacobson's organ in the cartilage of our nose. There is some evidence that this vestige still functions as a *common chemical* sense organ. It originally served to smell food after it was taken into the mouth and was connected directly with the mouth. These openings exist in snakes' mouths and receive the tips of the forked tongue; they can distinguish odors from tastes of food in the mouth. We cannot. For that reason "all food tastes alike" when our nose is stopped up with a cold.

13

Every human individual normal enough to live beyond the walls of an asylum lives because he has an equipment by which he can keep on making adjustments to changing conditions. The adjustments we make as individuals are individual adjustments, and they will be determined by many factors. But the adjusting mechanism itself has common features.

Thus we all are, and at all stages of our life are, *sensitive to change.* We sense change by receptors which are stimulated by change. But we fail to realize the nature of receptors, or understand what we sense, if we think our special sense organs are all or are the supreme receptors. We think of glands as *regulators,* and so they are; of our motor mechanism as *effector,* and so it is; and of our nervous system as *conductor,* and so it is; but they are also *receptors.* Our entire body is receptive, even as we are responsive.

Kinesthetic sense: a sixth sense, it has been called; or *proprioceptor,* to distinguish it from the five senses of sight, hearing, tasting, smelling, and touching—exteroceptors which receive stimuli from without. By the kinesthetic sense we receive information from within. Without that information our motor mechanism would be useless, nor could we ever learn to talk or walk.

Impulses arise in this mechanism: in muscles, tendons, joints. All have special sense-organ structure. They respond to pressure. With every contraction of muscle in talking, writing, walking, etc., pressure is exerted somewhere, nerve impulses are released. As these muscles are in opposite sets —to raise or lower the arm or head, for example—we come to know where our head, arms, legs, fingers, toes, etc., are without having to look.

We are not conscious of these countless stimuli, rarely think of them except in pain or fatigue. Nor is it easy to define the stimulus which affects them, largely because we learn to use our motor mechanism very early in life. But they are among our most important sense organs. Normally our muscles are in *tone,* neither fully extended nor fully contracted. Such explicit bodily movements as eating, drinking, talking, smoking, walking, etc., function as perfect habits, and, once acquired, with as little effort as though they were inherent habits. It is this kinesthetic sense which enables us to train the motor mechanism to function so perfectly.

The three semicircular canals in the inner ear are most important sense organs; by the information they furnish the body learns to balance itself. Without them we could not orientate our body along the line of gravity. Nor without the supplementary mechanism to the canals could we keep our head in equilibrium when the body itself is at rest. Orientation is quite as important as locomotion.

There is an *organic* sense. Organs, tissues, etc., in thoracic, abdominal, and pelvic cavities are on the autonomic line of nerves, but they are also supplied by *sensory* (afferent) nerves which reach the central nervous system direct. Mouth, stomach, heart, diaphragm, peritoneum, and urogenital organs are especially sensitive. Stimuli from these regions reach central and initiate movements in the motor mechanism. Indeed our most intimate and personal reactions are in response to stimuli originating in unstriped or visceral muscle tissue.

We have an "appetite," we are "hungry," "thirsty," "sleepy," "tired": these are real *senses*. Where or what the receptors for these senses are is not yet known. But we can speak of the viscera themselves as receptors. Thus the stomach is the "receptor" or organ of hunger when its muscles set up hunger contractions; the throat is an organ of thirst when its mucous membrane is dry; etc. Herrick distinguishes further: organs of nausea; organs of respiratory, circulatory, and sexual sensations; and organs of sensations of distension of cavities and of visceral pain.

These organic impulses lead to adjustment reactions: food, water, sex, voidance of noxious stimuli, etc. They are back of life. Impulses from these unstriped muscles must rouse action in the skeletal or striped muscles. And so we are *driven* to seek water, food, make love, etc. If the motor mechanism does not satisfy these organic impulses, they furnish the drive for emotional postures and attitudes.

As many of these organic impulses leading to bodily activity function rhythmically, we are supplied by our body itself with a reflex basis for a sense of time.

Our skin itself is a marvelous receptor, but it is organized for certain ranges and kinds of stimuli. These excite special nerve endings rather than special organs. One group is sensitive to touch and mild degrees of temperature. When stimulated the sensation is felt as though it belonged to the objects themselves. The other group senses pressure and pain, and heat above 113 degrees and cold below 68 degrees; the sensations are felt as on or in the skin and not as properties of the objects which excited the stimuli.

Stimulus to a heat spot is felt as heat, never as pain. Pain spots can be excited by chemicals, mustard, acids, by cutting, pinching, etc., by electric current, by freezing or burning, and by osmotic action such as salt in an open wound. Whatever the stimulus, the pain spot registers *pain:* it hurts!

And there are paradoxes. Why does menthol feel cold and carbon dioxide feel warm to the skin? Or a warm object feel cold when applied to a *cold* spot? Why do we have chills when we have fever? We speak of feeling "cold to the very marrow of our bones," but no temperature receptor has been located within the body.

A hand plunged into hot water presumed to be cold "feels" cold. A nurse, told to keep her patient's hand in water as hot as he could "comfortably" stand it, kept on applying heat. He could stand it—even up to the point where the skin came off! A frog shows greater ability to "get used to it." Put a frog in a pot of cold water and raise the temperature very slowly; the water can be brought to a boil without the frog showing the slightest sign of feeling. In both cases the noxious stimulus was too gradual.

Suggestion may explain why the hand felt hot water as cold, as it explains the difference in the sensation of a wisp of cotton and a lock of a girl's hair on one's brow. But *suggestion* does not explain the painless scalded hand, nor did it keep the frog's mind at ease while it got cooked. The hand became *adapted;* loss of skin was the price. The frog became adapted; it lost its sensitivity and its life. As we do in prolonged fever or in starvation.

"What hurts, teaches," says a Latin proverb. That is why

we have *pain* spots. That is why when in great pain we have little room for other feelings. A boy might forget a toothache at a ball game, but not an earache. Severe pain must have the right-of-way; it is not easily shunted on to a side track. This can be shown on a dog whose brain has been put out of action. Stimulation of a pain spot and a pressure spot in the same region of its leg excites two different nerves: one draws the foot up as though it were wounded, the other extends the foot as in walking. Both are reflex movements. But, obviously, the leg cannot be drawn up and extended at the same time. Which reflex does the brainless dog make? The one which answers the danger signal, every time.

We may be warned that "the tooth will hurt only a tiny bit"; we twinge just the same. We jump in spite of ourselves when we hear a big gun fired; wink, though we know the experimenter's hand will not reach our eye.

We have reflexes and reflexes. Those which respond to danger signals take precedence; they are prepotent. No matter where it comes from or what the excitation, whether cinder in the eye, frost on the ear, or gas in the intestine, pain is a call for help. Unfortunately, for many of our pains we have no adequate reflex response; we call in the doctor to become the *effector* of the reflex arc.

But normally we are free of pain. Only when this or that receptor transmits a message of greater intensity than the nerve is accustomed to conduct does the message break out of its beaten path to encounter a path of greater resistance. Any part of our body may be a receptor of pain. Even a new idea may be painful to a brain cortex which is all made up.

Life is sensitive to vital situations and must respond to meet such situations. But the excitability of living beings is not a particular this or that; it is an energy-complex played upon by countless stimuli. Some provoke one kind of response, some another; most of them none at all—no response is needed. The response must be adequate, of a kind appropriate for carrying on. To classify *receptors* according to the nature of the stimulus or the kind of energy which excites them, does not tell us all the avenues by which the world as stimulus beats in upon our body.

Because our receptors are specialized they are of enormous importance. Through them we keep in "touch" with our environment; we smell "the battle afar off, the thunder of the captains, and the shouting." Through any one of several receptors we can become excited by fire before its heat scorches our body.

Through our *special senses* we see, hear, smell, taste, and feel our way through life and learn of each other and of the world in which we live. They are good enough for practical purposes, but they fall short of human ambition. Science *sees* with telescope, microscope, fluoroscope, spectrum, etc.; *hears* with amplifiers: hears a bee change its mind and what wireless waves through the ether say. Herrick asks us to think of what the world would be to us if our eyes were like eagles', our noses as keen as dogs', and our bodies sensitive to Hertzian waves, X-rays and the like, and to other forms of energy manifestations as yet unknown to us. As we are, we are earthbound within the limits set by our physical sensory equipment; *"nor can our thinking transcend the realm of sense experience."*

14

A fly lands on my finger: it annoys me; I wiggle my finger: the annoyance flies away. There was a slight lapse of time between landing of fly and wiggling of finger: the *reaction time,* the time required for a stimulus to be answered by a response. It was about .05 of a second.

Why so much time? What was I doing all this time? *I* had nothing to do with it. I was not conscious of the performance; it happens also in our sleep. Had I been conscious I might have stopped the finger response to admire the tiny living airplane that had made a perfect landing. I might have given the fly leave to study my finger as long as it pleased, wondering why my finger, of all spots in the world, stimulated it at that particular instant to respond by landing.

It lands: stimulus. That stimulus, as impulse, is put on an afferent or *sensory* nerve for transmission to central. The impulse can lead to no response until put on an efferent or *motor* nerve ending in an effector, a *response mechanism*. In only one place can impulse be transferred from sensory to motor nerve: central nervous system—brain and spinal cord.

All the switchboards of all the centrals of all the telephone systems on earth combined into one would be a simple exchange compared to our own central exchange. This central, with the nerve trunks leading in and out and the ramifications of the individual nerves of the trunk lines and the ramifications of the branches of the billions of individual neurons—this is our *nervous system*.

That fraction of a second between excited finger and finger wiggle is the time it took for the impulse to be transmitted to central, there switched to another nerve to carry an impulse back to the finger. Same finger. But the impulse started on the *skin* of the finger; it ended in certain *muscles* of the finger.

Reflex action; there is a reflex arc; but central fills the breach in that arc. The skin of finger cannot talk to muscles of finger. Skin can inform central, central can give orders to muscles. Every message that comes to us from outside the body is carried to central, every response to such messages is directed from central.

The .05 of a second for that reflex assumes that the response was automatic: that it was a true reflex, that my conscious self had no part in it. Several factors enter into reflex time. Had the fly been a red-hot coal the time would have shortened: a *vital* stimulus gets a more prompt response. Reflex time is also conditioned by the nature of the stimulus: we respond more promptly to sound than to light. A third factor is the number of synapses that must be passed. They seem to act as switches or relay stations to control the direction of impulses—at one time open for, at another time blocking, conduction.

The physical contact of fly on finger skin called out the reflex. But the sight of the fly or the sound of its wings could have led to the same reflex. In other words, any one of several distinct kinds of receptors might be excited by the fly and lead to the same reflex. The messages are distinct: one from eye, another from ear, another from skin; the answer from central may be the same.

I was stretched out on a blanket under a tree in Colombia, sound asleep—noonday siesta. I suddenly found myself on my feet—and a long green snake in front of me. I was unaware of awakening or of getting to my feet, or of having seen the snake until that instant.

What had been the stimulus? My companion, dozing on his blanket a dozen feet away, had turned over just as the snake was crawling across my chest. He yelled, "Snake!" I jumped to my feet. My whole body could perform a reflex action before my conscious self could take charge of the situation and make human response: kill the snake. A *cultural* reaction. Had my interest been *ophidia* and not ethnology, my behavior would have been different. Brought up as a Hindu and without influence of Serpent-Eve tradition, that snake would be alive to-day, for all of me.

Something happens to messages from the outside world when delivered to central. The word *snake* might have led to the same impulsive reflex—an avoiding response; but the messages already handled by central determined my reaction to that particular message. We come to have *reaction patterns*, complexes of behavior. We *condition* our reflexes; we condition ourselves. Our nervous system itself becomes conditioned, is conditioned, day by day, from birth. The conditioning factors are environment—an East Side tenement or the Babbitts of Main Street.

In other words, what behaves is not brain nor central

nervous system nor reflex arc, but this boy, that girl, this woman, that man, integrated by an integrating organ, adjusting through an adjusting mechanism. Behavior, like life, resides in individual packages. The response of a crowd may be more intense; even as one wolf hesitates to tackle a lion, but as one of a pack takes a chance. Crowd and pack behavior occur because man and wolf vary their response with the nature and intensity of the stimulus.

The business of the central nervous system is to regulate and adjust behavior according to the nature of the stimulus. Few, if any, tissues, structures, organs, glands, muscles, or vessels of the body are beyond its reach. Our *vegetative* processes normally go on without conscious thought, nor can we control them by our "will." But let one of these processes go on a strike, central knows. Knows because, as all roads led to Rome, all nerves end in central. All nerves deliver their messages to central. Central is responsible for the behavior of the individual.

Certain nerves end here, others there. There are centers for this, centers for that. But *central* functions as a unit; it functions for a unit—the individual. Nerves so knit together all parts of the body that central can organize the body as a whole for life—and finds ways out of difficulties that baffle man.

A child is born deaf, dumb, and blind. What kind of mental life is within its reach? That was Helen Keller's fate. Yet her mental development was astounding and little less than miraculous.

15

A snowball aimed at me hits a dog. The dog jumps, yelps, and runs. The next ball hits me. Can you predict my behavior, as I do the dog's? I cannot. I might jump, yelp, and run; I might make no outward response. Ten years later I might marry the girl who threw the ball; or forty years later read with dry eye that the boy who threw it had killed himself with wood alcohol.

The message from snowball was delivered to the spinal cord. The cord could answer it by making certain bodily adjustments. Meanwhile the medulla had been informed and was ready to contribute to the reaction; by a wink or a sneeze or a cough, or orders to heart or blood vessels to prepare for action.

What action? What next? Here is where the 10,-000,000,000 neurons of the cerebral cortex get into the picture.

Spinal cord and *brain stem* (chiefly medulla) are the two *lower* divisions of the central nervous system. *Cerebellum* and *cerebrum* are the two *higher*. The cerebrum itself is the supreme central; larger in man in proportion to weight of body or of spinal cord than in any other animal; it is evolution's latest improvement as *central* of a central nervous system.

The eighteen inches of spinal cord is *central* for a few important automatic reflexes and receives the thirty-one pairs of *spinal nerves* which supply skin, motor mechanism, and parts of the viscera. It ends in and is intimately connected' with the brain, which consists of the other three divisions of central: brain stem; cerebellum (little brain); cerebrum (brain).

The *medulla* of the brain stem, an enlargement of the spinal cord just inside the skull, is probably the busiest center of central. Here end all but four of the twelve *cranial nerves;* through here almost all impulses pass from one division of central to another. Every mark I make with my pencil has first traversed the medulla. It is also a real central of its own, the center for such important reflexes as winking (in part), sneezing, coughing, chewing, sucking, swallowing, vomiting, and the secretion of saliva and gastric juice. It is also the center for breathing, for regulating the size of the

310

blood vessels, and for speeding up and slowing down heartbeat.

The medulla is only one-twentieth of the weight of the entire brain—and hollow at that! How does it control so many vital functions? By receiving impulses and setting this or that mechanism at work. I step into a tub of cold water. The cold receptors of the foot transmit the news to a center in the medulla, the medulla orders the blood vessels of the skin to close in: there is an enemy to proper body temperature about.

And so it works. On behalf of the medulla? No; on behalf of the body. The body is always adjusting itself: to bad air, to poor food, to cold water, to thirst, to fleas and flies, to summer and winter, to tight shoes and high collars and corsets, and countless other frills and fads listed in civilization's catalogue.

The catalogue is prepared in the *higher* centers of central. We can live with a bullet hole in the "higher centers"; a bird-shot in the medulla stops the heart.

While sitting in a chair or walking about the *little brain* center is in control. The chief function of the *cerebellum* is to keep us right side up. This is more important for fishes and birds than for some men, and more difficult for men than for any quadrupeds. But all vertebrates have a well-developed cerebellum. To preserve our balance and adjust our equilibrium is an enormously involved process. No wonder the cerebellum is convoluted and covered with gray matter. Probably 1,000,000,000 neurons take part in every move we make to keep straight. To the cerebellum come messages from the pressure receptors in our feet, from the receptors in all joints, tendons, ligaments, and muscles, from the sight receptors of our eyes, and especially from the *position* and *motion* receptors of our inner ears. The cerebellum correlates and co-ordinates these messages; adjustments are thus made possible. We can walk like a man, or swim like a fish, or fly like a bird.

A blindfolded person maintains his equilibrium with difficulty: the cerebellum is denied one important source of information needed to adjust the body. The blind man *learns* to preserve his balance. Every movement of his motor mechanism registers in the cerebellum; the motor mechanism itself, in whole and in detail, is a *receptor*. The cerebellum interprets messages from this sensory field.

The claim has recently been made by Japanese neurologists that the cerebellum also co-ordinates movements of tongue, lips, and vocal cords, and therefore regulates speech. In that case it is both *balancing* and *talking brain*.

16

Spinal cord; mid-brain; cerebellum; higher, higher, higher. Further away from the simple life. But as the spinal cord is the region which contains the mechanism for effecting many reflex actions, so the whole central nervous system is the region for the mechanism for effecting all actions and reactions. The brain differs from the cord only in the fact that it contains more and longer reflex arcs or nerve paths and more numerous connections. *Centers* are regions where diverse impulses can be co-ordinated and appropriate adjustments thereby become possible. There are higher and higher centers. The *cerebrum* is the *highest* or *supreme adjustor*.

In a well-filled head the cerebrum does most of the filling; and what the icing is to a cake the *gray matter* is to the cerebrum. This gray matter is called *cortex* because it is the *bark* of the cerebrum. The cortex is also found on the cerebellum and inside the medulla and spinal cord. It is made up of actual neuron bodies and their synapses—hence its color, *gray*. *White matter* contains the fibers or conducting structure of neurons. Because of the many deep infoldings or convolutions of the brain, the gray matter contains enormous numbers of neurons. Degeneration of that gray matter, whether from syphilitic "general paralysis of the insane" or from other causes, ends in death.

We walk through life like men because we are human beings and our motor mechanism calls for an upright body balanced on two legs, one of which must be off the ground half the time we are walking. Meanwhile, to preserve that gait, all our body weight except that of one leg is delicately balanced on a ball half the size of a billiard ball. This is a very clever trick and requires many months to learn, during which we get many hard falls. Once learned, we do it without effort the rest of our life, provided we keep sober and receive no injury to our cerebellum.

Injury to the cerebellum need not be fatal but does throw us off our stride. We stagger about and in general suffer from lowered muscle co-ordination. But we can get over this. The stagger need not be permanent, though the injury to the cerebellum is. Why?

The *cerebrum* has taken over the function. This is the clue to cerebrum. It is neither special organ nor performs special function: it can learn to do anything. Its capacity is incalculable. Its switching capacity alone runs into figures which make German marks look like gold coin and distances between stars like diameters on a mile track.

It is because of cerebral gray matter's range of behavior permutations that a Greek professor could devote a lifetime to the solution of a new diacritical mark on an ancient manuscript—to discover just before he died that it was a fly speck.

A child born without cerebrum lived four years. It preserved the reflexes it was born with: sucking, crying, sneezing, grasping, etc. It never learned to recognize its mother nor how to hold a bottle. It never learned any *controlled* or *voluntary* motions. It would lie for hours and hours in unchanged position. Of nervous or mental growth there was none, of intelligence less than that of a decerebrate frog.

If the cerebrum must be labeled, call it *the organ of asso-*

ciative memory and *the structural foundation of human culture.*

The cortex of the cerebrum is a clearing-house, or, as Child calls it, "a deliberative assembly to which reports of matters requiring consideration come in from the various groups or bureaus and in which they are considered and action taken through the proper channels." But before they enter this highest court they must pass one or more of the lower correlation centers.

In other words, with a toothache on my mind the snowball that hits me is relatively unimportant and gets scant attention from me, and could be answered by a mere jump reflex. But under ordinary conditions the stimulus of snowball reaches the cerebrum. Then I become conscious; this or that region of the cortex is intensely active; connections are made with other regions. A conflict goes on; the solution of the conflict will determine my reaction. Hesitation on my part means that the problem is not yet resolved. When a decision is reached, reaction follows. While the matter is being adjusted a boy knocks my hat off. This also reaches the cortex: the lower centers cannot make adequate response to such an insult! Another region of the cortex becomes the scene of violent activity.

Consciousness at this or that moment, then, is determined by the field of our cortex at the moment active: impulses have come in which must be answered and which cannot be answered except with the aid of the cortex. Only the cortex has the complete files of all that has gone before. Only the cortex can hear all the evidence from all the body: eyes, ears, and the million and one receptors of a body which itself is receptor and effector and which in consciousness calls upon the superadjustor cortex to govern its behavior. If a stimulus is not of enough importance to require cortex adjustment, it is not strong enough to get into consciousness.

What messages reach the cortex: odor of a bad egg, burst of thunder, flash of lightning, taste of a quinine pill, feel of a red-hot poker, sting of an insult, colic, toothache? They do, but they cannot reach the cortex direct. As Herrick points out: "No simple *sensory* impulses ordinarily reach the cortex, but only nervous impulses arising from the lower correlation centers." Of all the messages that reach the cortex, those from the eyes are the purest: they have less subcortical matter to deal with first. "It is no accident that the visual sense plays a dominant rôle in human cortical function."

That the lower courts of the body can perform so many living functions so well is why so little is referred to the supreme cortex adjustor, and also explains why so many have nothing to think about: their body does their thinking for them.

17

Gall, a Viennese surgeon, was the first to suggest that the cerebrum or brain proper is a group of organs, each performing a separate function. Out of that suggestion grew phrenology and nonsense and finally a disregard for the cerebrum. No one disregards the cerebrum nowadays, except under penalty of losing control of all that distinguishes man from his lowest ancestors. The cerebrum is a single organ, not yet well understood, but known to be the most complex structure yet thrown up by the 100,000,000 years of evolving life.

Real individuality in life begins with the cerebrum. The less cerebrum, the less power to learn. The greater the cerebrum, the greater the capacity to learn from experience. Of all the structures man has inherited, he knows least about the one which made human culture possible; and because he has used it least, human civilization has become the senseless thing that it is.

A lion can learn to lie down beside a lamb, but a moth cannot learn to let a flame alone. The moth has no cerebrum. The cerebrum is one organ, but is the central for several centers or areas of motor and sensory function. These areas are connected by *association areas*, large regions of the brain cortex which have no direct connection with the brain stem, and stimulation of which leads to no known effect. They are as yet the unknown, the great silent fields; the "deepest mystery" of the brain, Mitchell calls them. They are the *new* parts of the brain: "probably blanks at birth and upon them is recorded the story of a lifetime." At any rate, without them we could learn no new habits, no conditioned reflexes, nor become *intelligent* human beings.

The sensory areas for sight, hearing, and smell are definitely located on the cerebrum. The taste areas are not well known. The skin and kinesthetic sense areas are known; they are at the endings of the afferent paths from skin, viscera, muscle, and skeleton receptors. A pain area has not been localized.

The following motor areas have been localized: face, body, opening of jaws, closing of jaws, mouth, tongue, neck, vocal cords, nose, eyelid, ear, chest, shoulder, arm, elbow, wrist, fingers, trunk, hip, leg, knee, ankle, foot, toes.

Which means that injury to a certain small spot on your brain cortex puts your toes out of commission. Your right thumb is paralyzed: injury in the cortex of the left cerebrum. But when a deformed limb wastes away, it means that the lower motor neurons of the peripheral nerves are destroyed.

Look again over the list of motor areas localized. How many of these structures can you see with your eyes? Those localized motor areas of the brain cortex are called the *pictured movement areas*. You wiggle your thumb: do your eyes see the muscles involved? No more does the brain see or know anything of muscle. It knows muscle sensation because it receives impulses from movement in muscles. It knows thumb movements through the eyes. As Woods Jones puts it, the cortex comes to have a vast store of knowledge of concrete movements, not only of thumb, but of every movement the body makes that the eyes can see.

No repeated pictured movements ever become reflexes. They must be initiated in the cortex of the cerebrum. With one-half of the brain cortex injured, we cannot walk or perform any voluntary or pictured movements with the other half of the body. With all the motor areas injured, there is no learned action in the motor mechanism; certain reflexes only may remain intact.

The baby learns to put its finger on its foot, to put its toe in its mouth, to walk, to make all purposive pictured movements, through the conditioning of and learning made possible by the association areas of the brain cortex. The cortex itself is the receptive area for different impressions. In the association areas they are sorted, stored, blended.

Thus, early conduct is *pictured* in terms of action. The child really begins to organize its motor mechanism when it has memories of past movements. It can then begin to form pictured concepts of possible future movements. A little later it can estimate its ability to make movements. And with this ability, we have dawning consciousness and youthful ideals of conduct.

Davenport speaks of his nine-months-old son: "He cannot talk, dress himself, or attend to his animal needs. He is word and figure blind, cruel to the cat, appropriates others' property, and wants everything at the inconvenience of others. He is a low-grade imbecile without moral ideals." Which simply means that of altruistic behavior we have none at birth and gain none in the first nine months.

Insanity is a disorder of conduct. The pictured movement area of the brain has gone out of action. The body does not track: one part goes one way, another part does not go at all. Impulses from all the different parts of the body no longer have a meeting place where they can be co-ordinated, and as a result of such co-ordination adjust the body as an individual unit.

The ideals of conduct conditioned in the growing brain

will have much to do with the roads that will be open or closed to the adult brain.

The blind boy's brain has its pictured movement areas, only the "pictures" the eye sees must be supplied through the aid of other sensory organs. But no sense plays such a rôle in human affairs as the visual. No impulses are delivered to the cortex with so little delay or pass so few sentinels en route as those from the eyes.

But to take localization areas too literally is to overlook the real functions of the cerebral cortex. They are *associational* rather than specific. The cerebrum is a *superimposed* center. It takes on habits—localized centers presumably thereby come into being; but it can form new habits. It is the dominant center only when the lower centers fail or disagree. But no area of the cortex is the exclusive center of this or that or of any particular function. The centers of the so-called sensory and motor areas are merely "nodal points," as Herrick calls them, "in an exceedingly complex system of cells and fibers which must act as a whole in order to perform any function whatsoever." In any other sense, a cortical center for the performance of a particular function is an absurdity.

Herrick distinguishes two prime functions of the cortex. First, correlations of great complexity and with many diverse factors; of value because of the capacity for choice between many possible different reactions to the situation. Next, retentiveness of past individual impressions in such form as to permit of being recalled later and incorporated into new stimulus complexes. This is a high type of *organic memory;* it makes for modifiability of behavior. The mechanism of correlation functions may be innate; the retentiveness or "memory" function is presumably acquired after birth and is the supreme factor in the education of human beings. With the correlation function we are enabled to give expression to our *original nature;* with the memory function we can modify our innate tendencies and take on the trappings

318

of the culture which happens to be the fashion in our own home town.

18

The first raisin I bit into was wrapped around a quinine pill. About that time I traded a jackknife for a chunk of chocolate, which I devoured on the spot—and got sick. I was thereby prejudiced against two people and thereafter disliked two things. I can recall no detail of the chocolate or raisin incident; I only know that the sight of chocolate is disagreeable, the odor of a raisin unpleasant.

I left a dark kitchen in a hurry and nearly split my head on an outstretched pump handle. The pump was removed. Twenty years later I returned to that house. Leaving the dark kitchen that night, I ducked the pump handle and was conscious of a tingling sensation on my forehead. I had forgotten the pump: my body had not forgotten the handle. Even now, I sometimes feel queer when I leave that kitchen in the dark.

There are two kinds of *memories:* one is built into the body reaction-system and generally is beyond recall; the other is conscious memory and presumably entangled in the meshes of the neurons of the brain cortex.

I may search all day through these neurons for a mislaid name. The next morning I hear some one whistling "Annie Rooney"; the name pops into my head: Rooney! Conscious effort failed to stimulate the "Rooney" cells: the whistled tune excited the right spot.

Every neuron has potential connection with every other neuron of the nervous system. The connection may be incalculably indirect; the paths are there.

A look, a smile, a dimple, may excite a thousand sparks to fire, a thousand million neurons to activity. The total reaction will be the product of untold individual reactions, each complex. Every one of these reactions modifies the

319

reaction-system. It is not that we pile up experiences, but that experiences themselves both change the nature of the system and are themselves determined by the nature of the system.

The first "dimple" we experienced in life may have been wrapped around a quinine pill or too much chocolate; we are thereby "conditioned" against dimples.

Pawlow's classic experiments on dogs laid the foundation for an understanding of the *conditioned* or *psychic* reflex. By an ingenious mechanical device he could determine when and how much a dog's mouth waters: a reflex action of the salivary glands. This reflex normally takes place when the hungry animal sees or smells food.

A dog fed by one certain person only secretes saliva when this person appears. The sight of the person sets off the reflex mechanism: there may be no food in sight. Another dog, fed only when a certain musical note is sounded, eventually shows mouth water whenever it hears that particular note. If the note were one of 1,000 vibrations per second, a note of 960 or of 1,100 vibrations calls out no response. Another dog easily learned to distinguish 110 beats per second from 100 beats per second of a metronome.

A dog is fed exactly two minutes after a bell is sounded. Its mouth waters just two minutes after the bell sounds; this is both a conditioned and a delayed reflex. Many persons can "set" themselves and dispense with an alarm clock. I invariably anticipate an alarm clock by about three minutes. The nervous system itself can keep time.

Another dog was always fed with a ringing bell *or* a flashing light: no food when both stimuli were present. Now note. The dog's mouth begins to water when the bell begins to ring; while the bell is still ringing the light is flashed; the flow stops: light *and* bell are no stimulus.

We go through that countless times in our lives. Suddenly lose our appetite—for innumerable things besides food. A stimulus which calls forth a voiding or conflicting reaction inhibits a previous stimulus. We "lose" our appetite: for a man who betrays us, a woman who deceives us. A hair in the soup shuts down many a salivary gland, a worm in the salad ends many a meal.

Another dog was fed with a painful electric shock at a particular spot on his leg. He learned to like it. With no food in sight, his mouth would water with the shock. The same shock an inch away from the accustomed spot brought pain but not salivary reflex.

For "dogs" read "human beings"; especially, "children."

Destruction of this or that area of the cerebral cortex wipes out such conditioned reflexes as are dependent on the mechanism of the area destroyed. Destruction of all the cortex washes out all conditioned reflexes.

Conduction paths develop with us. They get well worn with use, rooted in habit. Paths that conduct pain impulses to central may finally fail to deliver "pain" messages because they have grown accustomed to carry such messages to the salivary glands or to the gonads; the impulse which should have registered as pain sets up or heightens activity in food— or sex-hunger mechanism.

A smile may stimulate a miser to tighten his grasp on his purse; but he must be a rank dyspeptic in whom the sound of the words: "Let's eat!" provokes no conditioned reflex of salivary glands.

19

We get more energy per fuel unit from our own internal-combustion engine than from any engine we can make, but our body uses up 75 per cent of it and says nothing about it. That only leaves us with a quarter of the energy we transform from food for consciousness. But that is enough. The vitally important functions of life go on as unconcernedly as though Nature had never invented nerves nor evolved brains.

The heart is the star performer. Remove it from the body, strip off its nerves: in a nutrient solution it keeps on beating. Cut a sliver from it: the sliver keeps on beating. The embryo chick's heart begins to beat before nerves find it. The heart is muscle, *striated* as are ordinary muscles, but *involuntary*, as are the muscles of the viscera and blood vessels. "Involuntary" muscle is automatic: contracts and expands on its own. Rhythmic movement is inherent in such tissues.

These internal movements—of heart, countless muscles, miles of arteries, arterioles, veins, venules and capillaries, and big glands and little glands—all keep plugging away in the dark. We cannot *will* them to stop. Nor by conscious effort can we slow down the heart or open the valves that control the progress of food through the alimentary canal, or stimulate the adrenals to give the blood a few molecules of its magic-working hormone.

"Involuntary": yes, beyond volition. Automatic: no. Man is no automaton; nor is heartbeat or gland activity or any process of life "automatic." Living processes are responses to food and oxygen; matter is transferred, energy is unleashed. But some living processes have learned their lesson so well they seem automatic to us, who must puff and blow before we reach the crest. Even if we decide to give up and sigh no more, the most we can do is give up consciousness for a moment: the lungs will sigh out our excess carbon dioxide for us. We may cry: "Give us air!" but life learned to get air millions of years ago. We may demand our place in the sun, but life learned to climb to the sun millions of years before man was dreamed of.

Life is motion. The capacity to move in response to life's needs resides in all living things—has always resided in life, is inherent in life. Life must move to keep in touch with the air and water and food of life. Man and higher animals have taken over some phases of movement—and are "go-getters." They go after water and food. By their sensory nerves they can see water and smell food. By their motor nerves they tell their skeletal or striped muscles to go get it; sometimes called the *peripheral* nervous system. But non-striated muscle and other "vegetative" organs know what to do with air and water and food when brought within reach.

And if the air, water, or food is bad, they speak up: a growl in the stomach, a flutter at the heart, a pain in the kidney. When they speak the cortex listens in. We may not know what spot or organ is speaking, but we know that something has gone wrong.

We begin to investigate. We find that our heart, seemingly without nerves, is singularly well connected with the nervous system. In fact, no other single organ in the body is subject to such nervous control. Why not? Its work varies with endless conditions. It knows how to beat, but how is it to know when to speed up for a race or slow down for sleep? Or whether to beat eighty times a minute for a man, or only seventy times because it is working for a woman? The heart must have accurate and detailed information if it is to give the best it has.

It gets this information from two sets of nerves. One is the great vagus or pneumogastric, tenth of the twelve trunk-line nerves ending in the brain. Its messages slow the heart, inhibit action. The other nerve is on another line, only indirectly connected with central: it is an accelerator, speeds up heart action. The two together hold the heart steady as a bit holds a horse: "gee" means fast, "haw" slow.

A man looks me over—scornfully as it were, and says, "Oh, gee!" The mere look was enough: it was an accelerator, my heart beats faster. By what nerve did that look or word reach my heart, speed it up, and slip the leash on fighting mechanism? A look can do it. One word can transform a man as pale as a cool cucumber into a red-faced fury and prepare him to take on his weight in wildcats.

A fighting man or a weeping woman is in a "state of mind"—an emotional state. Some dogs and people have their "emotions" under control, some are always emoting.

Emotions are born of biologic necessity: to meet the sudden demands when we must run or fight for our lives. To run or to fight for life requires reorganization of the body. No battleship ever carries out clear-decks-for-action order with the speed that the order itself prepares the bodily mechanism of the sailors who hear the order.

Such co-ordinated visceral action takes place through the *autonomic* system. "Autonomic" because in control of activities that function with so little reference to the higher brain centers they seem automatic. It is not an independent system (nothing is, in the body), only an extension of the peripheral, and is dominated by the motor nerves of the central nervous system. It is a *motor* system; it makes for speedier action in the motor mechanism.

The cortex may be busy with a poem under a tree. The sight of a bull puts cortex out of action and switches on the autonomic system. As a result, the poet can now break his own record for the hundred-yard dash; or he can climb the tree. The cortex is still there—if he can use it. Prepared to run and running are different things. Whether he runs or climbs, or decides to wait for the bull to make the next move, will depend, among other things, on how his emotions have been trained, how his reactions to fear, rage, pain, hunger, etc., have been conditioned. Even a poet inherits life's capacity for inhibition as well as for excitation.

The great *effector* of the body is the skeletal muscular system. With this the autonomic system is only indirectly connected. It is more directly connected with muscles which control the pupil of the eye and change the crystalline lens; with glands in the mouth, nose, stomach, and pancreas; with most of the arteries, the hair-raiser or goose-flesh muscles, and sweat glands; with the bladder and reproductive organs.

The sixty-odd *ganglia* or knots of neurons in this system presumably form subsidiary centers from which orders are relayed from the central system.

The fact that the autonomic system can be trained is important. It means that a reflex mechanism necessary for brutes can be educated to behave as befits intelligence. The manner of its education determines whether life is emotion or science.

The autonomic system is sometimes called *sympathetic*—not because it has any sympathy, but because the system connects widely distributed activities. What the system is called is less important than the realization that nerves carry impulses into and orders from central, and that nerves and central function as a unit. The autonomic nerves are simply part of that organization. It is not nerves that go to school or are trained; it is the individual.

20

Ever have cramps—in the sea, a half-mile from the shore? It is bad enough in bed; sometimes sends you out on to the floor before the cramped muscle unlocks. In the water a cramp is serious; it may lead to panic. Some one is generally lost in a panic.

Why does the muscle lock? If I knew I could rewrite the history of civilization. Whatever cramps are, fatigue is. Fatigue is as yet one of life's baffling mysteries. Is sleep a fatigue-killer? We know when we feel rested and when we are tired. What is tired? Why did it get tired? What do we feel fatigued with?

Fatigue is a physiological process, as is living, but it plays such an important part in all learning processes and is such a responsible factor in human behavior that it must be talked about even though it cannot be described.

In a cramped leg the muscle is locked, contracted. The cramp disappears when the muscle unlocks, relaxes. But contraction is not the normal state of any muscle—why does it lock? Neither is relaxation. Muscles are normally under some tension—"tonus." This renders them more capable of response to nerve impulse to contract or relax. But why a muscle, quite on its own, as it were, goes into a chronic contraction, no one knows. Nor is it known why it often requires more time for relaxation than for contraction.

Muscle works best under certain conditions. That at least is known. These conditions include hydrogen-ion concentration, temperature, and load. Under these conditions its energy yields more work and less heat than under poor conditions. For example, two of us run a mile in six minutes: poor time, but that lets me in. At the end, you are cool and fresh and I am dripping with sweat. Most of my energy went into *heat*. That is the difference between the labor of a trained and an untrained performer. But it does not explain why my muscle engines got overheated.

Nor why, when I begin to tire, my muscles relax more and more slowly in proportion to the contraction time. Finally, they do not relax at all, although there has been no change in the stimulus. This failure is cramp—*contracture*. If the cramp occurs in cold water, it is called "cold contracture"; does cold cause the cramp? Otherwise, the cramp is called "fatigue contracture." Does "fatigue" cause the swimmer's cramp? Do lactic acid, CO_2, and acid phosphate result from fatigue and cause contracture? Not in my legs. My toes cramp only when they are tired of being still. That cannot be "fatigue." The more I use them the less they fatigue; nor do they then ever cramp.

Non-striped muscles of viscera may possibly have a rhythmic beat of their own, independent of any action of the nervous system. But skeletal muscles perform under impulse only of nerves. All striped muscles go out of commission when their nerves are cut. As they do in deep sleep. Ever pick up a sleeping child? It would fall apart if not held together by skin and ligaments; complete relaxation of all muscles of the motor mechanism.

Which shows no "fatigue" if there are sufficient rest intervals between contractions. But after complete fatigue, at least two hours are required for recovery. All this has been experimentally proved.

326

But what is not cleared up is why a repeatedly stimulated muscle steadily loses its irritability, relaxes more and more slowly, contracts less and less, and finally refuses to contract, which fatigues us greatly; or refuses to relax, and that cramps us.

Is it the nerve ending? Do the nerves which conduct impulses to muscles, *motor-nerves*, have their own discharge rhythm? The nerve joins the muscle fiber at the motor end-plate. The poison of a plant juice called *curare* kills that plate. A nerve impulse cannot pass that plate if there is curare in the system. But the muscle itself, of course, is not killed, only removed from nerve impulse, *paralyzed*. From which it is assumed that there is some substance at the motor end-plate which transmits impulse from nerve to muscle. This substance gets tired or is made tired by a tired muscle. And whatever fatigue is, or whatever it is that causes fatigue, this substance when fatigued upsets the all-or-none law of nerve-impulse conduction: the impulse now passes from nerve to muscle with a decrement.

It must be so. Muscles are all-or-none performers. Nerves are all-or-none conductors. A tired muscle is not receiving the whole impulse, held up by some substance—which gets fatigued, and makes us all tired.

Here is the point, and a large one: living protoplasm balks at endless repetition. Life itself is a response to change. It wakes up at dawn, goes to bed with the sun. Sunrise and sunset are change. When Johnny's motor mechanism tires with the lawn-mower, let him take a swimming lesson; that will rest him. No normal boy suffers *fatigue* while swimming; although, if the water is too cold, he might suffer a cramp.

Whether fatigue is CO_2 or a function of lactic acid or hydrogen ions, or whatever the substance it affects, the presence of fatigue is the sign of enough. It is as though life said, Give us a change. Even the brainless reflex knee-kick knows enough to tire of repetition.

Knowledge of the human nervous system is miles from complete or satisfactory. Whatever "mind" is, the mind of a human depends on nervous control. When a nerve is cut, the *mind* of the part beyond the cut vanishes; when the spinal cord is severed, life itself vanishes, and with it the last trace of mind—even though excitability remain a few hours longer in the members.

Living matter is excitable; that is its nature. The nervous system is the mechanism through which excitation is conducted; its nature is such that excitation is speeded up and is transmitted over considerable distances. This may involve the transport of electrons. But whether by this means or by chemical change, the facts of transmission can be observed in any biological laboratory.

The nervous system as a whole has come to have what amounts to a monopoly of the excitable nature and transmissible quality of all the other cells of our body.

We may sleep through a hair-cut—so long as the hairs are cut. Let some be pulled, and we come to. Each hair is rooted in a nerve; the nerve cries out when excited. If many are pulled, we change barbers. Which means that the nervous system functions for the entire organism, knits it into one individual. It is the mechanism of integration. Through this mechanism individual behavior, individual response, is made possible.

Our nervous system, then, is more than mere mechanism of adjustment to environment, more than something which has excitation and transmission capacity; it is itself the product of such adjustments as have been made, the up-to-date product of the original reaction system that began with life. It has become increasingly complex. That complexity is the visible expression of that relation to environment on which all individual existence is founded and which starts with all individual existence.

Our individual existence starts with an egg which responds to environmental relations. Our nervous system, at any one moment of our life, is the *conditioned* product of the responses that have been made up to that moment. These responses have been made on behalf of an individual. This or that reaction may seem only *part* response, but all responses are individual: any particular part response sufficed for the whole organism. The organism of billions of cells can act as a unit because its nervous system accepts that office.

The organism is the individual—man. The cells of his body live their individual lives: they feed and breathe as individual cells. But they are welded together for a common purpose—the unified body they serve. The nervous system permits of individual action in that unified body. It thereby performs two groups of functions: "the physiological adjustment of the body as a whole to its environment and the correlation of the activities of its organs among themselves; the so-called higher functions of the cerebral cortex related to the conscious life."

As Herrick points out, our own conscious experience has nothing to work with except the sensory data which is transmitted through the lower brain centers to the cerebral cortex. Consciousness, then, is action of a kind in the cerebral cortex: the materials of consciousness are the contents of sense, sensory data.

We eat and sleep and snore and dream and work and play, hunt and fish, get rich and get poor, and in short do and think the usual and unusual things that men do and think. Sometimes we are conscious, sometimes we are not. Consciousness is an organic mode.

Excitation is movement of ions—charges of electricity. A tired muscle shows an increase of its normal hydrogen-ion concentration. Does this account for the failure of the nerve to conduct excitation in extreme fatigue? A nerve conducts an excitation; time must elapse before it can again be stimulated: about 1/100th of a second. During this interval the ions are probably restored to their original positions and other changes that occurred reversed.

There comes a time when we cannot reverse—nor change our mind; the reaction-system cannot restore our equilibrium; the motor mechanism cannot be relieved of the waste products as rapidly as they are formed. Stimuli which disturb the equilibrium of the physico-chemical reactions necessary for life cease to be stimuli. Changes in ion concentrations may disturb the equilibrium but no longer serve as stimuli to excite changes necessary to meet the next upset. "I will" is a fine slogan, but the kinetic energy which kicks down doors and tunnels mountains is never released until the mechanism is in such position that the potential energy is there. Our potential energy is force. There must be equilibrium back of "I will." Back of each heartbeat is a reaction which restores its equilibrium: it is always dynamic—potential. It can reverse.

With change to which we cannot reply, to which we can make no compensation, death comes to heartbeat and to consciousness. The protoplasm coagulates; *death is an irreversible change*.

The egg by which life is transmitted is a clean slate; the record of change has been erased. At birth the recording process begins all over again. With adult life most of the irreversible changes have been made; we have reached dynamic equilibrium.

Do *we* do it? Can we explain the nature of our reactions? Something is known of the nature of water and many of its reactions have been described, but none explained. Man is not quite all water. How much of the remainder is hydrogen ions, catalyzers, and drugs, is not yet known. Nor is it quite known what fires our consciousness; the processes of chemical combustion in living things are not perfectly understood. But it is certain that all brain work involves change or metabolism in brain tissue. Metabolism in the nervous

330

system is yet to be worked out in the biochemist's laboratory. When it is, we shall know more about memory and consciousness than we do now. But enough is known to give us a working hypothesis and to rob *memory* of some of its mystery.

Neuron metabolism is presumably not essentially unlike that of other reacting protoplasms, but because neurons are especially organized for conduction and are highly irritable, it seems reasonable that they should not only be architecturally unlike other cells, but should also be chemically different. They are. In their *neurofibrils* is presumably the substance which facilitates conduction of impulses; their *chromophilic* substance presumably is the *explosive* in excitation.

The chromophilic substance is an iron-containing nucleoprotein and is found only in the larger neurons and dendrites, never in the axons. It is presumably not concerned in the general metabolism of nerve cells; it does presumably contribute to the rapid liberation of much energy during excitation. Herrick finds a rough analogy with fire in gunpowder and in a lump of coal. The coal burns only at the surface in oxygen; the gunpowder, once brought to the proper temperature, liberates oxygen internally, so that the combustion can take place simultaneously throughout the mass.

During intense activity or in extreme fatigue the chromophilic substance seems to disappear, to be used up; when the neuron is at rest it reappears. In a way, its action suggests that of an enzyme. For the present it may be regarded as a catalyzer of neuron energy liberation. It furnishes the kick back of brainstorms and the explosive in flare-ups; it serves as a storehouse for the release of energy in long-sustained mental work.

But a catalyzer is not used up; no more, presumably, is the chromophilic substance. During rest or inactivity it reorganizes, as does an enzyme; it is free to enter into a new complex. Like enzymes, its action is both analytic and synthetic. It is conceivable that every action of the chromophilic substance leads to a structural change in the protoplasm of the neuron itself. The neuron, therefore, is not what it was before. It has learned a lesson; it will react more easily the next time. There will be less internal resistance, as Herrick puts it. "The change in the 'set' of the reacting substance makes a repetition of the discharge easier. It may be transitory or long enduring. This is *organic memory*. The same principle may work out in modified form in the cerebral cortex in connection with conscious memory."

One other point of great importance. Theoretically, if not actually, every neuron in the body is in contact with every other neuron in the body; but presumably no one neuron is in *direct* contact with any other neuron, at every junction is a *synapse*. This junction stops impulses or it lets them by. It is modified by what it does; it is "impressionable to individual experiences." The real importance of this fact will appear later. The point to be made here is that simple atmospheric vibrations of certain lengths may strike my ear drum and be conducted by my auditory nerve as such, but when these vibrations have been translated by my cortex and found to mean a word of five letters having an odor like a polecat, my entire body may suddenly be mobilized for action. More, I shall be extremely conscious at the time and a different man for the remainder of my life. And all because the different protoplasms of my body are knit together by correlation mechanisms of varying degrees of complexity, all integrated into one mechanism which adjusts me and with which I adjust myself.

And as for consciousness. Sometimes I am conscious, sometimes I am not. During sleep or at rest, the brain is probably in a state of dynamic equilibrium. Some stimulus disturbs this equilibrium; where the stimulus ends will depend on synaptic resistance and neuron thresholds. If the stimulus reaches the cerebral cortex, I shall probably be conscious of it—it will then be "conscious activity, the kind of consciousness depending on the kind of discharge."

When psychology has become quite divorced from *psyche* and gets in bed with living beings we shall be able to throw the word "consciousness" into the discard—along with "mind" and "memory." Human behavior then will be on a scientific basis and not a branch of literature or philosophic or religious speculation. "Mind" will give way to personality, "consciousness" in general to specfic exhibitions of learned behavior, and "memory" to the calling out of some part of the individual's striped or unstriped muscle-tissue organization.

Do I *remember* something? Only if I can react it with my manual, verbal, or visceral mechanism as the case may be. Am I *conscious?* Only when the higher brain centers are stimulated to activity. Have I a *mind?* Well I am alive— and must keep on making adjustments until I am dead. And *that* adjustment ends my personality and any further behavior as a living being.

This conception of a dynamically active cortex is helpful in understanding several phenomena of general psychologic interest—sleep, dreams, consciousness, etc. In sound sleep it is presumably in equilibrium. When we are widest awake, its equilibrium presumably is quite upset; changes go on until equilibrium is restored.

But in this connection Watson's warning against overemphasis of the rôle of the nervous system is useful.

Every sensory structure can, when stimulated, excite a segmental reflex, a reflex involving neighboring segments, or a reflex involving practically the whole central nervous system. Herein lies the neurological basis for the complex types of instinctive and habitual reflex acts. Central affords a system of connection between sense organs and glands and muscles. Interrupt the connection, the organism no longer acts as whole; some phase of the behavior pattern drops out. But, in stooping to tie a shoe, for example, or jumping in fright following a sudden explosion, the tonus of every muscle, striped and unstriped, in the body, is changed, and the glands become activated. *Action* takes place only with bones, which means more food, strain on the heart, elimination of waste, etc. While a simple eye-hand co-ordination brings a well-ordered and integrated response from the whole organism, such response only takes place with central, but it can not take place without action in heart, bones, glands, and muscles.

As to the nature of the processes due to change in equilibrium, Herrick assumes, for example, that the irradiation of a nervous discharge into the visual area of the cortex through the association tracts will be determined by the existing pathways at the moment open. Which pathways are open will be determined by previous experience (facilitating transmission) and by stimuli of other senses, which will reinforce, inhibit, or modify the visually excited nervous discharges, partly by particular patterns of memory vestiges in the association centers, partly by temporary states of fatigue, lassitude, interest, etc.—"and it may be by countless other factors." But, cortical equilibrium having been disturbed (by a withering look or a trim ankle), cortical activity will continue until a new equilibrium is established— "by motor discharge, by fatigue with no practical outcome, by the fabrication of a new pattern of cortical activity or by a new enduring 'set' of the reacting system which will modify all subsequent activity of this system and may appear in consciousness as an idea, a judgment, a decision, a purpose, or an ideal."

Consciousness is like life: there are criteria, manifestations, of living things; but, as there is no life in general, so there is no consciousness in general. There are conscious modes. The reaction of ameba to vital change is one conscious mode, or form of consciousness. Call it instinct, impulse—what you will; but it is a definite kind or form of energy transformer. In man, this energy becomes an object

334

of observation because it influences other centers of energy transformation. I have the energy to do several things at the same time—even to be conscious that the robins are greeting the dawn and that it is time for me to take the air. The fact of that consciousness is a factor in my behavior and I adjust myself accordingly. Any other animal with my kind of adjusting mechanism and with my experience would do the same.

CHAPTER VI

ACQUIRING HUMAN BEHAVIOR

1

THE stork leaves the baby and flies away home. The baby knows how to live; all it has to do now is to learn to behave. It can learn many things; it will be expected to learn certain things. It is fitted for life; it will be trained to fit into this or that kind of life. It has an inheritance; it will be asked to invest this inheritance in the coin of the realm. Its potentialities are unknown; they will now be tested and given rein to develop or checked by the bit of custom. In short, every baby is born at a specific time into a specific community with definite ways of living and set opinions of those who do not live that way; to that life the baby is expected to learn to adjust itself—or, as it is sometimes put, to become an ornament!

How does it do it?

How does the stork know its way home? We do not know. We know how to find our way home—and what happens when we arrive home and cannot find the keyhole, or when we promise to be home at one and arrive at four. Even a bee knows its way home—and makes for it in a "bee line."

336

Marked terns carried by Watson in a hooded cage on a steamer from their nesting grounds off the coast of Florida to Galveston, returned home in less than a week across the six-hundred-mile trackless waters of the Gulf of Mexico.

Uncanny? Only because we cannot describe tern behavior in the familiar terms of human psychology. We only know that with this *homing* instinct birds get home; we do not yet know the nature of the stimulus, whether one or many, or how this stimulus so excites the bird that it makes its "uncanny" response. But this we can say: any bird born with a reaction mechanism that is not responsive to life-or-death excitations will never grow up to be proud of its offspring.

An eel travels down the Rhine to the sea, and keeps right on until she reaches the Azores; lays her eggs; dies. Her progeny return to the Rhine. Salmon are as "uncanny"; from the sea they enter fresh-water rivers and ascend far inland; deposit their eggs; die. They are in such hurry to make this journey to the grave that they do not stop on the way to eat. Young salmon return to the briny deep to grow up, and find their way back up the very same river to pay their debt to their kind and to their nature.

During evolution, life has encountered endless situations and has learned—sometimes only indifferently well—to meet these situations in endless ways. Some of these ways are still miles beyond us—as Huxley remarked of his crayfish after studying it all his life. We see the responses—and too often interpret them in terms of our own likes and dislikes, pains and pleasures, work and play.

We think we know why we travel a thousand miles to die in the old home, and how we find it. But why should a poor fish of a salmon go hungry for weeks, travel a thousand miles, breast endless rapids and climb waterfalls, just to polish off life in the old home? It seems stupid! It is: it has nearly been the death of salmon. Think of all the salmon ever canned—all because they insist on going home to die!

We see the responses; we dissect out the reflex arcs of

nervous mechanism and distinguish receptors from effectors: the behavior still baffles us, because we have only just begun to try to interpret living beings as dynamically excitable organisms with a capacity to respond to excitations which to them have life-or-death value, and which transmit to their offspring both excitable structure and capacity for response.

We do not know what impels salmon to climb to lakes in mountains, eels to cross seas, birds to migrate halfway round the world, amebæ to chase their brothers, or men to beat their wives. We do not even know much about impulses. We do know that some things, some situations, and some people, excite us—sometimes more than we are willing to admit or is good for us. We respond: we may clean up or go broke.

But whatever it is that salmon, stork, or ameba responds to, we may be certain that the response is an answer to a question: is it poison or food—shall I eat it or leave it alone? Friend or foe—and if foe, shall I run or fight? And, in higher organisms, does she love me or does she not?

These are the three big things in life.

Plants and animals answer these questions, each according to its kind. One's poison is another's food; one's deadliest enemy is another's life-saver. Each has its own specific reaction system—range of capacity to act, range of capacity to learn. In short, to each species of animals the world is thus and so; to that world it must respond thus and so; the individuals of the species are born attuned to the world in which they must sink or swim.

The baby our stork left is in the same boat. Only, if we are to understand it, two things must be borne in mind.

Every species of higher organisms, both in plant and animal world, has its own specific life cycle. A certain caterpillar eats and excretes the livelong day to turn into a butterfly which lays her eggs while in the cocoon and dies before she has eaten a meal or flown a foot. A colt dropped to earth rises up to trot off with its mother. "Infancy" may be a minute, it may be years. "Adult" life may rise at sunset from an *imago* in the water on the wings of an *ephemera,* to mate, drop her eggs, and die before sunrise.

The world into which we are born has little relation to the world we were evolved to be born into: it is a man-made world, full of whispers and innuendoes, dark corners and bright lights, selfishness and greed, stupidity and cruelty, and many charitable organizations. In course of time these excrescences will be seen for what they are. Then the years of infancy can be so spent that the adult can make the most of his capacity to mend his environment, instead of being so misspent that he must use all his energy to fit into it or escape from it.

Eagles have nests, and coyotes holes, but a lamb has no place to lay its head except alongside mother, and she must keep in touch with grass. The lamb begins to jump about before it is a day old: it may have to run for its life that same day. Having frolicked fleetness of foot into its legs, it is prepared for the main business of life—tearing off grass between gums of upper and teeth of lower jaw.

The baby the stork leaves can neither fight nor run, but in its innate instinctive nature are biologically useful modes of response to the two big crises which confront a human infant. The response to hunger is one. Back of this response is a mechanism which works like a charm. Sucking begins when the lips are stimulated, even by an empty rubber nipple. Food in mouth leads to the next step in this reflex chain—swallowing. The reflex chain ends with the stimulus of a full stomach. All this is *instinctive* behavior. The reflex is the simplest and most persistent mechanism of instinctive acts. The two represent a primitive response in a predetermined direction.

Nor does the newborn have to learn to "throw up" a meal or spit it out, or to lick, hiccough, sneeze, breathe, or make a face—at quinine, for example. Or draw up its leg when tickled. These reflex responses are instinctive acts, written into its inheritance.

339

In short, we are born with much valuable knowledge picked up during the millions of years we have been living; but we are not born with the knowledge where food and water are to be found, or with a motor which would take us there if we knew.

Which means that our viscera know how to live; our motor mechanism does not know how to carry the viscera to the things it must have to live on. And we are infants-in-arms until our motor mechanism learns to perform that service for us. When that mechanism learns to go after food as well as the viscera know how to handle food, we are *going* concerns, we have some *sense*. The first sense we acquire is movement sense, kinesthetic organization.

2

Animals must eat or die; must breed or their kind dies with them. Their structure and their nature make them responsive to these two urges at periods also determined by their nature and by their development. It is also in their nature that their structure will enable them throughout their life cycle to make adjustment to vital stimuli.

The higher the animal life, the less set are the inborn responses, the more flexible the adjustments. A monkey is interested in more things than is a cat or a dog: it has a more excitable nature. It learns more rapidly.

The response mechanism and the response repertoire will be conditioned by the world the animal faces. The lion learns to jump through a hoop of fire—a situation the lion at birth did not confront. A monkey learns to pick a lock or untie a knot. But it is enough for the monkey at birth to know how to eat and how to hang on to mother: she will provide the meals and carry the baby along with her. But it is also necessary that the baby know when it is in pain and have some means of letting mother know.

With man, "helpless infancy" reaches its maximum duration. Whatever instinct is, man has less need of it than a flea or even a monkey. A monkey at six knows everything; man at six has just started to school. But, like the monkey, he is born with enough to get by the first day.

A wasp leaves its cell fit to fly, sting, and get food. That is *instinctive* behavior. It has nothing to do but live; nothing to learn but death. The human newborn yawns and looks about. It does not know what it will have to do. Why instincts when there are mothers to teach it habits?

The mason wasp *(mud dauber)* is not so clever with her stinger as is the saddler with his awl; she does not always reach the spinal ganglion of the spider she stings; she may kill it, which then will be no good for wasp's larvæ. But if she does reach that ganglion, the spider is paralyzed and will live for days. She drags it home, lays an egg on it, and seals egg and spider in a mud tomb. The egg hatches, the larva eats the spider, and digs out, leaving the empty shell of the spider's body within the tomb. The wasp's stinger was ready-made and her stinging of spider an *inherited habit*, instinctive. The saddler has to learn to use his awl. The awl finally functions *like a machine* because innumerable reflex arcs bound like a chain-gang have learned to work together. The saddler can then use his *mind* for other things.

Habit is the most important element in human behavior. Any animal that cannot form a habit must depend on instinct. Instincts make for routine and stereotyped behavior. The greater the capacity to form new habits, the wider is the possible range of behavior. This range in man is so great that stereotyped thought and action are evidence of an abnormal mind.

Human culture is back of human habits. Human nature is back of human instincts. For example, suppose we are about to enlist or buy life insurance. Are we physically fit? The doctor puts us in a chair, asks us to cross our legs, and raps the patellar ligament just below the knee. Our foot flies out. We smile: we used to play that trick on each other when we were boys. What can the old *knee-kick* trick have to do with fitness for military service or life insurance? Or with instincts?

Much. The rap on the ligament was carried by a sensory nerve to the spinal cord, from spinal cord by motor nerve to the *quadriceps femoris* muscle (in which the knee-cap is embedded) ending in the tibia. This muscle contracted; the foot kicked out. Spinal cord O. K. No paresis, locomotor ataxia, or such.

Every rap on that ligament is followed by a knee jerk. It is a reflex act and implies a definite reflex arc; such an arc exists; we have countless such arcs at birth. It is not learned or acquired or under control of the will. A ray of light strikes a newborn's eye: the eye may or may not close, but the pupil will contract, as will ours under similar stimulus. That contraction is a reflex act, instinctive: *we could not help it*.

We often say, "I simply couldn't help myself!" It is the gospel truth; by no conscious effort are we ever complete master of ourselves. We may gaze in open-eyed delight at a blinding flash of lightning and never turn a hair at the most deafening burst of thunder, but there is a limit of control in all human flesh; it is the nature of flesh to be sensitive, of nerves to transmit sensation.

To blink at lightning and jump at thunder and pull at the nipple and swallow food and relieve the bladder, etc., are all *instinctive* activities. Because they are more complex than mere knee-kick, pupil contraction, and other reflexes, they are called instincts. Instincts are compound reflexes. If we could analyze them, we should find an arc for each of the component reflexes.

Instinctive behavior is *unlearned* behavior; it functions with the first adequate stimulus; it is common to man and to many higher animals; it is complex; it is accompanied by but not dependent on consciousness; it is explicit or implicit; it is *modifiable*.

Go to the ant, sluggard! is no advice for any human being.

The ant is a slave to its instincts. It can only react in a certain way, predetermined at birth, working on an inherited preformed mechanism. Requiring no experience, it gains none. The ant is nature's masterpiece of quick and accurate uniform behavior, as predetermined as an oak tree. Its nervous system is a ladder; it must climb that ladder. Go to a monkey, is better advice. No Primate is a slave, unless enslaved by man. Ants have been living the same life for millions of years. A monkey lives more in a year than all the ants have lived since ants evolved.

Our nervous system is no ladder; it is built around a tube. It has plenty of reflex arcs, but it is surmounted by a brain whose big business is to learn and to profit by experience. The baby's spinal cord is largely organized at birth, but its big brain is a clean slate. There is nothing known it cannot learn. With man, plastic behavior reaches its highest point.

We do not *inherit* instincts, but an instinctive mode of vegetative and reproductive reactions; also an instinctive activity which by the nature of the stimulus says "yes" or "no," a positive or a negative response. With such activity, we can learn to walk and pull the cat's tail; we can form habits. We bump our head against the table; our next response to table is *conditioned*. We pull the wrong cat's tail; our habit of response to cats' tails is conditioned. All our responses are conditioned. That is the way we learn to behave. We do not require instincts; we can acquire habits. If we get set in them, we can forget our brains and live like ants.

Add it up: *instincts are inherited habits*. Have we more than a chimpanzee? We cannot say. But we can say that both of us have enough to start out in life; if not, we are defective and do not go far. We can also say that our inheritance of reflex arcs exceeds that of the chimpanzee by several ounces of neurons. As a consequence, we have more nervous machinery in general, more neurons to load, more paths to carry the load.

But the fundamental difference between man's and chimpanzee's inheritance is in parents. Once a chimpanzee, always a chimpanzee; but a man may become a skunk or a saint. Think of all the kinds of people you know!

Man's inherited habit-to-live can be modified into thousands of ways of living. We do not inherit habits of shaving, wearing kimonos, three meals a day, plug hats, skyscrapers, abhorrence of pork, four wives, faith in Sunday schools, or belief in higher education for women. We do inherit parents who do not want us to disgrace them and who do their best to bring us up in the way we ought to go.

Which means that human inheritance varies from age to age and cradle to cradle. Little the newborn cares about a silver spoon in his mouth—he inherited the habit of responding to an empty stomach; or whether the roof over his head is copper or thatch—he inherited the habit of crawling in out of the wet.

To describe human adjustments in terms of instincts or analyze specific human behavior—or our own consciousness —into instinctive acts, is to stir the mud. Human culture is the accumulated responses of the man-animal to his man-made environment. It accumulates, it varies, because man can and does talk. This seems a handicap at times, but in the long run it has had enormous consequences. Without speech as an organized tool of exchanging, acquiring, and transmitting experiences, human culture is inconceivable.

Life learns. An ameba probably learns new tricks not inherent in original protoplasm. Man also must learn by experience. But if you tell me "The water's cold," or "That's a toadstool," it saves me time. It is this enormous assemblage of others' experiences in the form of objects and descriptions which makes human culture what it is and man's birthright to-day what it is.

An engineer will build an airplane in less time than it took him to learn to drive his first nail. But in an entire lifetime he could not alone assemble the materials for the airplane, or, without benefit of accumulated knowledge, learn how to make one nail.

We inherit no nail-driving habit. We do inherit a motor mechanism which *feels good* when functioning. We took our first lesson in driving a nail when we banged the rattle on the side of the crib. Later, stimuli of nails, hammer, soft pine, an environment holding other stimuli to activity; countless reflex arcs, some already learned in responses to such stimuli; thumb smashed, probably! but the nail is finally driven. And more nails, and more, until finally the carpenter drives nails from *force of habit* like an instinct.

3

We learn to skate in summer and to swim in winter, said James. He meant that our gradually rising curve of learning reaches a crest—and stops for a while. During summer, we consolidate all that we learned during winter. With the next winter, we start from a new level. It is even more true that we learn both to skate and to swim when we learn to walk, just as we have made progress in learning Chinese when we have learned English. But to learn Chinese, or to skate, or to dance on our toes, we must start early; our muscles soon get *set* in their ways.

It is the first walk that is the hardest. The *steps* we acquire later in life are mere child's play compared with the first step the child learns to make. Balancing the body on one foot on a wire rope is only possible because we learned first to balance the body on a ball a half-inch in diameter. We speak of such complex acts as tennis, typewriting, piano playing, etc. They are complex, but the complex and difficult part was learned by the time we could walk across the room and put a finger in the cat's eye.

Do we learn these acts, or are they innate responses that appear in due time? We know that the newborn's legs are not only weak, but are not yet shaped for an upright gait, and that its spine has not yet taken on human curves; legs and spine grow human. Several years elapse before they are entirely human in character. But they are human enough to walk on within twelve or fifteen months.

The response to the first pin-prick is not the simple reflex of hand going to the spot that is injured. Rather: random, aimless, uncontrolled, uncoördinated, unadjusted movements of body, arms, legs. Possibly driving the pin in deeper. Contrast these vain random motor-mechanism movements with the prompt and coördinated pattern-reaction to pain or noxious stimulus; or that of visceral and glandular systems to pain of pin-prick or to any pain or to any stimulus which the little mite of protoplasm interprets as deadly.

It may seem much more important that the infant should know where and how to put its hand on that pin than it is to get so upset it loses its appetite—and possibly its dinner. And the madder it gets, the less likely it is to find the pin. But man was not evolved in a thorn tree, nor were there pins when the human adjustment system was perfected. Nor has man yet progressed to the point where he is born adapted to "all the comforts of a home" and the tenseness of civilization. We have to learn to walk and to train our hands and fingers in such space and to such keys as our fate allots us.

Random and uncoördinated movements represent the range of our motor mechanism inheritance at birth; except, of course, the grasping reflex. That comes with us. Many newborns can support their body by either hand; by a hand so tiny and by an arm so frail that it does not appear strong enough—and does not know enough—to support a half-pint bottle.

Swimming is not an inheritance. The newborn is afraid of water, and if introduced to it under painful circumstances may carry the fear for life.

The earliest body movements are chiefly of an avoiding nature. A three-days-old infant's nose was lightly pinched. It began to strike out with its hand. In eighteen seconds the hand found its mark: it struck the experimenter's hand. On the second trial it found his hand in two seconds. By the fourth day the infant's hand had learned its lesson: it could at once strike the experimenter's hand.

The newborn can turn its eyes toward the light. Not until days later can it fix its eyes on a light or move them with a moving light. It will reach out for a lighted candle. But only after 150 or more trials has it learned to direct its hand to the flame. A few trials suffice for the infant's hand to avoid the flame. The more flame the hand discovers, the less the hand tries to discover. For "flame" substitute "stick of candy."

These early months lead to simple eye-hand co-ordinations. But only after long and repeated experiment can the little hand or finger be directed to the spot which stimulates the eye. So with body and leg movements. Their actions become definite and sharp only after months of trial and error. Meanwhile the entire motor-machinery grows in size and in strength.

Every movement that comes under control is a movement learned, useful in the next adjustment movement. Muscles, tendons, ligaments, become coördinated. Thus habits of motion and movement are formed. A few years later these will be put to use in making pies or playing marbles, or shooting a rifle, or chopping wood.

Hundreds of muscles. What can they not learn to do? But in all this learning countless little habits are formed: *habits* because learned. A time comes when the youngster can pick up a glass of water from the table and carry it to his mouth; over one hundred muscles involved. Each performs at the right time, does just the needed work and no more. The levers involved! The wonderful coördination! No machine works so perfectly as the body machine can.

The great, the essential, the refined, the delicate movements are learned within three years. That little mechanism grows up with us. Throughout life we call upon it to run, to swim, to climb, to dance, to jump, to "hold 'em," to "knock 'em stiff."

Movements and motions of the body mechanism can be learned because muscles, tendons, and joint surfaces are themselves sources of impulses: *receptors, sense organs.* Our brain can thereby organize our body. We walk along new gravel beds, plowed fields, dusty roads, sandy beaches, or city pavements, without stumbling or missing a step. We kick a cat, but not a brick. Nor a hat on April first: we kicked that hat once—it had a brick under it. We learned. By experience we learn to walk through plowed fields, through grass, ashes, leaves. Training, learning, habits of the motor mechanism.

With this kinesthetic organization we *sense* hard stone, soft grass, heavy lead, the resistance of water, bushes, walls. If we learn to sleep on a feather bed, a hair mattress is as "hard as a board." The city-bred boy stumbles all over a farm: his kinesthetic sense has something to learn. Water looks soft: it feels as hard as rock if we dive in flat. Only by experience do we learn whether it is safe to jump from a height upon a pile of leaves or a load of hay. By falling off a bicycle we learn enough to stay on.

This kinesthetic organization is of enormous importance. It carries us through life if we have built it up well, giving us time to choose. The individual who is always stubbing his toe, spraining his ankle, stumbling over others' feet, running into doors and sharp corners, falling downstairs, picking up hot pokers, barking his shins, and "didn't know it was so far" or "so high" or "so hard" or "so deep" or "so steep" or "so slippery," has poorly developed kinesthetic sense: he is inexperienced in movement or without a full complement of kinesthetic habits.

The motor mechanism starts to school the day the baby is born. And every mother knows that it is "not still a minute." Within thirty months it has fallen down a thousand times; walked or backed or bumped into everything available; handled everything greasy, sticky, smooth, rough, hot, cold, dry, wet, hard and soft, within reach. Falls out of crib and chair again and again. Finally learns to climb in and out. Bumps its nose, its head, its shins; gets its fingers caught in doors. Learns that it can slide down the banisters and the cellar door and climb up a rope but not a lace curtain.

Very busy months these. There are not enough words to describe all the motor habits a healthy youngster learns within thirty months.

The kinesthetic sense only gets into consciousness when something goes wrong. With our motor mechanism we swim along, unconscious of the unending and beautifully coördinated movements of bony levers worked by myriads of microscopic muscle engines. Then, without warning, cramps! We are suddenly conscious of our body machine. Pain anywhere in muscles, joints, tendons, ligaments, brings our body machine home to us.

4

Practice makes perfect. Even a car "drives" better after the first thousand miles. And as for the driver himself! At the end of the first day he ever drove a car he was a wreck. For two reasons.

Fear lest he wreck the car: too emotional. He suffered enough in anticipation to lose a dozen cars, several legs, ribs, eyes, lives. Other fears under his belt moved him deeply: was it safe, any possibility of its blowing up, would the gas hold out, etc.? He did not know his car; it was a great unknown; the unknown is always a threat. He did not know his road, nor its manners and its customs, its curves and its grades. The new way is always a threat: what is around the corner?

The other reason. His own motor mechanism was tired all over. Throughout the day his muscles had been tense, taut as fiddle strings, keyed up for emergency action. His eyes saw too much, his ears heard too much, and his nose was on the *qui vive* for hot boxes, burning rubber, scorched grease. His control over his car's brakes and gears was better than over his own. It was as though he were running his body on high with the emergency brakes on. More than that: his hands and feet had not learned to coördinate. To do one thing with one foot and quite a different thing with the other, steer with one hand and work a brake or gear-shift with the other, is a *learned* operation. He had not yet learned it. He could do it, but at an awful price.

Now he drives three hundred miles a day; is as fresh as a daisy; has a good time, sees the country, talks his hat off, smokes a dozen cigars. Does not give his car a thought the whole day. He is as automatic as his engine.

Same car, same road, same driver. And the same process in every act of learning, beginning with the act of standing up or the first walk in life. We have time for the high spots in life if we have learned how to cross the routine valleys by force of habit.

Watch a small boy at his first copybook. Face screwed up in a knot, brow furrowed, mouth open, tongue out, one fist clutching the desk, the other the pencil, legs tied up tight. Every muscle in that boy's body is engaged in learning to write. Finally he learns to write with one arm, and can smile and wink and let his legs go to sleep. But when we go to the theater we help kill the villain and embrace the heroine: we sigh, we groan, we clench our fists.

Do you know which stocking you put on first this morning or which trousers' leg you filled first? Do you recall how you felt the first time you ever wore a dress suit, or how long it took you to put it on, or to learn to tie a bowknot? Can you bathe, shave, and dress in six minutes? I can do it in less than five.

A skilled performer at the piano or typewriter or on the tennis court acts like an automaton. But no mere automaton —human or otherwise—ever makes a great performer.

For this reason: heightened sensitivity of the central nervous system increases the response of the reflex arcs. A tap on flexed patellar tendon elicits no kick when one is asleep. Sleep means that central has hung up. But try out the knee-kick with your teeth clenched or your fist tightly doubled up: more kick. Get real mad: more kick. A lad of sixteen is given a little instrument squeezed in the hand to measure muscle strength. He squeezes: so many pounds. "Best you can do?" "The best." His best girl enters the room. He now beats his record by several pounds. Central nervous system more active; everything more active, except viscera.

A *good* habit is a well learned habit put to useful purpose.

The competent driver guides his car as a clever boy his bicycle: the right muscles work to the right amounts at the proper time and in proper order. A car or a curve or a hole or a honk ahead is stimulus enough for eye or ear; the adjustment is made as though it were a reflex, as easy as pie. It is an *acquired* reflex. Paths have been worn for such highly complex responses as driving an auto, an airplane, a tennis ball, a pair of chopsticks, knife and fork.

All our habits act by *force of habit* because these paths are worn. We awake in the morning and "before we know it" we are at the breakfast table, or possibly "come to" only when some headline in the paper catches our eye—perhaps already half through our breakfast. And yet, before we "came to," we went through a thousand acts: dressing, shaving, etc., etc., some of them really complex performances requiring delicate adjustments. And the whole bag of tricks performed as a result of a single stimulus: a bell, a call, a ray of sunlight, gastric tetanus, what not. After that one stimulus one act followed another: as Paine's "Fall of Pompeii" followed from one match.

Yet there were a thousand responses available for that *breakfast* stimulus. The stimulus was not necessarily followed by a yawn, a stretch, push covers down, one leg out, other leg out, slippers, etc., etc., etc.—one conditioned reflex touching off another. But that chain of reactions had been performed so many times that the paths connecting up these countless reflexes had been worn; all the other possible paths of response offered more resistance because they had not been worn by constant action.

A habit, then, is an act so often repeated that it runs itself: it does not need our conscious attention; we can give our attention to something else.

The dropped colt picks itself up and walks off: walking reflex paths all ready for use; he does not have to learn a thing about walking. Think of the ways a child can learn to walk, and with only half as many legs as a colt! But whether the child learns to walk goosestep, Spanish, or in Chinese size-minus-four, depends on incidence of parents and accident of locality—for each insists that its own style is right. Nearly all our early steps are conditioned into habits backed up by: "Walk like I walk or I'll . . . "

The average mortal has only one habit. The one stimulus which rouses him from sleep carries him through the day and back to bed and to sleep. All days look alike to him. Saturday night is also conditioned into the chain: no fresh stimulus needed for the bath! His body's clock is likewise set for Sunday. That day, too, goes by according to schedule, and when done is itself the stimulus to resume a new week. One habit after another, like a chain, functioning as one. Works like a clock wound up for life. Makes a perfect clerk, "hand," or maid.

This one-habit mode of existence is fine; it gives the brain a complete rest. The possessor need never have a thought! He is a *skilled* performer, but never great, on piccolo, at lathe, behind counter, or on a stool. He does not even make a good soldier. There must be visceral dynamics—generally called "guts"—behind a bayonet charge; and high-strung central—called "brains"—in control for a sharpshooter.

The difference between action in an automatic machine and in a human genius is *brains*.

5

I smile when you tickle me; I cannot help it, it is a reflex. If you smile back, I will learn to smile when you smile. The drive in life is hunger. The action in life is to secure food and mates to satisfy hunger. Play is preliminary action— trying out, testing the capacity of range of action. It differs from the reactions of adult life in that it lacks the consummation response or adjustment. The action has no ulterior motive.

Play is not an instinct; nor is it unique in human beings or identical in the human race. It is a form of acquired behavior. The games I play as child or adult will be conditioned by my bents and especially by social environment. What is played, who plays it, how it is played, all depend on learned habits of individual response and can only be interpreted in terms of situation, stimulus, and response.

The stimulus back of play—whether of puppies, children, or adults—is a motor mechanism which was built for action, glows with action, and in childhood grows best by action.

Weeding the garden or picking potato bugs is action. But there are drawbacks. Repetition—same stimulus, same response; and no end in sight—there seem to be so many weeds, so many bugs; if they are to be cleared out, the pace must be kept up. That means that the impulse to respond to other stimuli that may rise and do keep rising up to beckon the child aside must be repressed.

Play is generally actions of several kinds at the same time. Even in a game of marbles a half-dozen different activities may function together. The difference between marbles and professional baseball is chiefly years: the men have their game better organized; are better players because more habituated to it; and stick closer to their game. But sometimes their game becomes lost in a fight with words, catcalls, and pop bottles.

Margie making mud pies and mother making apple pies further illustrate the difference between play of children and of adults and between play and work. Mother's work ends when the pie leaves the oven. Margie may grow stale over her pie before she has made one, or she may go right on making pies until she uses up all the mud. Her impulse is for action rather than for consummation. She will stop when the impulse for mud-pie action is replaced by another with more pull. Such as: "Let's play dolls," or, "Dinner is ready."

Impulse to action; gratification of that impulse; hang the consequences: of such is the play of children, the daydreams and castles-in-Spain of adults.

It is of little consequence to Margie if her pie is dough or too big or too little for her pie pan. And of less consequence to Johnny when as Heap Big Injun he "scalps" Margie with a celluloid paper cutter. And if Margie plays the game she will pretend to be scalped, catch her "blood" in her apron, and fall down "dead."

What man tied to his job all day does not yearn now and then to be a Dick Deadeye, a Jesse James, or a Captain Kidd! Boys can be. They rob, they hold up trains, they capture ships, they bury and dig up chests of gold. We come from a long line of freebooters. There is nothing in our inheritance which savors of factory, treadmill, or office stool. We must acquire these priceless habits, and often at the loss of our entire original inheritance, which included freedom to fight or run, and everlastingly to fool around.

The sheer joy of being alive, the supreme joy of action in the child! Watch a four-year-old work off his surplus steam. Not only is every muscle of his body in action, but his face and his speech box are at work. It is as though his entire being were so sensitive to excitation that the slightest wind that blows excites him to new effort.

Why not? He has only just discovered the most wonderful,

354

the most excitable, the most insatiable mechanism in the world: a growing human being, himself! That mechanism discovered, the boy or girl now sets out to discover the world, and does easier than later in life. Life's innate curiosity has not yet been crushed; nor has imagination, the capacity to make believe, yet been killed by the "realities" that grown-ups cling to like shipwrecked mariners to a rotting spar in midocean.

Spontaneous. As all life is, outside hoopskirts and boiled shirts. Impulsive. Where does the impulse come from? Where does every living impulse come from—without or within? Both. Living beings are expressions of the relation-ship between conditions that invite life and beings that re-spond to these conditions. And back of the gratification of food and mate hunger and the decision to fight or flee is knowledge, information, trying things out. Testing oneself, learning one's own capacity.

Play is the beginnings of knowledge. Banging the rattle on the crib or getting a toe in one's mouth is an early lesson in wisdom.

Which means that there is no sharp line between playing Jesse James and being Jesse James. But the child who stops with a stick for a gun will bring down no bigger game in later years than he can kill with a daydream. Those of us who live only in hopes build only castles in our own air.

The practical application is this: two boys will pick more than twice as many potato bugs as one and pick them faster if a definite goal is set—a quart, or a quarter. Still better re-sults can be had by setting a phonograph near by with a good rhythmic swing to it—say, the "Sambre et Meuse" or the "Washington Post March." Life hates monotony, but loves rhythm; in heartbeat, in intestinal contraction, in canoeing, in poetry, in music.

But do not expect the child to be like you through mere *imitation*. The child will smile when smiled at, laugh when others laugh, yell when others yell, look at what others are looking at, listen when others listen, run with or after or from others, and duck when others duck. One sheep over the fence, all over. Not a sound at night: one dog barks; in five minutes fifty dogs are yelping. We also applaud, hiss, whistle, yawn, light up, with the crowd. Stimulus and response. Your lighting up is stimulus for the same reaction on my part.

There is also a more direct conditioned stimulus. I cut my finger: it bleeds, it hurts; I wince. You cut your finger: I see blood, I wince. Watch the crowd at a prize-fight. They duck, they dodge, they "Ouch!" They are only less affected by the blows than the receivers, or only less jubilant than the man who delivered them. There is much human nature on exhibition at the prize ring and swimming hole.

6

Without habits we are in a bad way, as poorly equipped for life as though we had surrendered to habits—then we are in a bad way. The clock striking twelve may be adequate stimulus for me to remove my clothes. If I cannot control that stimulus, the authorities will: the clock strikes that hour twice a day.

This is an extreme case, but it will serve. The clock strikes twelve: bedtime. But noon is not midnight. The mere strike of twelve is not an adequate stimulus. My bodily mechanism is not in the habit of running down at the noon hour.

If noon is my hour for food, the stroke of twelve sets off a different mechanism. If my noon behavior is routine and well learned, habit will carry me through. I close my book, adjust my desk, reach for my hat and coat, etc., etc. By one o'clock I am back at my desk. Habit carried me through the hour. My *conscious activity* was planning a vacation.

During that lunch hour I performed hundreds of individual acts, one after another, in regular order; constituting a fairly distinct routine or habit cf behavior. Although my *mind* was busy with fishing tackle, canoes, and such things, *I* did not have to look out for lamp-posts, breaks in the pavement, or step-downs at the curb. I had *learned* to thread crowded streets, remove my hat on entering a restaurant, eat with a knife, pay the meal check, etc. All *habitual* performances: learned responses, acquired reflexes, habits. Otherwise, the one hour allotted for my meal would not have sufficed. One unlearned in city streets might spend a half-hour crossing Times Square; if unaccustomed to a menu, much time in deciding what to order.

We begin with no acquired habits; we begin at once to acquire them; with these, to acquire others. But when we get to be *mere bundles of habits*, when we *know*, when our mind is made up, when nothing can move us, *we are through*; we have used up all the blank pages we inherited on which to write our life.

People do get that way. They lose capacity for new experience, ability to form new habits, plasticity for new modes of response to change. "Life is not what it used to be." In reality, they cannot respond to change. The cab-driver who cannot learn to drive a car is out of luck. Whole groups find themselves in midair because they cannot change their habits fast enough to keep pace with change. Their *emotional* reaction is wasted, misspent energy. They do not thereby change conditions, nor are they themselves thereby adapted.

The champion golfer is not thinking about his stroke: he knows his golf: it is a habit. He is thinking about the Cup, or his Girl. If he had to think out each stroke, he could not even qualify. Ask him to describe any one particular shot after the game: he probably will not even be able to recall it.

> "A centipede was happy 'til
>   One day a toad in fun
>   Said, 'Pray, which leg moves which?'
>   This raised her doubts to such a pitch
>   She fell exhausted in the ditch,
> Not knowing how to run."

Habit formation—golf, tennis, pitching hay, eating spaghetti, chewing tobacco, going to church—is at bottom like any other form of learning. Learning to play the piano or checkers, to read Greek or talk Choctaw, to solve puzzles or problems in higher mathematics, involves no new principles not used in learning to walk or in forming the habit of rushing to the window every time the fire engine snorts by.

Most men shave themselves, but go to the barber shop for a hair-cut. It was not always thus, nor is it thus in all lands. Custom. Custom also is habit. Our repertoire of habits is conditioned by the company we keep. It is not immoral to eat with a knife, or a vice to drink tea from a saucer; but men are socially executed for less.

Take shaving. I move from Fiji to Main Street with a normal face of hair. Decide to shave in sheer self-defense. Do not like the idea—emotionally wrought up. Two things follow: I am not likely to forget that shave; if I am not too excited I will be able to give it the best I have. Law number one of learning: *emotional reinforcement;* the reflex arcs are keyed up for new experience. I may so dislike the idea of shaving that my emotion takes a real fighting mood; the reflex arcs are keyed up to resist.

Not having the shaving habit or habituated to razor-sharpness, I cut myself. More emotion. Never will forget that shave. Nor am I likely to forget the move which resulted in a cut. Second law: *attention* or *vividness.* Learning to shave is learning to confine the razor edge to the surface of the face. Old school of hard knocks. If the cut were serious, my learning to shave might end with the first lesson. Many boys stop with one lesson on a pipe.

Cut not serious. And it is finally all off. Shave again next day. Much easier this time. Suppose I had waited a month: less easy; too much time to forget what I had learned well enough to remember a short time. Memory of first shave and memory of movements made are different processes:

358

different reflex arcs involved. Third law: *recency*. No one learns to play the fiddle with one lesson a week.

The fourth law follows—keep it up: *repetition*. Practice makes perfect, wears paths through the nervous system.

I may begin this first shave at the age of forty. I have had no opportunity in life to form habits of action on a reflected image, nor have I formed habits of using hands for more delicate operations than digging yams. I try a half-dozen times. My face is a sight! I give it up—as many men do; it is hard to teach an old dog tricks. That is why the boy beats his father at golf. Law five: every man has his *limit*. But with enough stimulus the limit can be extended. If the father had to beat his son or have his allowance cut off, he would be more likely to succeed.

7

Every living being has an inborn emergency equipment. For countless beings the equipment is inadequate; they go down like flies before new foes, new diseases, new situations. A large percentage of all the human beings ever born died before maturity; the *emergency* may have been a rusty nail, a venturesome spirit, a backward disposition. Anything which threatens life or disturbs its peace of mind or upsets the system is an emergency.

Emergencies cannot be listed; they are too numerous. Nor can they be described in general terms; they are individually discrete. Half a loaf is always better than no bread, but there are times when a half-loaf is the dynamic equivalent of a human life, when half a minute spells victory or defeat, or life or death. There are few of us whose life at one time or another has not hung by a thread.

What do we do, what is our response to crisis? Fight or flee? It depends. The cry of "Women first!" on the *Titanic* was enough to keep the men from fighting for the boats: life was not worth fighting for when the loser was a woman. Nor worth saving when a spar would only support one: a man let go of a spar that a woman might live! *This is human behavior at its highest.* Possible because our inborn emergency equipment can be trained, conditioned, educated, made to obey the orders of our head. But it is so well organized and so powerful that few can turn its command over to the cortex, fewer still who can conquer it. Greater is he who conquereth self than he who taketh seven cities!

Greater, because self-preservation is the first law of nature; and the higher we climb in nature's scale, the better organized life becomes for self-preservation. Man has more means at his command for self-preservation than any other animal, largely because he has more ways of destroying his enemies. Cities and the "taking of cities" arose in response to man's desire to anticipate emergencies.

The difference between *self-preservation* and *self-control* is the difference between all gorillas and some men. If man used only his inborn emergency equipment in a fight with a gorilla, he would lose—or die of fright before the gorilla could lay hands on him. Fighting instinct, yes; and fleeing instinct also. But a worm will turn. A rat will run for its life; cornered or caught by a leg in a trap, it will fight for its life.

There is another kind of response, the kind we keep on making during our unconquered-self lives. We are dressing, already late for dinner. We break a shoestring; we cannot find a certain shirt stud; and then that crowning insult, we drop the collar button and it rolls under the bureau. Now we are mad. We roar like a caged lion; we say words, stamp the floor, kick a chair, yank out the bureau. Battles have been lost on account of such trifles.

What happened? Almost everything. Upset—literally. Lost his head: that is true also. Also lost his appetite. The wife is so *disgusted* she loses her *temper*—and calls him "brute."

It is a brute reaction. It is a biologic reaction: it requires neither learning nor headpiece. Out of our inborn **emergency** equipment we build up our attitudes, fight **windmills** and straw men, and rip and roar up and down the world, **or** tremble like a leaf at every breath.

I saw the commander of a United States warship run like mad four blocks to prevent a black cat crossing his path. That, to him, meant certain death. Such fears are norms of behavior; they furnish countless impulses for action. Another commander might also have been moved by the fear of black-cat-calamity, but more moved by his uniform to die in his tracks rather than run four blocks to head off death.

To be moved though we move not, is no mere figure of speech. Some movements we can control, if we have learned control; but not the visceral mechanism which tells motor mechanism to move, nor adrenin which prepares the whole body for action.

Even a cat prepares for action. It assumes a fighting posture, lashes its tail, and spits. Man has no tail to lash and when he is mad or scared cannot spit because his salivary glands are out of action; but his internal responses to emotion are as real as the cat's; the visceral organization retires in order that the motor mechanism can have all of the body's energy available. When we are so mad we cannot eat, the viscera say: "All right, we are not asking you to eat; kill somebody, or move."

"Every little movement has a meaning of its own," as the old song declared; it is also true that every movement moves something. We are never more physiologically correct than when we say, "That moves me." Between birth and death many are "moved" enough to dig a Panama Canal, yet they never move themselves up out of the cellar of life.

The difference between being moved to disgust at the sight of a dead cat and moving to remove the cat is one of life's little jokes that make human life so interesting.

We are *moved* with unstriped or visceral muscle. We *move* **with** striped or skeletal muscles. To make a *gesture* is to

361

make an excuse for moving. We are moved with less effort than we move: our unstriped muscles function without the cortex. They run themselves, and if we are not in charge they run us. In mobs and panics they run riot. Every emotion—anger, love, merriment, jealousy, grief, fear, remorse—is an implicit bodily movement.

Emotions vary, in individuals, communities, nations, races; are under different degrees of control; are aroused by varying situations. Emotions are older than the human race; but outside the human race are put to no such sublime or ridiculous ends. We do not begin life with specific *loves, hates,* and *fears.* Some can go through life without set hates and loves. They can look people and things over and decide whether they are worth loving or hating, and if they are, possess them or do their best to clear the earth of them. But as we are, not one in ten can love a Hindu or a Jap or the other political party. And much of thinking and talking is in terms of hates and fears and loves. We murder at least something, if not somebody, every day. And love—there are quite as many things to be loved as people. In fact, there is nothing, it seems, that cannot come within range of our love, except our enemies. Yet there are those who "hate the whole . . . sex"; that means half the human race.

Is it in our very nature to hate our enemies, impossible to love them? Why is the very cornerstone of Christ's teachings so rarely taken literally? James thinks those "swayed by it might well seem superhuman beings. Their life would be morally discrete from the lives of other men, and there is no saying whatthe effects might be: they might conceivably transform the world."

They might indeed.

As the world is, hate is given freer rein. Recently it reigned; and each half of the world besought the same God to help it kill the other half. We can hate enough to kill, but killing no longer solves problems, nor hating an enemy convert one.

Fear is old stuff, out of date. It should be thrown off with our swaddling clothes. And yet it probably plays a greater part than hope in the daily lives of most men and women. Fears are played upon by all sorts of propagandists for political, social, and religious purposes. Fear of hell-fire is supposed to lead to love of heaven; fear of "ign'runt foreigners" to hatred of aliens and so to the closing of the doors. And the only reason this nation could not be led to hate Germany as France did was because we could not be made to feel the fear of Germany as France did.

But for most of us life is only meat and the body raiment. Same reaction system, same environment: stereotyped behavior because our world stands still. And an enormously valuable emotional reservoir of energy, capable of moving mountains and giving all life a joy-ride, is expended in hating those we envy and kicking against the pricks or in fleeing in terror from our shadows because we cannot shake them off.

And so it is that an instinctive emotional endowment rooted deep in the body of life and inherent in man and mammals and all living beings that meet dangerous situations with complex mechanisms which must function as a unit and without warning, becomes personal and individual. The organization of that endowment into specific fears and hates and general attitudes favoring negative and positive responses begins the day we are born.

8

"When I was a child, I spake as a child. I understood as a child, I thought as a child: but when I became a man, I put away childish things." Some childish things we do put away, and we do forget most of the rag dolls, tin soldiers, and mud pies; but we get our start in childhood for much of our bent and most of our *set*. We do not *put away* our nature. Paul was an exception.

We are afraid of the dark, of little green worms, of hundreds of things. And get emotionally excited about them. Some react to a cabbage worm as they would to a wild elephant or to a mouse; and are as nearly scared to death as life lets them. It is no merit of their own that they have not died of fright a thousand times.

We are not born that way. The newborn sets up a fear reaction only to *fearful* stimuli: the bang of a door, being dropped, a sudden push or pull at its blanket; especially by removing its support. It catches its breath, clutches at anything within reach, closes its eyes, cries, voids waste. Memories of life in the trees? Why not: sudden noises and movements and withdrawal of support were real dangers then. The infant could not flee, but it could be scared; later it runs and hides when it is afraid.

A rat learns to thread a maze for food: it must pass a trap which always terrifies it. Remove the trap: it jumps as though the trap were present. A dog chases a cat up a tree four times a day. Every time the dog appears I appear. By and by the cat takes to the tree without the dog—my face is enough to make it climb a tree.

A small dog was tossed into the carriage of a 180-days-old child. The sudden and unexpected move terrified it. A year later it showed the same kind of terror at tame white mice. A door was slammed and at the same time a cat was shown to a child; thereafter it was afraid of the cat.

The child is afraid of a sudden and loud noise. It *hears* the thunder, *sees* the lightning; it *learns* to be afraid of the lightning. If the flash is blinding, it is afraid of the room. If there is some particular person in the room every time the lightning flashes, the child learns to be afraid of that person, lightning or no lightning.

With a what-not loaded with what not in the parlor and a dresser covered with hand-painted junk in the spare bedroom, and both parlor and bedroom in perpetual gloom, means must be found to keep little Willie out. A short-cut is found in the fact that Willie can be scared. And Willie is scared. By the time he is three, or sooner, he is as big a coward as his mother was when she was three. He is afraid of the dark; jumps every time a door is slammed; squeals at the sight of a mouse; and if a bat flies into the room, the whole household is in a panic. And everybody has bad dreams. And little Willie comes out of his nightmare in a cold sweat with a scream: some ghost story has done its work.

We move about in a lighted room with the aid of our eyes. In a dark room we are not distracted by what we see and consequently are more alert to what we feel and hear. We keep meeting with the unexpected, sometimes the sudden—crash of a falling chair, bark of a dog, bump on the forehead. And by the time our fear of the dark has become further conditioned by ghosts and hobgoblins, we are more than afraid of a dark graveyard. And if mother is afraid of strangers and shows it, we are afraid also, because our habit of expectancy of her behavior is dislocated.

So with rage. The baby cannot fight, but by cries, slashings with arms and legs, stiffening of body, flushed face, clenched fists, and held breath, it shows its rage when its nose is pinched, head held, or its body hampered. And it soon acquires the ability to kick and slash and scream. I have seen a boy of two beat his head on the floor in a rage at being denied something. Such early outbursts are signs of the coward and the murderer that are in us. The way these potentialities are trained is the key to character and the clue to most of our attitudes.

A nurse bathes a child each day, first tickling its feet or pinching its nose. A habit grows up, functioning like an instinct on reflex arcs. The mere sight of the nurse calls out a gurgle or a rage. If the nurse wears a blue dress habitually, the blue dress is enough. If the baby knows only one blue dress and that blue dress always means tickle or pinch, any blue dress becomes enough for gurgle or a fit.

We come to hate everything associated with our early hates; afraid of everything associated with early fears. The ran-

365

dom fears and rages come to be attached to new objects not contemplated in the original scheme of kill-or-cure emotional reinforcement. They become specific. The baby is not naturally afraid of lightning; it is afraid of a sudden crash. Nor is it naturally afraid of darkness, snakes, strangers, graveyards, or black cats.

Our emotions are conditioned in the same nursery in which our growing body learns its first steps. As the movements of motor mechanism become habits and so function on smooth-running reflex arcs, the emotions themselves become organized: the live-or-die glands and the autonomic nerves learn special modes of behavior. They take on habits, learn new responses, acquire new friends, new foes, new fears. The mouth waters under certain conditions. Fear is called out under certain conditions. Certain persons, things, situations, call out tantrums, cries, rages; others are sources of attachment, loves.

Practice makes perfect—hates and fears as well as tennis-players and card sharps. One does not naturally love a cat or hate a nurse or fear a mouse. But with practice the *threshold* is lowered, the message gets a quicker response. Only intense stimuli at first called out these emotional responses. But a youngster "nearly scared to death" is already on the way to be a coward. The child "nearly tormented to death" has laid the foundation for a vicious temper.

It is like a cork. First time out requires effort. Thereafter, any old corkscrew will suffice. By and by, a thumbnail.

The function of emotion is quick action and a long memory. If I am the victim of a $100 counterfeit bill to oblige a stranger who needs change, I am not likely to oblige the next stranger requiring change. I might even "take it out on him." We do such things. The horse-buyer knows that a horse which has had the mange does not forget it: it is tied in. He strokes the flank of a prospective purchase. Lip quivers: that horse had the mange.

Love, fear, and hate start out together; they grow up together. Meanwhile, the reflex which enables the newborn to
support its body by its hands soon disappears; the human
mother does not hang her baby on a limb to dry, nor does the
infant have to cling to her while she climbs down a tree. It
disappears from lack of use. The primitive hate and fear
types of behavior would also disappear if they were not at
once set to work.

The adjusting mechanism learns—only too blindly. Until
we ourselves are blind. Having eyes, we see not what there
is but what we think we see. We see with a body that by
nature has a huge capacity to hate that which threatens us,
to fear that which endangers us, to love that which protects
and feeds and tickles us. Our ancestors had to have a fear-
response to the new, the unexpected, the sudden, and the
strange. That is no reason why we should jump, turn pale,
sweat, gasp for breath, close our eyes and open our mouths,
and feel creepy every time we hear thunder or backfire, or
are left alone in the dark, or confront a novel and strange
idea. Nor should the same emotion that makes us fear the
novel and the strange impel us to hate reason—even though
reason interfere with our routine behavior, including attitudes, desires, ideals, ambitions, and loves. We do not get
jealous of reason or want to fight it; but we do get so enraged
at a book that we throw it in the fire, so mad at an opinion that
we would like to crucify the man who expresses it.

The haunting fear in Dickens's day seems to have been
poverty; the supreme dread, the almshouse. What is our
haunting fear, our supreme dread? Have we progressed
very far?

With "pep" we can make decisions, use our heads; but
when the visceral nerves take charge, decisions are made for
us—we are as *human* as iron filings around a magnet or
famished hogs around a swill barrel. A man in a "towering
rage" is more physically fit for murder than one in cold
blood—that is what a towering rage is for, prepare the body

for action with adrenin. Hate is biologically useful. Do we save it up for the hateful occasions and get the work out of it it can do, or squander it right and left?

Fear and rage are twins: born of the same necessity. But we are born of human parents in a state of civilization. Civilization clings to savagery and brutality because fundamental emotional states are retained as weapons in the endless battles of religion, society, and nationality. Biologic fears, hates, and loves are put to a thousand uses that could never have been contemplated in the original scheme of evolution. That scheme says: if your neighbor's eye offend you, pluck it out; but that scheme made no provision for theft, swindling, lying, blackmail, slavery, war. Our scheme does.

Our bottled emotions find curious outlets: giggles, tears, laughter, shame, remorse, rage, grief, love, fear, as the case may be; and take us to fights, dances, games, theater, speculation, futile argument, Monte Carlo, or the Count of Monte Cristo; or they may end in hysteria, phobias, manias.

The big question for each one of us individually is whether our acquired repertoire of specific loves, fears, and hates will suffice to keep us on good terms with ourselves and at peace with the world. Many a man loses his job because his viscera have never been educated nor his emotions trained. Note too that under stress of strong rage or fear activity in the digestive system closes down, predisposing to intestinal disorders including bacterial toxins and consequently to other far-reaching organic changes. Love on the contrary hastens food digestion and heightens metabolism. Love is a better tonic than rage or fear.

9

Look at a thirty-months-old boy; better yet, *mind* him for a few days! You are looking at Freud's *Unconscious Mind*, Watson's *Unverbalized Behavior*.

Why can we recall nothing of those first thirty months,

most of us nothing of the first forty months? Enough happened. If all our bumps, knocks, cuffs, and "repressions" are locked up in the Unconscious, it is a spacious place.

What became of all the food our blood absorbed during those months? Some was built into our bodies, some was used as energy, and what was left over was stored as fat. What happened to the Don'ts, Naughty-naughtys, and Shame-on-you's? Some got built in as parts of habits of response. We *learned* to love our mother, nurse, anybody or anything that got conditioned into our response mechanism for loving. We learned likewise to hate the butcher boy who pulled our ear or pinched us every chance he got; and forever after disliked everybody who suggested butcher boy. Butcher boys should be more careful.

Horses also.

A young man is upset by the sight of a horse and will cross the street to get away from one. This is "strange," we say. It is a "psychosis," says Freud; and by analysis of the *Unconscious* can be cured. It is next to nothing, says the psychologist; all of us have our little peculiarities: some of us are delighted at the sight of a horse and will cross the street to pat it or kiss it on the nose. Further, says the psychologist, I know when I am conscious and that "consciousness" is simply being conscious; and that I know nothing that I cannot name or describe. Abnormal behavior toward a horse or anything else seems mysterious only because we are not in possession of all the facts or even principal factors back of the behavior of the individual.

The horse that bit the child made him dislike all horses. He cannot now recall the bite; his reaction-system can and does. In one lesson he learned to mistrust a horse. Many big things are learned early in life with one lesson. Few pick up a red-hot poker or stick their tongues to an ice-cold bit of iron twice. One lesson was enough: it took the skin off.

I have no memory of my red-hot-poker lesson, but I have a scar on my hand; I can recall to memory the skin of my tongue I left on the ice-cold iron I was invited to "taste," although it left no scar on my tongue. One incident happened when I was two; the other, when I was six. We have no memory for our early kinesthetic and emotional organization —the Freudian *Unconscious*.

The story of an elephant balking at a bridge where he had had a mishap seventeen years earlier, although the bridge was now concrete, may or may not be true. The point is that if I have an *unconscious mind*, the elephant has. Also dogs, goldfish and oysters. Every animal has a dynamic mechanism that can be shocked at one shock and profit by experience.

Which means: we can all learn and what we learn makes us what we are—and determines whether we want more of it or not. Our bodies learn thousands of things we cannot describe or name. We have a thousand likes and dislikes for which we can give no explanation beyond: "I just like it," or, "I simply can't bear it!"

We remember back to a certain fairly definite period of our lives; beyond that our *conscious memory* is a solid blank, yet our *body* acts as though it remembered. It does, but that is not memory; not by such remembering are we conscious. If so, there would be no excuse to postulate Unconscious.

It is behavior—no doubt about that. Call it *unverbalized*. The unverbalized in us is all that the body learned before our babblings were organized into speech: modes of response learned without words. We cannot *think* about it because thinking is talking without perceptible movement in speech mechanism. We cannot be *conscious* of it—as conscious is used in psychology, the "act of naming our universe of objects both inside and out"—because we cannot connect it up with the mechanism by which we name our universe of objects. For the same reason, we cannot remember it. Nor will any amount of *psycho-analysis* bring it into memory. Often it can be brought to light with outside help—mothers, nurses, etc.

Before we take on habits of speech we take on a huge

amount of *habits of mind:* kinesthetic and emotional organization. Innumerable actions are performed with the skeletal
muscles so often that they function like inherent reflexes.
So also innumerable mental attitudes—prejudices for and
against all manner of people and objects—are called out so
often that the body-mind *instinctively* reacts. The visceral
muscles and the entire autonomic system "work like a charm."
These early conditioned habits have enormous influence on the
future of the individual.

Watson contrasts the child of four just home from the
movies, who talks you deaf, dumb, and blind, with a child of
twenty-seven months who is a skillful performer on a large
kiddy-car. He could guide it, coast downhill, and make all
the adjustments. His kinesthetic organization was complete
master of the car. But "Billy ride kiddy-car" was his only
parallel word organization. Which means that Billy has no
memory organization of these bodily processes except when
he is so placed that he can exhibit the bodily organization.

Billy had been a bottle baby. At the age of twenty-seven
months he was tested as to his *memory* for a bottle. At the
regular hour he was told, "Dinner ready," and put in a crib
and handed a bottle, as was the custom fifteen months before.
Billy reacted like a tramp who asks for pie and is given an ax
—he got mad. Dinner? In a crib with a bottle of milk?
Crib meant nothing to him. He had never learned to be
afraid of it; he had forgotten it. The *crib habit* was gone,
buried beneath other habits. Bottle also. "Dinner" to him
was meat and vegetables. When the nurse said, "Take your
milk," Billy began to chew the nipple— thought it was a new
kind of meat! And he looked at his mother with disgust for
cheating him out of his dinner.

The entire crib-bottle-nipple-sucking-smiling habit was
gone. Neither objects, faces, nor words used when Billy was
a bottle baby could now call out any of the old habit responses. Adults often choke when they try to suck through a
straw: it has been so long since they used that inherent habit.

Infancy is infancy, the next stage after fetal life. During infancy we prepare to shift for ourselves. That is the biologic significance of infancy. It is no more *unnatural* or *unconscious* than fetal life. We learn, take on, acquire, habits of behavior.

We may form incestuous attachments: have an *Œdipus* or an *Electra* complex. But such attachments are not talked about, because, as Watson says, "society is not organized to ban incestuous attachments in the making"; there were no *repressions*. Habits connected with "the slowing or speeding of the sexual organs" have not been verbally organized. Few men and fewer women have paralleled their sex organization with words.

Most of our emotional organization, from infancy to old age, is never verbalized. There are neither adequate words nor social mechanism for word conditioning of the infant. Elimination, eructation, releasing gas, masturbation, etc., were verbalized only when exhibited in the presence of others. In short, nearly all visceral and emotional habits are as a rule learned without parallel verbal organization. They make up our *unverbalized* behavior.

10

An Egyptian king wanted to learn the *original* language, possibly the speech of the builders of the Tower of Babel before their language was confounded. He had some children brought up by deaf mutes. The children learned the deaf-mute language. There was no more an *original* language than an original bill of fare or an original wardrobe.

The bullfrog's spouse call has probably changed little since the first frog, impelled by love and with the aid of vocal cords, lifted up his voice. If there is an "original" language, we shall find its purest form in a frog pond on a summer night. In the years of evolution that voice developed in various directions and was put to various ends, but wherever there is voice there is a sensori-motor mechanism back of it. This mechanism reaches great perfection among birds and mammals, especially among Primates.

Can monkeys talk? They do: in articulate speech, by grimaces, by signs. They talk all they need to; they under-stand one another. To that extent their language is as definite as ours. The more one studies the apes, the greater the puzzle as to why they do not learn to speak English; we do not yet know that they cannot. But it is conceivable that a chimpanzee, brought up from birth and conditioned by human voices, could learn to distinguish and make response to several hundred words.

Accustomed as we are to regulated flows of conversation, monkey and other mammal talk seems largely exclamations: cries of rage, fear, pain, courtship, etc. It is *emotional* language. Monkeys especially have a large repertoire of finely shaded emotional calls. How many and what the shades and tones signify, we do not know. There are individual variations; the mother monkey knows when her own youngster shrieks for help.

That is about the extent of our inherent repertoire. We can all cry and grunt, and we have our own key and pitch; with that our voice training begins. A mother easily distinguishes the cry of her child from among twenty-five babies in a nursery. These cries presumably differ with emotional states—hunger, pain, rage, fear, etc.

Within thirty days a normal infant's voice begins to roam around, as its hand and arm do; as though it were trying its voice out. It has a vocal mechanism; it exercises it. All living mechanisms are excitable, tongue especially. A current of air is always available in breathing; that current flows between vocal cords and through a resonator. Lips in certain position, tongue in certain position, cords vibrating: sounds result.

It is a long road between early random sounds and the first word, as it is between random reachings out and grasping a cup. But a sound is a sound and the ear of the child hears the sound. The sound means nothing definite to the child's ear at first. Early sounds are as general and as aimless as random squirmings elsewhere in its body mechanism. Some excitatory stimulus—a pin, a tight bandage, oxygen or food starvation, thirst, slamming of a door, the glow of a full stomach, the comfort of a warm bed—is impulse for action. Its range of reactions is limited and as yet unlearned, untutored by experience. It has not learned definite responses. It has not yet learned to walk to the tap and draw a cup of water; it has not yet learned that "Dink!" will bring the water.

The baby's ear hears the sound; it makes it again, as it reaches for its toe again once it has discovered how. And again. And again. In all living matter nothing functions as fast as babies. M, N, NG, H, W, Y, R, OW, O, E, long A, short A: all in thirty days. Hearing others produce these sounds becomes stimulus for repeating them. Baby is given a rattle and says, "Oh." Mother says, "Oh, baby." Baby bangs the rattle and chatters, "Oh, oh, oh," like a magpie. It has begun to learn English.

But habits of language begin somewhat later than other activities such as are performed with hands, arms, legs. Before baby can say "water" or "drink" it has learned appropriate responses to hundreds of objects and many complex situations.

With more vocal building-blocks more sounds are produced. There comes a day when baby wants something. It jabbers away. And finally says, "Dada." Great excitement. Wants its father! He is produced. It was not father that was wanted. Other articles are produced. A rag doll. That is what baby wants! "Dada" means rag doll! "Dada" may be the baby's word for rag doll for months. Every baby has its own vocabulary. Words become substitutes for bodily movements. Language habits replace bodily habits. Before the baby can understand the language of its parents, the

parents understand the baby's language—and jump accordingly. For babies, as Watson says, enjoy such tyranny as is
rarely displayed by the crowned heads of history.

Endless repetition. Tryings out, tryings on. A slow process. But fast time once a real start is made. "Dog" at
first means dog, also cat, also bone. The meanings of words
become restricted; the words themselves, whether spoken or
heard, more definitely conditioned. "Dada" gives way to
"doll" and "daddy." The baby's vocabulary is replaced by
parents' vocabulary. The useless and random sounds and
words disappear; those which bring results are retained.

The *learning* processes involved in conditioning the appetite, using knife and fork, and taking food, are all the same.

A girl of twenty-eight months has a vocabulary of 400
words; a boy of forty-three months, 960 words; a boy of
fifty-four months, 2,000 words—enough to carry a moron
through life. The college graduate rarely knows more than
5,000 words.

Language is part of human adjustment, learned as other
actions or habits are learned. Every normal newborn has the
potential ability to learn to talk English, Kwakiutl, Chinese,
Zulu—any language. He learns one—English, let us say;
learns it well. At twenty it will be difficult for him to learn
French, more difficult to learn Zulu; by the time he is fifty
it will be very difficult, so difficult that few do it. English
is of little help in learning Kwakiutl: one goes head first, the
other goes feet first.

Each language employs certain phonetics and proceeds
after its own grammatical form. In learning English, speech
organs and ears are trained to English phonetics, to the rules
of English grammar. Over a hundred muscles are involved;
delicate adjustments of an extraordinary complex mechanism; to say nothing of the tongue itself. This neuro-muscular
mechanism learns English: English is its habit. To learn
English phonetics, other hundreds of possible sounds and

word combinations have been neglected; they can be rescued, if at all, with difficulty.

A pair of chopsticks and knife-fork-spoon are about as different-looking objects as one can easily imagine. They seem to have nothing in common. So with English and Chinese, spoken or written. The two languages do not look alike; they sound as unlike as cat and canary talk. With the same inherent equipment of muscles and organs the child learns to eat with chopsticks and talk Chinese if brought up in a Chinese household; or to eat with knife-fork-spoon and talk English if brought up where such eating tools are the fashion and English is the mother tongue. Children of English parents brought up in India or China often learn first the manners of eating and the speech of their native nurses. A resounding belch after the meal is "good manners" in certain parts of the world. Manners are habits.

If the baby hears *baby-talk*, baby-talk will be its first language, its *mother* tongue. It may never feel so much at home in any other language. Even tones are learned. Every child can learn to whine or talk through its nose, or to speak in coarse or harsh tones. If such have value in the household, the baby will learn to fix their value. A dozen words from a two-year-old may "speak volumes" for the household.

In hundreds of languages there is a distinct word meaning *water;* and several ways of pronouncing "water" in English. Why so many words for the same thing, so many ways of pronouncing the same word? Each language has its own short-cuts to verbal activity, its own verbal response to H_2O. You pronounce w-a-t-e-r one way, I pronounce it another: we learned it that way. Having learned it that way, we react to other pronunciations of "water" as we react to other forms of behavior differing from our own. If we wait until we are grown, we find it difficult to pronounce *"l'eau"* as the Frenchman does—or understand his idea of water. We get set in our ways. Our vocal structure gets set in its ways.

Especially the larynx. Between twelve and fifteen it under-goes great structural change.

Removal of the larynx removes the vocal cords and so destroys the capacity to speak aloud. But as long as an air passage is open from lungs to pharynx and mouth, *whispered* speech is possible. If the passage is closed so that one must breathe through an opening in the trachea below the larynx, there can be no whispered speech. Such cases are known: they can speak neither in nor above a whisper; yet they learn to make all the movements necessary for articulate speech.

From all of which Watson argues that *thinking* is action in a certain motor mechanism, as winking is action in a certain motor mechanism. We think in words; words are language mechanism activity. Hence, thought is language mechanism in action. Destruction of enough of that mechanism to make impossible any of the movements involved in speech is to make thought, and probably life, impossible.

Certain phases of human culture certainly would be impossible without language. Nor is any culture known without its linguistic constituent. As Kroeber says, it is difficult to imagine any generalized thinking without words or symbols derived from words. Religious beliefs and certain phases of social organization such as caste ranking, marriage regulations, kinship recognition, and law, also seem dependent on speech. But it is conceivable that certain inventions might be made and the applied arts developed in a fair measure by imitation among a speechless people. How and why primitive man alone of the Primates developed the faculties for speech and culture remain a profound puzzle.

11

For over two years the child has been using words, but only after two years' trial and error and constant effort and endless corrections can the child be said to have a *well-organized verbal* behavior. From the age of three and on, word and kinesthetic organizations are put on simultaneously. By the time we are four we have added to our kinesthetic and emotional organization a third element of behavior: we can talk; we can react with words.

We begin our word organizations early. We learn "ball" and a ball. We learn what follows when we do not respond to "Don't!" "Blow your nose!" "Stop teasing little sister!" "Bad boy!" "Shame on you!"

Very shortly the infant's world is largely words—together, serving as stimuli to call out reactions. The times without end that we react to "Let that alone!" As a consequence we come to answer a vast word-world with words. *The word-organization dominates.* The sensori-motor throat-mechanism becomes the controlling segment of the body. The tongue becomes gifted!

We can remember our games of marbles and ball, and the birds' nests we robbed, and the early swims in the creek, and the arrowheads we found, and the hundreds of actions performed after three or four years of age, because we *talked* about them at the time. How well we remember them depends on the extent to which our word organization paralleled such bodily actions and the amount of emotional reinforcement accompanying such actions.

Thus, word organization that accompanied explicit body organization plays two rôles in behavior: we can always talk about it, memory; we can by words begin, correct, modify, or control the total reaction.

I can talk about learning to swim; I cannot talk about learning to walk. Learning to swim was accompanied by talk—of swimming. Learning to walk was accompanied by bumps and bruises—often vocalized but not verbalized. In later years a bump on the shin or a fall on the ice generally finds us speechless but rarely emotionless.

By the time we reach school we solve problems on paper: build houses and bridges, explore the Amazon, cross Asia with Marco Polo, conquer Europe with Napoleon, write

378

books, edit newspapers, make love to Dido. There is no end to this verbal organization, no limit to our capacity to make verbal response. Only memory sets the limit to the problems that can be solved with words.

But we do not always say the word. The stimulus to call a man a *cur* may be great: we repress it and "get hot under the collar"; or to pronounce the name of a loved one: we repress it and blush or giggle; or, think it over.

Every word of the 400 the girl of twenty-eight months knows is a conditioned reflex. Her eye sees candy; her mouth waters candy; her voice says candy; she says candy until she gets it: all learned responses, all habits, all reflexes. To say "candy" is an explicit act of behavior; it implies stimulus, receptor-conductor-effector. The effector was the voice mechanism, the speech organ. Suppose she had not *said* candy but *thought* candy: would this have been an act of behavior? Is *thinking* candy a reaction?

We talk to ourselves, some incessantly. We call it "thinking out loud." It is: thinking aloud. Many never learn to read without moving the lips; closer inspection of their throat shows all the muscular movements involved in reading aloud, except in the vocal cords. They move their lips because they have never completed the transition stage between *explicit* and *implicit* language habits, between *talking* and *thinking*.

Children talk; and keep on talking. They are responding to stimuli. There comes the stimulus: "Keep still or I'll . . . " They keep right on talking—but to themselves. They learn the new habit of talking without articulating; the vocal cords do not participate in the action. By and by they learn to drop even *overt* lip movements. They can think the word *hunger* without overt movement of any of their laryngeal-throat-mouth mechanism. The taking on of such habits begins early and involves no new or strange process either in learning or in the conditioning of reflex arcs. Almost as soon as the child can talk it is told not to talk. But the child has already learned to make adjustments with words. By trial

379

and error it learns to drop its voice, to whisper, and finally to dispense with all overt movement. It is now a real *thinker*. A shrewd observer and a good lip-reader can read the thoughts of others who have not learned to think except in overt movement.

"Now think of something; think hard!" You think of, say, *beefsteak*. To your chagrin and amazement, the clever observer says, "You are thinking of beefsteak!" Try it on yourself. But there are those whose thoughts cannot be read. They can think without overt muscle contraction, so short-circuited and abbreviated has become the habit. The observer's eye detects no sign of movement, but could we apply delicate instruments capable of picking up nerve impulses and detecting faint muscle contractions, we should find that *thinking* "beefsteak" differs from *saying* "beefsteak" only in degree of action.

I enter a restaurant with my stomach crying food and my mouth watering beefsteak and my throat thinking beefsteak. I sit down in a chair. That stimulates the waiter: he responds with ice-water, etc. But I want *beefsteak*. I can make that want known by several methods: I can make a picture of it; describe it; point to it on the menu or to a plate of it on another table; or produce one from my pocket and make signs of more. Any one of these methods might stimulate the waiter to action. But he is in the habit of responding to word stimuli. I say, "Beefsteak." That word spoken within his hearing brings quick results. And with a beefsteak I am *adjusted*—to food.

The chief business of thinking, as *implicit* language processes, is for individual adjustment. The supreme value of language is as an instrument of adjustment in social organization. Because of language the situations which confront individual members of society are extraordinarily complex and infinitely varied. Most of these situations, or stimuli, are *word* situations; we can adjust with words. Sometimes we "Katy did!" "Katy didn't!" the whole night long.

Of course, we think with our entire body. Our entire bodily organization is at work: at times at a high rate, at times low; at almost all times one part is more active than another. Rarely do we get into action with our bodily organization functioning as a unit and to the limit of its capacity. The body thinks, now here, now there, and the responses are always in keeping with the conditioned reflexes in implicit as well as in explicit mechanism. We do not *reveal* all our thoughts, nor always even *think them in words* to ourselves; nor does an ameba or a cat. Our bill of inherited "rights" is not less.

12

Man is a talking animal and because he can talk has increased his response mechanism beyond measure. Most of our adjustments are with words, and for most of us the older we get the more we rely on words. Our verbalized organization dominates our life. But our earliest and our last responses, and many in between, are speechless, part of our unverbalized behavior; we only look the part, by a smile or a frown. Response without words is the more ancient mode of adjustment.

Language short-cuts work and play and makes culture possible, but because of language we become complexly integrated. Words become loaded. One word can set more men marching to death than any one earthquake ever killed or volcano drove from home. "Lend me five dollars" can lead to action as overt as a wink or a kick on the shin. If "Lend me five dollars" leads to explanations, the explanation reaction is also overt.

To the thousand petty annoyances, discomforts, and senseless situations of life, few of us have any reaction beyond words: "What a nuisance!" "Isn't it a shame!" "That ought to be remedied," "Some day they will do better," etc., etc. We pick our way about through the flotsam and jetsam of stupidity and ignorance of yesterdays, without a move to

381

clean up the mess beyond words, words, words. We grow indignant and with clenched fists and flushed face exclaim that we could show them what we etc., if etc. We have thereby fought a righteous battle for the good of the cause. Words, words, words. Even the air is full of words these days.

We bandy words as boxers spar for position. We play our *best golf* in the club-house; *turn the rascals out* in hot argument in the smoking car; bring *peace on earth good-will to men* at church; and correct our bad habits and save up money in bed.

If you will listen to me I can prove to you that I am an expert golfer and that I am really interested in good government: I can prove it with *words*. And if you are a good fellow you will take me at my word; but if not, you will brag about your golf and tell me what you would do if you were President.

There are many star performers with their verbal organization who rarely let their bodily motor mechanism get into action: *he-men* who never fought a fight or played a game of one-ole-cat, golf, or tennis in their lives; *reformers* who were never in a voting booth.

Even talking wears some people out. They just *think*. They are content to *think* themselves good golfers, good citizens, good Christians. They think beautiful thoughts, poems, pictures, music, peace on earth, etc., etc. Even thinking tires some people. "In winter I set and think; in summer I just set."

"Don't bother father; he's thinking." One might suspect him of being asleep. What is father *thinking* with? His mind? Is *thinking* action? If it is, and if he is thinking hard, he will be consuming energy. There is no action without energy. If father can think without energy consumption, he should be removed to a museum where they keep mermaids.

After an hour "father" rises, puts out the light, and goes to bed. That may have been his regular hour for bed. Yet in that hour he may have done the "biggest day's work of his life." He may have reached a decision "momentous" in his own and his family's life. Great Scott! his decision might affect the destiny of nations!

What was the decision? How can I know: he said nothing, made no move or sign, no overt explicit act of any kind. For all I know he may have decided to *sell the car, give up smoking, change his bootlegger, run for President,* or *declare war.*

"Well, fellows, what do *you* think about it?" One nods; one shakes his head; one turns his thumbs down; one shrugs his shoulders; one winks; one whistles; one clears his throat. The last "fellow" rises to emphasize his remarks: "Well, fellows, if you ask me what I think, I say: Oh, hell! That's what *I* think!"

The "fellows" usually voice what they think. One word stimulates another: many cannot stop, once the first word is uttered. We fight countless battles with words. With words we fly to the moon and build castles-in-Spain. In fact, the range of our activities is only limited by our vocabulary. That is why we *think* so much: one word stimulates another; we cannot stop. There is no problem we cannot wrestle with in thought. Thinking is so easy, Watson calls it *laryngeal itch.*

When our thinking is in words we are thinking "out loud" or "to ourselves." The latter is *silent* laryngeal itch. The stimulus for such thinking or silent verbalization need not differ from any other stimulus to which other mechanisms or *higher* or *lower* centers of the body respond. It is called *itch* because we can make such varied responses to such varied stimuli without "turning a hand"; it is so much easier to turn it over to the mind. "I will think about it."

The stimulus that sets us thinking may come from within: hunger, sex, etc. More generally from without: anything in the environment, from a house falling on us, to, "Come!"

And so we "think it over" in unvoiced words. If our vocabulary is large we can think widely. But the poorest of us can in our thoughts take journeys on yachts, endow charities, win ball games, paint the house, kill off our enemies, write novels, compose operas. Our only limit is words. As there is a verbal substitute for every object in the world the limit of the world we can carry about with us is set by our verbal organization.

Father may have thought out a way to buy a new car, the stimulus for such thinking having been any one of the countless stimuli which excite people to think *new car*. The family will ride in the car when father says a word, nods his head, or writes a check. It is the thinking that gets into the picture that counts.

The stimulus of an empty stomach serves the newborn for its first thought: it *says it* with certain general bodily movements; two years later it says it with a specific mechanism which makes a sound like "hungry." Sixty years later the response may be the same, even though no ear can hear the word of the man who thinks it. In other words *thinking* may be kinesthetic, verbal, or emotional. If we are hampered in our bodily actions we talk; if our verbal thinking is blocked emotional thinking dominates us. The final act may be an unverbalized "judgment"—which need not be a rational conclusion but is likely to express our irrational dislikes.

In silent words we make countless adjustments. To *think it out* is an *implicit habit* of response. There are also *implicit hereditary* or instinctive responses, as in changes in respiration, circulation, and the whole system of hormone secretions. *Explicit habits* of response are eating with a knife and fork, playing tennis, staying on good terms with one's own and the opposite sex, etc. There are also *explicit hereditary* or instinctive responses, as in grasping, sneezing, etc., and in the emotional reactions in rage, fear, and love. If the solution of a thought-out problem is not translated into overt explicit action, spoken or written, or other explicit bodily reaction, there has been no adjustment: the world of environment is just what it was.

Man's responses are uniquely his own because he has so

many words to respond with, so many ways of modifying his explicit instinctive responses, so many degrees of emotional outlets.

13

We recall *Mother Goose* without effort, even long poems of childhood. I have forgotten my Latin, but certain *Odes* of Horace and that good old resounding *Dies iræ, dies illa,* I do not forget. Not for twenty years had I thought of a certain jingle. I find myself in the midst of some girls. Without warning, and to my surprise, I begin: "Briar, briar, limber lock . . . " Where has this counting-out rhyme been these twenty years?

There is no short-cut to learning, nor *system* by which the memory can be improved. Goose, Odes, Hymn, and Briar were learned, over and over: overlearned. We overlearn many things in childhood we "never" forget. We learn much in childhood we do forget.

Forgetting is in proportion to learning; the more we learn it, the longer we remember it. Learning is a *soaking-in* process. Some things must be learned many times before they soak in. The idea that we forget the *unpleasant* or the *painful* because it is unpleasant or painful is nonsense.

We learn to swim in youth. If we began each spring where we left off each autumn, we overlearned it. We can jump in forty years later and swim. So with driving nails, playing marbles, etc.

We know how to swim. But vivid swimming memories are mostly accessories: the thrashings we received when we arrived home, the knotted wet shirts, the frenzied efforts to dry our hair. They were emotionally tied in.

Every reaction we make has its instinctive and emotional background, its explicit and implicit factors. Rhymes, Bible lessons, poems, particular conversations, etc., remembered from childhood were emotionally tied in as well as overlearned. The emotional factor is of great importance in con-

385

ditioning reflex arcs. In learning to swim, drive a nail, recite a poem, these factors get tied together and work together.

They become so tied together that one of certain stimuli can set them off. What was in the situation to set off, "Briar, briar. . . . " I do not know. It may have been one of a dozen stimuli: the general situation itself, something peculiar in the situation, etc. This is certain: my overt act in repeating the jingle was in response to an adequate stimulus. We call ourselves *self-starters*, but we start in response to a stimulus whether to run, climb a tree, recite a poem, or *think*. There was some stimulus in that situation which recalled past experience to me.

I had been there before, as it were. We often say that, knowing well that we never have; and call it mysterious. There is no mystery about it. Some detail in a situation, in a room, in a man's face, vividly recalls some past experience. The recalled detail is so vivid that we feel we have "been there before," have "seen that man before."

Memory does play strange tricks. But it seems less tricky if we think of it in terms of situation and stimulus. When we cannot remember our own name—and sometimes we cannot—the situation is one in which we have had no experience in remembering our name, or in which no adequate stimulus is at hand to break through other stimuli clamoring for attention. *Trying hard* to recall it makes it hard for the adequate stimulus to appear. The next morning the name may pop into our head. The stimulus for recalling persisted; there had been no adjustment. During sleep or on waking the adequate stimulus gets a hearing: the name "pops into our head."

As did "Briar, briar. . . . "

Between the years we learned to swim and the day forty years later when we jump in again, arms and legs learn no new habits which make swimming mechanism hard to function.

The childhood lessons that are forgotten were never over-

learned or were built into other learning. We remember our
A B C's because we continue to use them. But of the stories
in the *Readers* we remember only our favorites. The counting-out rhymes were repeated so often—as was *Dies iræ*—
that the conditioned reflex chain was grooved. "Ene" was
adequate stimulus for "mene," and so on.

It requires longer to learn "Ura, eyuk, ro, duni" than to
learn "Ene, mene, mine, mo." "Ene mene" does not make
sense, but it jingles. It requires ten times more practice to
learn nonsense than sense material. And the longer the nonsense series, the longer proportionate time required; each
syllable must become tied up with the one preceding. Hence,
nonsense syllables are quickly forgotten. To relearn them
eight hours later requires two-thirds of the original learning
time. There is no such forgetting during the intervals in
learning to play the piano or the typewriter.

Boys quickly learn to swim; it becomes a *habit* more
easily than skating. No school in summer. One habit is
learned more quickly than two. Learning *lessons* in school
formerly progressed slowly: practice periods too close together, too little incentive.

We can learn only so much of any one thing in one day.
But between times we can learn something else. If it is a
poem, game, or complicated process, we learn it more easily
and remember it longer if we learn it as a whole. The way
to learn *Paradise Lost* or a part in a play is not line by line,
but as a whole. When learned as a whole it is remembered
as a whole; when learned line by line it is so remembered:
it is not so well tied in. We know a thing "by heart" when
our memory anticipates every reaction in the chain.

It is the stimulus that counts. Rats, mice, guinea-pigs,
birds, and cockroaches learn to thread an elaborate maze;
even at the cost of pain if the stimulus be adequate. Hunger,
for food or for the opposite sex, is the stimulus used. Old
rats require longer effort and more trials to learn to thread

the maze. But no rat has yet been found too old to learn to thread it!

Within reasonable limits, youth learns more rapidly than adult age; both learn in proportion to incentive to habit formation and uniformity of height of incentive. A man is as old as he is incapable of learning.

We learn only if we have the incentive. But even the reflex time of knee-jerk slows up if repeated at once. A joke told is already stale, good thereafter only to the teller when he can find new victims. One lesson was enough for Eve.

Memory is looking backward; of biologic service when it impels us forward.

14

"Don't jump; *dive!*" Easier said than done. We are organized on head-up, feet-down plan. We learn to walk that way. The first dive is a new experience: it reverses our feet-down head-up and away-from-solids habit; the water looks hard; there may be rocks below. There were. The boy never forgot it—nor learned to dive. No will power inside his skull could cause the nerves outside to forget their lesson. He could not put his whole heart into a dive.

Some boys can; they have the do-or-die habit. They explore bottoms and dive in again. And again. By the end of the week they dive like frogs. Their sisters are just as good. Do-or-die for one is usually do-or-die for all in the family.

The boy who learned to dive in spite of his first mishap succeeded largely because of it. The problem was different, more difficult than he had anticipated. That tapped a new source of zeal. He became a high diver in the circus. A net is not water, but the skill required in manoeuvring a head-first body in diving was available in learning to dive from the top of the big tent.

There is always great complexity of stimuli in any given

situation; *the situation itself is always changing.* A pig quietly nosing along a swill trough is joined by two more pigs. New situation now: the first pig gets into the trough.

The family have just sat down at the dinner table. The door bell rings. Behavior of the entire family changes: mother jerks off her apron, father puts on his coat, sister wipes brother's mouth, brother kicks the cat. New situation; only one new stimulus, door bell. The family jumped to the reaction: well trained.

Baby alone went right on banging his spoon on the arm of his chair. Baby had just acquired that habit and found it so stimulating that entrance of stranger did not alter its situation. But the family now are suddenly conscious of baby's behavior. Mother asks sister to take baby into the kitchen, knowing that removal of spoon will set off the first habit baby learned (crying till he gets it). Baby is not likely to lose that habit: no other one yields him such large returns.

We become Dr. Jekyll or Mr. Hyde. Few can become both. We have our own level of organization, our habits of response to situations in which we feel at home. But Jekyll-Hyde was at home in two situations. His was a dual personality. In one set of situations he was Dr. Jekyll, in the other Mr. Hyde.

There are times when, to our astonishment, dog or child makes no response to name or other stimulus which ordinarily calls out a response. If we cannot predict a child's response, how can we expect to predict the behavior of an adult? How can we know when Mr. Hyde will turn into Dr. Jekyll?

We cannot. Even prediction of a comet's movements is simple compared with predicting the behavior of an ameba. But there are some general principles that are of general application.

Our response to a kick on the shin may be: "Well, I'll be . . ." That response does not follow if we are in church, even though the kick came from the same brother. The situation as a whole is a determining factor. The response is *delayed* until the situation is right. In Rome we do as the Romans do. Ditto in church, at a ball game, at a ball.

The response is likely to be a repetition of one recently called out. We have not been to a movie for months: a friend drags us out; we go to a movie every night for a week. I have just visited a maple-sugar camp: I now notice maple trees everywhere; and see sugar cakes in the grocer's window. I passed them by this morning without noticing them.

A fire engine shrieks through the street several times a week. I have long since ceased to notice it. I do to-day: my fire insurance expired yesterday. I am all excited because I intend to listen-in to-night: the President's speech is to be broadcast. I make certain that my radio is in order. At eight o'clock I have the colic: the President's speech means nothing to me.

My response to a knock on the door may be to open the door; I may lock it, turn out the light, and reach for a revolver. I may pray. Vast numbers of our responses are made with words. This doubles our response repertoire, complicates our behavior.

Four brothers—a banker, a preacher, a paleontologist, and a bootlegger—read the news of the sinking of the XVIIIth Amendment: predict the response of each. The door bell rings, a man enters; it is their enormously rich Uncle Bim from Australia. The situation is again changed. But to each and to all situations an almost unlimited number of varying responses was open to each of these four men. And is open to all of us.

There are also two ways of clothing our nakedness—for we are born naked and are not ashamed of it. But the over-dressed man and the underdressed woman had the same start and are only happy when they are noticed: on the stage or platform, or in the pictures or a lodge parade. When a woman cannot make an exhibition of herself any other way she can start a dress-reform movement.

Human beings, acting and reacting. The situations which call out reactions are diverse. The response any given individual will make to any given situation is a variant and depends upon that individual's previous experience, including such things as cold toast that morning, the reading of *The Marble Faun* ten years before, a fight twenty years before that. Individual behavior.

Yet, as Watson says, it is almost impossible for a balanced man to be so torn as to steal his neighbor's purse or child, or to commit suicide or mutilate others. Such responses are possible only to the extent that the co-ordinations used in committing such crimes are in his behavior repertoire. Furthermore, his total reaction systems are so tied together that the moment he starts to commit suicide or a crime a new situation is created and leads to a different act. It is quite impossible for most of us to commit suicide; our conditioned fears and our unconditioned responses will not let us. Practically all our suicides are pathological—diseased personality. Suicide in Japan or China may be normal behavior.

We are not mosaics of inherent reflexes and learned habits, but we are going concerns. How we go, how fast we go, and what we go in or out for, depend on the situation and our experiences with previous situations. "We act in line with our training and in conformity with our inherited points of weakness and strength." The situation we are in dominates us and releases one or the other of our all-powerful habit systems—we exhibit our learning in the manual, laryngeal, or visceral field. A cross-section of our habit systems in these three fields gives us a picture of our personality.

15

We learn new responses for adjustment purposes and in taking on habits are subject to factors which condition all learning. We become *adapted, positively* or *negatively:* the stimulus reaches us more easily or we inhibit it with less effort.

A doctor asleep beside his wife hears only the telephone; she hears only the baby. But if the baby cries long enough he will hear it, and if the telephone rings long enough she will hear it. There is a limit to adaptation. Both can hear a mouse or a burglar. Most boys can hear a penny drop; most men's ears pick up nothing less than silver.

Tight shoes are only tight until we get used to them. It is the sudden drops in the temperature that we notice. We grow accustomed to change if it is gradual: bad air, bad food, bad government, bad wives, bad husbands, bad children, high cost of living. Life can make huge concessions if it is not crowded or pushed. As long as the breaking point is not reached, we can stand it. Wives at fifty will look just as good as at twenty—if the change has been gradual. We can become adapted even to lethal doses.

When any given stimulus sufficient to set off the response mechanism is repeated, the threshold is lowered and the response hastened: we are positively adapted, favorably disposed. We are negatively adapted if the stimulus is gradually increased without increased or with delayed response, or if the threshold is permanently raised. If we fail to get up with the alarm clock we soon fail to hear it.

We have a "hangover" after intense and emotionally stimulated activity. After a long session at cards, our minds go right on playing cards. We "pop the question" on a moonlight night after a preliminary *warming up*. Warming up lowers the threshold and has psychologic value in all fields of activity where we are out for victory.

Why do we like certain poems, pictures, songs, melodies, hymns? I sat through a Georgia camp meeting recently. The preacher exhorted and exhorted; no one came "forward." Then another old familiar air was set in motion: many went forward.

Leaders—in religion, politics, and business—get "results"

because they know how to play on us. We buy or bite not according to our requirements or on the strength of the merits of the "goods" they sell us (for they rarely talk merits), but according to their appeal to our *attitudes*.

We go to a political rally. Flags everywhere; pictures of Washington and Lincoln on the stage. That stage is set for us; the trap is baited. We do not need these settings; but they do their work: they make us favorably disposed. We cannot look at *Our Flag* or the *Father of Our Country* without being moved. Prayer follows: God, save America and bless the man who is about to save it. Etc. Then the speaker talks about Lincoln and drags in other matter irrelevant to his own fitness. And we are further moved. And with an, "All together!" we sing "America." That decides us: he is the man we want.

The successful politician may never have heard of "emotional tendencies built up through association processes" or of "conditioned emotional responses," but he does not try to sell himself to a Georgia rally with a eulogy on Sherman or ask all to rise and sing "John Brown's Body." Nor does the salesman try to sell refrigerators to Eskimos or the complete works of Darwin to South Carolina.

Whether we are positive or negative all depends. But we are positively adapted for anything and everything that interests us. Whether a particular thing is to our interest or not also depends. We can learn.

16

The principle back of breaking habits is the same as that back of forming them: substitution. Substitute another. Sometimes it is difficult; the path may be worn too deep. Then it is a habit: if useless, a bad one; if dangerous, lock him up.

A farmer breaks a colt gradually. He accustoms it to the sight of things, to the feel of things; little by little. The first thing the colt knows, it is hitched up. It is *broken* to harness. But a colt can have its conditioned fear reflexes. And when the stimulus comes—umbrella, locomotive engine, auto, red dress, any fool thing—it scares. One way to keep it from scaring is to keep it away from fearsome things. A better way is to condition it to men. With fear of men gone, the colt begins to have confidence when there is a man about.

The human infant has almost no specific fears. Its particular fears become conditioned and terribly real. They can be conditioned out, gradually. The old habit of being afraid of certain things or persons is replaced by other habits.

As the weaning day approaches many babies take to thumbs. The thumb satisfies the sucking reflex, an instinctive act. But if the baby is not allowed to get its thumb in its mouth, the sucking reflex will disappear along with other infantile actions. Elimination functions are instinctive and many habit activities are built up around them. Such acts cannot be broken up, as can the sucking reflex, but they can be socialized and the infant can be taught continence with respect to them very early in life.

Habits, whether inherent or acquired, can usually be broken up by altering the stimulus. Horses often show their fighting instinct by kicking or biting at a passer-by. But a horse which has bitten into a sleeve of cayenne pepper is not likely to bite into another sleeve. If the figure passing behind him is a dummy, and if his feet are jerked from under him as he kicks at it, he will think of his feet the next time he is impelled to kick. The dog which instinctively sucks eggs loses his appetite for eggs after he has crushed a cayenne pepper prepared egg. The instinctive chain reflex now reads: *smell egg, hang out tongue* to cool; instead of: *smell egg, crack* it, lap it up.

Specific fears and other forms of emotion generally run in families; they are handed down, conditioned in. Children of lion-tamers, snake-charmers, steeple-jacks, etc., grow up without conditioned fears of lions or snakes or high places. The son of a snake-charmer may go in for the ministry, but the minister's daughter is not likely to become a snake-charmer.

The child that has everything it wants is no more likely to form habits of thrift than a Hottentot or a monkey. Habits are not formed by uttering precepts. Nor is moral conduct founded on preachments. Nor a bad habit broken by warnings. But a little common sense and a few lessons in the biology of reproduction have not yet been known to encourage youth to bad habits and have been known to make for sanity, peace of mind, and normal behavior. Much of the drive behind *morbid* curiosity in the young springs from society's ban on such matters. The ban itself only makes a natural curiosity morbid and adds zest to the gratification of that curiosity.

Our *erogenous zones,* as Ellis calls them, function from birth: they respond to stimuli. The baby can gurgle and coo and smile when it is tickled or patted or pleased. The hug response follows the outstretched arm movement. Just where *love* comes in it is not easy to say. It does come— early; it does get conditioned into our emotional fears and hates, strengthening them, modifying them, coloring them. Especially into our attitudes, even toward a sunset. Our emotions get more or less saturated with sentiment. Often the mate-hunger impulse receives more than its share of rebuffs. These lead to definite attitudes backed by emotion.

The lovesick maiden seeks sympathy and the lovelorn youth solitude. And few there are who do not know the meaning of shame, envy, hate, jealousy, shyness, embarrassment, pride, suspicion, anxiety, anguish, resentment, etc.; emotional habits conditioned on to instinctive tendencies. They upset us in dozens of ways; they make or break or prevent marriage; they are as much a part of us as our arms and legs.

Emotional attachments are of value only when attached to serviceable or useful behavior, when called out under stress, and when directed to the big business of life. It *hurts* to be scared and we *boil* when we are enraged. But the life that always boils or is scared cold has little time for routine business of life.

The time to break such hurt and boil habits is before they are formed: before the emotions have become specific for things, places, and people that are not changed by tears or smiles. Then we can talk of moral and political issues without slopping over into useless sentimentality or boiling over with worse than useless vindictive animosity.

This is not easy. It is easier to allow our emotions to move us than to restrain our emotions and inquire: where do we want to go and why do we not move in that direction? Easier, because that is our habit.

17

Your family physician can put you to sleep with a drug, but he cannot tell you why you suffer insomnia or why you can walk in your sleep. Or why you sleep—or wake up.

One popular theory solves the problem with *thyroid hormones*. Muscle activity generates poison—"fatigue products." Iodine is anti-toxic. The thyroid furnishes iodine. Hence . . . But inasmuch as the infant sleeps early and late and cannot be presumed to have generated much fatigue product from muscle activity, sleep itself was assumed to be instinctive biologic defense mechanism to *prevent intoxication!*

Which *explains* sleep just as much as breathing is explained by saying that we breathe in order not to become asphyxiated. We cannot commit suicide by holding our breath, nor by withholding our sleep. Breathing and sleeping are reflex acts which travel on their own. The muscle toxins were assumed. It was then presumed that the thyroid—or some other gland—washed them out.

The *vasomotor* theory assumes that at the end of the day the center of the nervous system which regulates the size of blood vessels gets "tired." As a consequence the blood supply to the brain is partially cut off. That puts the brain to sleep. Then we sleep.

But is the brain robbed of blood during sleep, does action in skeletal muscles lead to intoxication? In other words, is there any basis in fact behind the commonly accepted theories of the cause and function of sleep? When we are tired we fall asleep more easily than when we are fresh. But the loafer does not have to be tired; he drops off to sleep at his regular hour—or any other hour. Nor is the brain robbed of its blood during sleep; the evidence points the other way. But whether the brain has little or much blood, the vasomotor change may be the consequence as well as a cause of sleep. Neither explains the release of the sleep reflex.

Kleitman and Lee, working on a human subject kept awake for 115 hours, could find no evidence of general intoxication either in the carbon dioxide content of the blood, in blood sugar, heart rate, respiration, temperature, or rate of basal metabolism. The theory of *intoxication* at the end of every sixteen hours falls flat.

Their experiments uncovered other facts at variance with popular notions about sleep, especially as to the effects of loss of sleep. After nearly five days without sleep, the subject showed no variation from the normal in a large number of functions. He ate and worked as usual. His knee-kick and eye-pupil dilation reflexes were unaffected. So was his ability to do mental arithmetic, to name opposites, and to react to eye and ear stimuli. There was no change in his sensory threshold for electric-current stimuli. He did lose some control of the muscles of his head; it wobbled. But that may have been due not to insomnia, but to tired neck muscles.

The subject could keep awake only by continued activity. An attendant accompanied him to prevent him from relaxing. Whatever causes sleep, its onset begins with complete relaxation of the skeletal muscles. As muscular activity invariably accompanies and is perhaps the most characteristic feature of wakefulness, the probable cause of the onset of sleep is relaxation, voluntary or involuntary.

Sleep itself may be due to *fatigue* of the highest centers of consciousness; but whether to loss of nutritive substance in the nerve cells or to increase of waste of cell metabolism is not known. The *highest centers* are those of learned control and association of motor and speech mechanisms. They are the most recent acquisitions to the nervous system, the least organized at birth, the most modifiable from birth. A small dose of alcohol affects the voice, a larger dose affects the gait; but only a large dose paralyzes the respiratory center: that is a *low* center.

In all the experiments performed, the subjects could not study after one night's loss of sleep. They could do laboratory work and mental arithmetic, etc.; but their highest centers gradually lost their irritability, as ours do after a long day's work. Sleep restores this irritability. But just what else happens during sleep is not known.

Dreams, for one thing. During light sleep sensations from the viscera or from outside the body may reach *lower* centers; they are older, better organized; presumably less subject to fatigue. Dreams are not critical. These sensations do not reach the highest levels of the cortex where only they can be correctly analyzed and interpreted. If they become so strong as to force their way into the highest level and rouse it to action, we wake up.

Sleep, then, takes the kick out of stimuli that in waking hours would receive attention and result in voice, thought, or motor mechanism reaction. But the sleep-walkers! Their dreams get into their *high*-level motor mechanism and they walk! Why walking does not wake them is not yet known.

What wakes us? Stimulus from stomach, bladder, or other visceral organ finally becomes so powerful as to break through synaptic resistance and rouse the cortex. We are awake.

Why do we sleep? What is back of sleep?

But, first, what is back of life itself? Sunlight. The sun is the primary source of the energy of green plants; in sunlight they build up their bodies. But the light fails, the sun goes down. They had to meet that condition, to find the energy required to prolong life throughout the night. The problem was met in two ways: by living more slowly—that is, consuming less energy—during the night; by deriving energy from breaking down and so releasing the stored energy of their own body. Process of katabolism, or destructive metabolism.

Katabolism, then, is an adaptation to the dark.

Throughout the ages since life evolved, day follows the night. Throughout the nights, the machine of life slowed down; it could not build up its body, but it could keep it alive until the day came, the body itself furnishing the energy.

We eat; the sun goes down; we go to sleep. The sun comes up; we wake; we eat. During sleep the processes of metabolism, especially the katabolic, continue.

Ages ago, our ancestors did not develop electric organs or luciferase; they did develop diurnal habits. The nights were given over to the vegetative processes, the days to action in the motor mechanism. Having nothing to do at night, they went to bed. There was no other place to go. With no electric light to switch on, the wires to and from the highest brain centers were switched off. Sleep became a habit. It worked like a conditioned reflex, sunset setting it off. Even to-day, some find it hard to break the habit; they go to bed with the chickens and are up with the dawn.

399

Judging from their behavior, all our four-footed friends dream. Presumably their dreams are as unique as are their individual selves. I find no explanation for my dreams that does not take stock of my experience. Dreams themselves are no more mysterious than is any other phase of adjustment. Dreams and sleep are processes of adjustment based on physiological processes.

It is assumed that dreams have a biologic function. "It is the dream that really keeps us asleep," says Humphreys. He cites the sleeper and a lawn-mower outside. The sleeper dreams he hears something else: if he "heard" *lawn-mower*, he would have to get up and go to work. "He can only consistently go to sleep by hearing noise as something else than the sound of a lawn-mower."

That explanation is too simple; it covers too much ground. True, many dreams seem to have the function of *guarding sleep*. But to say that the dream keeps us asleep is as lucid as to say that sleep *causes* dreams.

There are dreams and dreams, and sleep and sleep. Some animals and people are always dreaming; some seem never more than half awake. But inherent in life and human beings is the necessity to "come to" when life is imperilled.

When now I lay me down to sleep, what do I lay down? Obviously, not the same body that I carry to a Harvard-Yale football game. But the body that carries me to the game may be any one of 80,000 bodies in the Bowl. When half of them groan the other half cheer. One particular body may sob, another go into a frenzy of delight; another may yawn and say, "What a rotten game!"

The body I lay down may be so tired it is "dead to the world" and beyond stimulus of smoke, though my own bedclothes are on fire from my cigarette. I do not come to until fire stimulates my skin. No dream *kept me asleep*, nor did *nightmare* arouse me.

I may be very tired and yet wake at the low gentle gnawing of a mouse. I curse the mouse and try to go to sleep again. Why could I not have dreamed of squirrels in the wood gnawing nuts and have slept peacefully on?

I have worked late and am tired. I must be up and at work again within five hours: I need every minute of my sleep. I drop asleep, and come to with a start. I have had a horrible nightmare. I can sleep no more that night. I can discover no *excuse* for my nightmare: no fire, no mouse, everything quiet.

No excuse.

I sit in my chair on deck in the sun: not asleep, not thinking, not daydreaming. "Without a thought in my head." I feel that I could sit there forever, the day is so fine. Suddenly I am up and off. I go to my cabin and write for hours. I do not hear the dinner gong. The steward brings hot water; I do not notice him. He now knocks twice before I hear him: "Not going in for dinner?"

I may know, I may not know, what brought me up out of my chair and started me to work. But when because of drugs, alcohol, or toxins, we are quite beyond reach of messages from without or from within, we have passed out. But, as a rule, we are as little conscious why a particular thing pops into our head as why we have a dreamless sleep, or a silly, lascivious, or nightmare dream.

Sleep is primarily relaxation—general dropping off of the motor mechanism. But activity keeps on, though slowed down a trifle, in the digestive, respiratory, and circulatory systems. The bodily functions continue; the motor mechanism goes out of action, including external receptors for outside stimuli. *Consciousness* quits, the *mind* stays on the job. Consciousness is a functioning of arcs of the cortex of the brain, where knowledge is stored and sorted. When certain parts of the cortex are injured—by disease or wound—we lose control of something, as though we had quite *forgotten*. It may be use of part of the motor mechanism, or the speech mechanism, etc. But with the cortex out of action, we forget what we have learned.

Roused from deep sleep with the porter's admonition: "Gotta get outa here in five minutes," we make a mess of dressing. Seems as though we have forgotten which shoe goes on which foot, and we blink at collar and tie as though we had never seen such things. We are not "in possession of all our faculties."

Hence, dreams mix things up. The right shoe on the left foot. A shirt means nothing. And we wake up the next morning with the "funniest dream; can't make head or tail of it."

Or, the nightmare wakes us up and finds us in a cold sweat. Nightmare behavior is *jumpy* behavior. The child terrified at dusk by goblins and ghosts and Red Riding-Hood wolves, carries an easily terrified body to bed and may carry it for eighty-odd years: jumps at every sound while awake and in sleep is *subject to nightmare*. Such a body is always prepared to jump, until its hypersensitivity is educated out of it. This is not an easy process if the early fears have been branded in.

A dream may be anything. If A's dreams are *wish-fulfill-ments*, A apparently is a Spanish-castle-builder and keeps at it in his dreams. If A's dreams are also sex, it is because A's mind dwells on sex. As wishes and sex enter into many lives, they are likely to enter many dreams.

Sometimes the frankness of our dreams amazes us. Life is frank. With the cortex out of action, we lose the guardian of our morals. The mind of the dreamer rambles around aimlessly and shamelessly. For the same reason scientists often solve problems in chemistry, mathematics, etc., in dreams; their mind was free from inhibitions, it was not *afraid* to try out new combinations.

We solve many different problems of conflict just before we drop asleep, or we drive them from our head long enough to fall asleep. That problem is likely to form the subject of our dream: the body mind carries it on from the point where it was dropped by the conscious mind.

Children and morons do not solve problems in chemistry in their dreams. As in waking states, they deal with the simple affairs of the day or of yesterday. Adults' dreams may drop into childhood imagery and symbols. Starting with some unsolved problem or conflict of the day, the mind drops into earlier levels of mental functioning. Few of us go through the day without some early memory rising up like a ghost or blissful experience to haunt us or make us sigh for the barefoot days. In sleep the mind wanders, and easily and naturally into childish things or into childish methods of *playing cars* with four chairs, one dog, one cat, two dolls, and Johnny for engineer and Mamie for conductor.

"My dream has come true!" Often they do. As I write, my body's mind wanders fore and aft and up and down. It will be surprising if it can anticipate nothing of my behavior or my family's behavior to-morrow or next week. When our dreams do not come true—and generally they do not, for truth has little interest for dreams—we say nothing about it.

"Prophecy lies in my name, saying: I have dreamed, I have dreamed."

19

We land at Bombay, deposit our belongings at the hotel, and start out to see the sights. We need not move a foot: there are *sights* all around us. All is new; nothing seems like home. The very atmosphere has a peculiar odor, a different feel. The sun is not the same. The houses, trees, birds, shops, signs, noises, voices, cries, cattle, carts, carriages, trams, are different. Swarms of human beings unlike any that we know; different in face, build, gait, dress, coiffure, foot and head gear, and personal adornment.

Bombay is a new world. Nothing in our past experience has prepared us for it. Suppose we have come to settle

down in Bombay? We realize that we have much to learn—
more than we can realize at first. We do not know how to
act. Why does that man stare at me that way? What is
the meaning of such behavior? We have no ready-made
behavior by which we can adjust ourselves to their behavior.

Even the flies, bugs, and insects are different. How are
we to know which are harmful or dangerous? At the edge
of a park we meet a little green snake. It appears harmless;
it may be deadly poisonous. How can we know?

How do we? How do we know the world outside our skin?

We enter the native market. Piles of strange vegetables
and fruits. But nothing that we know. We see only certain
shapes, sizes, colors. But what are they inside—sweet,
bitter, mushy, hard, juicy? We do not know them. Our
mouth does not water. Suddenly we espy a box of peaches.
Our mouth waters now. We have a very clear knowledge
of peaches. A rat runs out; we jump back. We have not
seen a rat for forty years, but we have not forgotten rats; nor
that a rat is not to be caught with the bare hands as a rabbit
may be.

The first rat we met bit us; the first rabbit we met we ate.
I know more now about rats than the mere fact that they are
ugly and are to be killed only at a safe distance; and about
rabbits than that they are harmless, defenseless, nice, and
good to eat. But there was a time when "rat" meant no
more to me than "hat"; or "rabbit" than "Babbitt"; a time
when neither a rat nor a rabbit meant more than something
which could stimulate my eye and provoke my reaching for it.

Because we are impelled to reach, and when within reach
explore, and because things either bite us or we bite them,
we do learn.

The world we know is the world we explore with our
fingers, tongue, eyes, ears, nose, and all the receptors with
which our body is so abundantly supplied on or in the surface
or within. We know some objects, beings, qualities, and
quantities, well; some, not so well. Included in this knowl-

edge of objects are attitudes toward objects. We learn eventually to let sleeping dogs lie, and many objects, persons and situations alone.

Don't monkey with that!

But we do. There is more monkey than rabbit in our inheritance. As a result, a lively boy or girl of fifteen years knows as much as the "average American."

"Is there anything that child does not want?" asks the harried mother. The child replies, "Nothing." And the child that cries till he gets it answers: "Why not? What are things for if I am not to be allowed to examine them?"

It is a slow, complicated process, but after the child can walk it goes on at an astonishing rate. Tireless, insatiable, indefatigable youngsters! "If I didn't stop them they would tear down the house and burn up the barn." Why not? They might build a better one, or learn a new culinary art, as Charles Lamb says the Chinese learned roast pig.

Here is a baby. It has learned the location of its eyes, ears, nose, and toes, and can reach and grasp and handle. Assume that it has been "carefully guarded"—which usually means it knows next to nothing. Offer it a peach, pin, stick of candy, match, red-hot poker, cat's tail, firecracker; same reaction: baby wants it. It may learn enough in one lesson to alter its behavior thereafter to each of these objects. Why? Because hot pokers, firecrackers, cats' tails, pins, candy, etc., have their own behavior. Sooner or later baby learns that the tail of a cat is not a handle to a plaything.

The first peach baby meets is, let us say, through the eyes. Mere visual stimulus was enough for the first lesson. The peach did not explode or bite or burn. Baby explores further. Peach can also stimulate the skin of hand or body or face; also the nose, the tongue, and sense organs in the alimentary canal and kinesthetic senses. By the time the exploration is complete the child knows a peach. Through the responses to the many diverse stimuli a peach can make, the child knows more or less of its color, shape, weight, hardness, odor, taste. That it has a skin, that the skin is tough and covered with down, that the down is unpleasant to skin of hands, face, mouth, and tongue, etc., etc.

Knowledge of peach was built up. Visual stimulus was adequate to provoke grasping response; odor stimulus provoked another response; and so on. By and by any one stimulus may call forth all the responses of all the other stimuli, because these responses are conditioned. While seeing peach, nose smelled peach, hand felt peach, tongue tasted peach, etc. Until at last the mere word "peach" on an empty tin can in the middle of a desert can be felt, seen, sniffed, and tasted—there may be no *peach* within a thousand miles. The response to the label on the empty can might also lead to verbal response, such as, "I'd give a thousand dollars for a peach," or, "I wish I hadn't eaten these peaches," or, "You are a peach!"

The kick-back, the response the object itself makes to our exploration, is not only part of our knowledge, but largely determines whether we shall "pursue the subject further." A child reaches out for a dog's tongue or a cat's paw: a bark, a meow, a bite, a scratch. If bite and scratch are serious, and especially if mother yelled, "Don't!" at the top of her voice, we are likely to know barks and meows, and when such melodies stimulate our ears we do not need sight of dog or cat to complete our perception.

We learn Bombay that way. We sample the fruit and vegetables, exchange our "good iron" dollars for their "funny paper" rupees, and take no chances with snakes. Learn to love mangosteens and how to eat a mango. Learn to distinguish Parsee from Moslem and both from Hindu. Get used to the idea of burning cowdung for fuel, and do not shudder when we pass the Burning Ghats. Etc.

We learn life that way—building it up, building it up. We know some things well. Many things we do not want to know; they bit us. We can even land in Bombay and walk through the city concerned only as a dog would be; in which case there would be other dogs, cats, places for food and drink and sleep, and endless things to be avoided lest one get run over.

Knowledge is power, no doubt; but what does it turn? Let society answer that question for its own collective and individual self. But what I know and what you know is that ice is cold, fire is hot, rock is hard, hills are high, stars are far, candy is sweet, vinegar is sour, rain is wet, wet paint comes off, wood burns, he is a good fellow, rubber stretches, decaying flesh stinks, roses have thorns, money talks, shoddy is shoddy, fleas bite, glass is smooth, mules kick, bulls bellow, roosters crow, corners are sharp, eggs are high, he is a scab, she is worth looking at, Tut-ankh-Amen is dead, the razor is dull, they are wearing them higher, all is not gold that glitters, babies are nuisances, parents are easily led.

"How do you know he won't lend you five dollars?" "I asked him: I know."

That kind of knowledge is power.

When the engineer turns the steam on he knows how the steam will behave. He has monkeyed with steam, he can anticipate its response. When the navigator leaves Aden he sets his course for Bombay. He knows the behavior of his ship, his compass, and the sea. At a certain hour of a certain day he expects to sight a certain light.

Education does not begin at six; like charity, it begins at home, and at birth, and should never stop. But it is equally important to realize the full force of what Herrick means when he says:

"There is nothing in our experience, there are no mental powers, no skill in ratiocination or logical analysis, no capacity to forecast future events, no flights of imaginative fancy, which do not depend directly or indirectly upon sensory data."

The astronomer figures a bit and announces that the diameter of Betelgeuse, a star in the constellation Orion, is 200,000,000 miles.

Most of us finished with stars when we learned "Twinkle, twinkle, little star," "Oh, look at the stars!" or, "Isn't that a bright star!" We stop our learning of many things when we can name them. We know many situations and solve many problems by mere phrases: "Chinese eat rats," "Sweet land of liberty," "Dirty foreigners," "Liberty enlightening the world," etc.

By the time we are ready to leave home we have a varied assortment of *facts* that we have learned ourselves; they are part of our own personal experience. This experienced knowledge is the result of our responses to external stimuli: stars, rocks, tacks, whistles, pennies, candy, rain, trees, etc.

Some stimuli are received by certain receptors, other stimuli by other receptors. Qualities especially are learned from stimuli to several receptors. Thus we learn most things as hard, soft, wet, dry, smooth, rough, greasy, sticky, etc., through no one sense organ. We learn that molasses is sticky not by looking at it, but by poking our finger in it; sweet, by tasting it. We know lard because we have seen and felt and smelled and tasted it, but neither eye nor nose perceives lard as greasy.

At first we had no organized sense of distance. We walked into and off things. The baby falls downstairs until he learns how far it is to the next step. He learns. He throws a ball and walks to pick it up; that gives him a sense of distance. At the creek he "throws a stone across," only the stone does not cross; he has not learned to distinguish distance on land and water. By experience he builds up a sense of distance, space, depth.

An Englishman announces to his Colorado host that he will work up an appetite for breakfast by a walk to "that little hill." He has not learned Colorado atmosphere: the "hill" is 10,000 feet high, fifteen miles away.

Our two eyes are not far apart; but my left eye can see what my right cannot unless I move my head. The nearer the object, the more each eye sees what is beyond reach of the other; the greater is the resultant eye-strain in binocular vision. The eye-strain is a clue to distance. As the background also is seen as two images by the two eyes, another clue to distance results. The child continually reaches for objects just beyond reach. As a drunken man does, having lost much of his learning through temporary derangement of his "higher faculties."

Our eyes were evolved before print was invented: they are not naturally adapted for close-ups. In reading or examining close-up objects, the axis of vision (center of fovea to center of lens) must change from parallel to an angle. Countless early adjustments of these axes are part of the experience which leads to sense of distance.

A silver dollar ten feet away looks different from a dollar a foot away—its image on the retina is smaller. If I know the object I see to be a dollar, or a man, or a tree, I have a clue to the distance of dollar, man, tree. One gets a new perception of the size of St. Peter's by standing at one end and watching a tall man walk to the other end. Smaller, smaller he grows; at last he seems like a child. "It is big!" we now exclaim.

Distance and depth learning begins with the fact that the stimulus itself changes with distance from the eyes, and that every response we make with our eyes requires action in a complex muscular mechanism. The photographer focuses his camera. As do I when I lift my eyes from my book to the clock tower a mile away: I must make far-reaching adjustments in both eyes. They are made by many muscles controlled by several nerves. I may not know I have such muscles: my body knows. Adjustment of iris alone involves three distinct sets of muscles that must work in harmony and at the same time.

We respond to stars by looking at them; to trees by climbing them, by seeing them in sunshine, in fog, in rain, by moonlight, in summer and winter and spring and autumn. By and by we *know* trees.

And hear them also, with two ears. On a dark night we hear a suspicious sound. We "strain" our ears, turn our head to the right, to the left: if now one ear does not receive more stimulus than the other we decide the sound is in front of us; it may be behind us.

Telephone bell, motor horn, railway whistle, footstep, mouse gnawing, bumblebee: we *know* these sounds. By their intensity we also judge of their distance. But if the sound is quite new to us, we can not judge its distance by its intensity.

When a child, I heard a chick in a pasture field crying for its mother hen; I began to look for it. Every now and then I would hear it again. For ten minutes I searched, all the while becoming more mystified. I happened to look up: high overhead a hawk was circling around. The "chick" was a *hawk!* Its cry was so like that of a chick that I had been completely fooled. But we learn to distinguish many diverse objects by the sounds they make. We may walk blindfolded through a street and hear ice, wood, and coal chopped; wood, ice, stone, and steel sawed; hammering, filing, the drawing of a rusty nail, jangle of coins and keys, rattle of dice, rending of silk or paper, scream of a terrified child, "the car rattling o'er the stony street."

Without eyes, much of the world vanishes; but the blind man picks up sounds and echoes so far beyond our untrained ears that we give him credit for "another sense." The woodman picks up sounds in the forest of no meaning to the city man, others that fail to reach his ears. But the city man gets even when the woodman comes to town: he cannot hear himself think, nor knows whether the fire siren is a mile away or around the corner.

The nose does its bit in our learning of life and things, and what to leave alone and when the other fellow should take a bath. We can get used to smells. We can also cultivate our rather inferior olfactory organ and without eyes or ears come to distinguish many cheeses, tobaccos, beverages, foods, salt air and all that pertains to the sea. With nose alone, in Manchuria, one can distinguish a Japanese from a Russian railway station. The Japanese are clean.

We learn time by the passing events. We have our own rhythms for heartbeat, breathing, talking, walking, eating, etc., all of value in acquiring time sense. The stomach is a good clock. Where is the sun? Daylight, nighttime. The banks are closed, the evening paper has come. Or the birds have tuned up. Or the cocks are crowing. What time is it: how far have we moved? How long have I been sitting here: how much work have I done, how hungry am I, how tired, or how many pipes have I smoked? Time does not stand still. We learn to move with it.

The body itself is the great learner. General kinesthetic and special equilibrium organs in our ears give us great knowledge of the world. Movement in muscles can serve as stimulus as well as a ray of light in the eye. Before we learn to dance or play tennis or introduce the speaker of the evening, we learned to walk on two feet. The knowledge the body picks up as it walks us through life is a reservoir of learning from which we draw as from an unlimited bank credit.

Some of us have no *sense*, but it is a misshapen, misspent, and unlearned motor mechanism which has no sense.

Our senses often fail us; our *perception* is at fault, our experience incomplete, our judgment wrong, our knowledge insufficient. But to live is to take a chance. These look like mushrooms; the cook says they are mushrooms: I take a chance. Were they mushrooms?

As the diameter of the earth is less than 9,000 miles, I do not like the idea that the diameter of Betelgeuse is 200,000,000 miles. It makes us small potatoes. I take no chance. I say: "Bah! How does he know? He has never been there!" Or perhaps I ask another astronomer. He says: "No, not two but four hundred million miles!" I like that less than the other figure. It is "hard to believe."

Which astronomer told the truth? Both, it seems. That star pulsates like a mighty throbbing heart in a vast universe, expanding, contracting. It was measured at two different times, hence the different results obtained for its diameter.

The immediate world that we come to know in our process of learning to be human also expands and contracts. Of many things we come to know more; of many things we thought we knew we come to realize we know next to nothing at all. But, expanding or contracting, the world we know is the world in which we live and believe.

21

From a sunlit street I enter a motion-picture theater. It seems pitch dark. After a few seconds I can see my way to a vacant seat; a few moments later I can recognize faces twenty feet away: the theater itself is no lighter than when I entered. My eyes had become *adapted*. How?

In sunlight, the pupils of my eyes were contracted to shut out some of the light-waves. Inside the theater the pupils began to dilate, thus letting the light-waves fall on the outer part of my retina, the region of the *rods*. In these rods is a substance called *rhodopsin* (rose-eye), or *visual violet*. It decomposes—"bleaches"—under light-waves as short as 320/1,000,000 of a millimeter in length. Light-waves are forms of energy. Pupil dilation exposed my rods to this energy. As a result, a photo-chemical change took place in the rhodopsin: my eyes were "adapted"; I could see.

The human eye is a complex mechanism of the general

nature of a photographic camera in which certain photo-sensitive chemicals are excited by varying amounts of light-wave energy. A chemical reaction takes place. The impulse of that reaction is carried by the optic nerve into the brain; if we are not color-blind we "see" red, yellow, blue, etc., according to the length of light-waves. But whatever we see, the fact is that we are of the nature of a mechanism which is activated by external stimuli. During the reaction, chemical changes take place under conditions which transfer energy. The changes made, the energy transferred, we are by that amount and to that extent changed. Each change is registered somewhere within us, and to that extent influences all subsequent reactions.

Those who lived through the Iroquois Theater fire cannot forget it. It is buried into their reaction-system and influences their behavior. During those few moments the dynamic nature of their reaction complex received impulses that changed the quality and quantity of its sensitivity. To thousands the name *Iroquois* is a cause of excitation, an energy-laden stimulus calling out avoiding reactions. The theater was renamed.

I am now in my seat in what was once the Iroquois Theater. I note the *exits* more attentively than usual, decide which is mine should "anything happen." That stimulus is so strong and memories so crowd my mind that I am hardly conscious of the preliminary music; it arouses no activity in the cortex of my brain. My revery ends when the music changes. My senses now become alert. I begin to focus my attention on the picture I am about to see, the picture that diverted me from my routine work and impelled me from the sunlit street into the darkened theater.

Meanwhile, certain cortical centers of my brain have become the dominant centers of activity. They are now consuming energy at a rapid rate; the arteries leading to the brain have expanded to supply the demand for more oxygen; muscles controlling the bellows which work my lungs have been stimulated to permit of the rapid elimination of the carbon dioxide of oxygen combustion and the rapid restoration of the supply of oxygen. Before the first scene is flashed on the screen, impulses of a hundred natures have been dispatched from brain centers and responses made throughout the entire bodily mechanism. And as scene after scene of "The Birth of a Nation" is unwound, new impulses are hurried along.

By the time the picture is finished, I have fled in terror; I have committed murder; I have fallen in love at least twice: all within two hours. No part of my body has been quiet, unaffected, unchanged. Few, if any, of my muscles but have joined in; few, if any, of my glands have lain dormant. Centers of activity have shifted—as one flees or fights, leads an army to victory or falls in defeat, or must remain in one's seat while lovely Mae Marsh is driven to her death by a madman.

The least active organ in my body was the digestive. Digestion is a complicated process requiring much energy; my energy was exhausted elsewhere—I had none to spare for alimentary canal. All I asked of it was sugar from the liver: sugar feeds the fires of hate and fear and love, and brainstorms.

In those brainstorms—and there are many in "The Birth of a Nation"—millions and millions of neurons listened in, gave decisions, issued orders; correlating, coördinating, adjusting the body, preparing it to fight, to murder, to mate. The body responded. Each bit of bodily machinery could respond because it was accustomed to respond to messages carried by the nerves of the body. The body grew up with the nerves. What the nerves know, the body knows: the nerves integrate the body and enable it to function as an individual.

And yet, with all the excitement and needs of blood to brain and to the fighting-fleeing mechanism, the long intestine kept its rhythm, the fine cilia lining air-pipes kept moving

414

like fields of grain, the glottis never forgot to execute its complicated movements, however hard I swallowed. Even my empty stomach kept its place: it did not growl or make hunger-contraction gestures.

It is the entire body that responds, the entire body that learns, the entire body that grows up. It was the entire body that recalled with bated breath the Iroquois fire, noted the exits, disregarded the music, and, spellbound, saw "The Birth of a Nation."

All living beings are excitable and must make adjustments; man most of all. Other animals come in contact with as many points of the outside world as man, but none can so vary its responses, because it has no such storehouse in which to store responses already made, nor so many words with which to answer back; none must respond to such diverse, complex, and rapidly changing situations.

On one side of me was a Negro; on the other, a Virginian; in front, a maid; behind, a youth. What was "The Birth of a Nation" to their minds' eyes?

CHAPTER VII

FROM THE STANDPOINT OF THE NEWER PSYCHOLOGY

1

ANY attempt to explain or to describe man by a set of rules or by a special formula, or as cast in a given mold, is predestined to failure. Man is a *something happening all the time*, a *going concern;* he makes his rules, revises his formulæ, and recasts his mold in the act of being and while going. It is in man's nature that he does not stay put.

Human behavior is individual behavior; it is the individual that grows up, that functions as a living being, that behaves as a more or less human being. Genetic history, visceral processes, and somatic behavior are only phases or aspects of the same behaving individual. To restrict our interest to any one of these phases is to let us into human morphology, human physiology, or human psychology, but not into the whole nature of man.

The blind men fussing around an elephant came to some interesting conclusions: the leg was like a tree, the tail like a rope, the trunk like a snake, the ear like a fan; but tree, rope, snake, and fan added up gave no real understanding of elephant. Nor does a lifetime spent in studying oxygen and hydrogen prepare us for understanding water; but a knowledge of water helps us understand living things, including vital processes in living beings and cultural traits in human behavior. In other words, psychology must take a very deep breath if it is to obtain a very broad view of human behavior. It must go to the bottom of life to discover how life behaves at the top.

And yet psychologists and sociologists continue to attempt to force human behavior into *specific* desires, wishes, traits, impulses, functions, instincts, what-nots, rather than study it in terms of specific protoplasms which have had a history and learned their lesson. It will be instructive to look at one of these attempts.

I select McDougall's list of "instinctive activities" not because it is the worst psychology, but because it is bad enough to illustrate what happens to a psychologist when he cuts himself loose from biology.

Instinctive behavior is blown-in-the-bottle behavior; and of that kind of predestined, foreordained behavior man has less than any other animal. Man's really distinguishing trait is his capacity for modifiable behavior. Without that capacity he is a moron ape, and not too clever at that; with it he is man, ruler of the earth, creator of human culture and so-called civilization.

Instinctive behavior is the crowning glory of bugs and insects; we cannot compete with them in that kind of behavior—just as we cannot compete with the earthworm's capacity to grow a new head to a tail and a new tail to a head when its body is cut in two. Ours is a *higher* nature.

Look at a silkworm. It emerges from the cocoon and lives a simple life of from ten to twenty days without a meal, but with a mate. The female deposits her 500 eggs in a single layer in a definite pattern, on a mulberry leaf or something just as good for her caterpillars to eat. *She has to do it, she cannot help herself.* Miss McCracken's experiments, reported by Herrick, show us why.

The silkworm has a brain and five pairs of ganglia or knots of neurons, one pair in the neck, four in the abdomen. Snip off her head: the headless body lives out its allotted days and does not seem to mind the operation. The headless body can also be induced to mate and lay the normal number of eggs in the normal way; but the headless body can not distinguish a mulberry leaf from blotting paper.

Cut the neck off also—the legs go with it: she cannot mate, but she can live; and if already mated, she can lay her eggs but not arrange them, because she has no legs; but her abdomen tries to arrange them by twisting around while the eggs are being laid. Cut the first, second, and third abdominal ganglia: she still lays her eggs.

Which means: the head is necessary for *choosing* a leaf and a mate; but not for living or for mating or for laying eggs. The brain sets off certain instinctive activities involving discrimination; but activities of the body segments, once initiated, carry on without the brain. Only when the last ganglion of the abdomen is cut is the egg-laying reflex abolished.

Instinctive activities, functioning on inherited reflex arcs of nervous structure: *predetermined* behavior, *instincts*. The moth must fly into the flame—its reflex in response to light impels it; it could keep away from the flame only with a surgical operation on its phototrophic mechanism.

Instinctive behavior is insect behavior at its highest; human behavior, modifiable behavior at its highest. Even birds have a picturesque repertoire of instinctive behavior, but the headless body of a bird does not live, let alone mate and lay eggs.

Now look at McDougall's list of our *instinctive activities*—with the "names of accompanying emotional qualities" in parenthesis:

Escape (fear); *combat* (anger); *repulsion* (disgust); *parental* (tender emotion); *appeal* (distress); *pairing* (lust); *curiosity* (curiosity); *submission* (feeling of subjection); *assertion* (elation); *social* (feeling of loneliness); *food-seeking* (appetite); *acquisition* (feeling of ownership); *construction* (feeling of creativeness); *laughter* (amusement).

There is a bird in Australia called the *Laughing jackass*. There is nothing in McDougall's list that that bird is not impelled to do at one time or another. But whether it is *social* because it feels lonely, *pairs* because it is lustful, *laughs* because it is amused, is *elated* when it asserts itself, or *appeals* because it feels distressed, I have no means of knowing.

Submission is not "instinctive" action in man, worm, or primordial protoplasm. Some of us know when we are licked and when it pays to throw up the sponge and cry *Kamarad*. And some unfortunates with defective glands, or whose "instinct" of assertion has early in life been kicked or beaten out of them, probably do have "feelings of subjection." Uriah Heep was so 'umble he cashed in on it for a while. But *submission* is no more instinctive in man than it is in wild cats.

Much is made of the "instinct to hoard, with its feeling of ownership, of possession." Some hang civilization on it. True, many are so in the habit of acquiring that hoarding seems as instinctive with them as it is with bees to hoard honey or with squirrels to hoard nuts. But acquisition of what? What is it that man *instinctively* hoards? Surely not capital; if so, it is a poor instinct these days. Only about four out of every hundred have hoarded enough to live on. The average Hindu has hoarded just one meal; that is all there is between him and starvation.

Pick up your toys!—how many times does every mother say that. The instinct of man- and monkey-child is the same: reach for it, taste it, smell it, thump it, throw it away. But try to take it away—or a bone from a dog! There is a *fighting* instinct. One of the curiosities of civilization is the things people fight for. Boys fight for marbles; no mother has to beg her son to hoard them. Born with an instinct for life, at six marbles have come to have life-giving value.

Construction? Destruction, rather. If we cannot eat it, we pull it to pieces. Sometimes this tendency to examine and destroy gets so overlaid with distorted habits as to result in sadism.

We are born with certain instinctive activities and emotional capacities; the so-called human instincts above cited inhere in living beings. What seem clear-cut instinctive actions are learned or *habit* reactions based or built on some innate emotional response or on attack and defense reactions as old as life itself. And any attempt to describe human behavior in terms of such instincts is to try to catch birds by salting their tails; worse, it is to fail to understand the fundamentals of animal evolution.

2

How does the baby know it is hungry? It does know: and if born of an undernourished mother, has been hungry for days and enters the world grub-struck.

We speak of drives, impulses, wishes, instincts, reflexes; but living beings must eat or they die. Hunger is back of life, the primordial drive in life. And if life waited for the doctors to decide whether *hunger* is physiology or psychology, life would starve to death.

The fact that an infant enters the world grub-struck may be the most momentous single factor in a lifetime of behavior. The way the appetite back of that hunger complex becomes conditioned may be the decisive factor in shaping that individual's career. Without hunger and its attendant appetite there could be no genetic, visceral, or somatic behavior. Even *psychics* are believed to be subject to hunger.

Hunger has led to crime, to suicide, and to cannibalism; and the fear of it, to war. It can make us feel faint, give us dull headaches and gnawing pangs—though we are not always certain whether the pangs gnaw in the head or in the stomach, or whether it is the mouth that feels hungry. But we can get so hungry that the sight of food makes us "sick," or "too dog tired" to eat. But why a fast can make one man cantankerous and fit another for a spiritual life is as yet a fair puzzler. What is certain is that if the way to a man's heart is through his stomach, the stomach is worth looking into.

It has been during the last fifteen years, and more learned of its nature than in 5,000 years' wondering about it. By cutting nerves, inserting balloons, and X-ray observations, Cannon cleared up much that was obscure. Carlson let in more light, chiefly by experimenting on a Czech who feeds himself through a tube in the wall of his abdomen because an accidental dose of strong caustic soda closed his esophagus years ago.

The *hunger mechanism* is in the muscular walls of the stomach. The stomach itself announces that it is *hungry* by violent rhythmical contractions lasting half a minute, alternating with mild normal or *tonus* rhythms of twenty seconds' duration. These alternating rhythms continue for from fifteen to twenty minutes. If this call for food is unanswered, the stomach gives up and remains quiet for from one to three hours. Then repeats the call.

That mechanism and an empty stomach come with every normal baby. With one big difference between baby and adult: the time between unanswered calls is not hours, but minutes. The adult has already built his body and can *live* on his fat; the baby has to build its body. Besides, the baby's skin area in proportion to body volume is larger than the adult's; it loses heat faster, hence needs more fuel for its furnace. And as soon as it becomes active, it is very active. No action without energy. If the infant has to keep yelling for every meal, still more food is required: even an infant's stomach cannot signal "more fuel" without burning up some that would be used otherwise for growth or exploration.

An adult's stomach signals *hunger* from four to six hours after a full meal; the baby's, within three hours—rarely more than three and a half or less than two and one-third hours. Thus nature answers a question often put to the doctor: when and how much? As much as its stomach will hold and as often as it cries for more. Colts, calves, and kittens grow up that way and seem to do well.

We *feel* hungry when, and in normal life only when, the empty stomach begins its hunger-contractions. The more violent these contractions, the hungrier we feel: it becomes "painful." Mild hunger is sensed less as pain and more as a general kinesthetic sensation.

We have no specialized receptors for the many sensations by which we are aware of our bodily states and emotions. But the entire body-within-the-skin is sensitive to pressure. Strong pressure anywhere on the body is felt within: hence *pressure receptors*, or muscle or kinesthetic sense. There is no special receptor for intestinal cramps, but we can feel them. There is no known receptor for hunger pains, but we never sense them as we do cramp pains in skeletal muscles. Colic pains in the intestine do not make us feel hungry.

The empty stomach contracts. Its contractions are stimuli. The reaction to such stimuli is completed with food. What happens in the meanwhile: what goes with hunger, what are the accessory phenomena? The animal gets more excited: beasts, babies, and men. Hungry protoplasm is more irritable than a just-fed man or baby: it can *think* of nothing else. Even the human cortex at such times has been known to get so crossed that only a divorce court could untangle the lines.

Also. The heartbeat rises from eight to even thirty per minute. Blood pressure rises. Salivary glands more active. All of which leads to *feelings*—emptiness, faintness, restlessness, drowsiness, headache, even nausea. It all depends on the individual: intensity of stomach contractions, condition of stomach's sensory nerves, especially the nervous organization or control.

Suppose the hungry baby is not fed, that the reaction begun with hunger-contraction stimulus is never completed? Death, of course. Meanwhile it lives off its own body, suffering much at first, then less and less. Carlson starved himself for five days. He lost eight pounds. The hunger contractions increased in intensity. The sensation of hunger was strong ten hours after his last meal and continued strong for three days. Food looked good throughout the five days, but on fourth and fifth days he could forget food. He felt some mental depression the last two days, also loss of physical strength. But never during the fast was his discomfort so great that it could be called pain or suffering, nor did it interfere with his work. Mental recovery from the fast came with the first meal; recovery from physical weakness, after the second day. He then felt as if he had had "a month's vacation in the mountains." He thinks an occasional fast for a healthy adult "may add to the joy of living and to the length of life."

In a Carnegie laboratory a man weighing 134 pounds began a *test* fast. With no food, but plenty of distilled water, he lost 28 pounds in a month. He lost some muscular strength, but gained in sharpness of senses and ability to learn new tricks.

The first three days of a fast are the hardest. Suffering thereafter is imaginary, due to fear or panic. "Voluntary starvation is in no sense a heroic act"; the "exalted" feelings, sights, and sounds reported by fasting ascetics are pure hallucination, thinks Carlson. Their brains are not more active, but less: they dream! Starvation changes the nature of the blood and the tissue of the brain. Hallucinations are children of the emotions rather than of the brain.

If the baby does not like its first meal, it will refuse it, as a chick does a bitter worm. Man is born with sucking reflex and hunger mechanism; his appetite begins to be conditioned with his first meal. We do not inherit a thirst for milk or beer, or a craving for pickles or alcohol.

All eat to live and some live to eat. We inherit a hunger complex; we acquire a complex appetite. Both hunger and appetite furnish their quota to prisons, but succeed fairly well in keeping out of the insane asylum. Hunger fills almshouses, appetite supplies hospitals. The complex appetite has become an important factor in human culture and has even "shaped the destinies" of some nations. For details, consult an historical index under "Nutmegs," "Spice Islands," "Opium Wars," etc.

3

He is a "born hog." *He* may deserve the epithet, but there are no *Suinæ* in man's ancestors. Human hogs are made, not born. Greed is not part of our inheritance, nor to the stuff we are made of has it biologic value.

Food has biologic value. We are born with a hunger complex and of parents who know by our behavior when that complex begins to act. Their reaction brings us in contact with food. That contact—physical and chemical—releases the sucking reflex, which continues until the stomach signals "Stop." The hunger complex satisfied, *we* are not hungry. The hunger mechanism retires and the infant can give its mind to other matters. Or, as we say, we can now get down to business!

That "business" may be "big," but it ends with, Where shall we eat? Later, What shall we eat? These questions are big business to millions of people—among the important "problems of life."

How are they solved? In relation to the hunger complex and the body's requirements? Or in reference to a complex appetite which ranges from soup to nuts and includes corned beef and cabbage on Monday, fish on Friday, brown bread and beans on Saturday, and a gorge on Sundays, holidays, weddings, and wakes?

The hunger complex is a biologic necessity and begins with a mechanism of special receptors in mouth and nose by which we distinguish noxious physical and chemical stimuli. We may turn up our nose at many things, but certain things make us hold our nose. The bacteria of decay are enormously important in the nitrogen cycle, but we prefer our ammonia in smelling-salts. Nor is it without biological significance that our taster for bitter is thousands of times more acute than for sweet.

We get "hungry for" this or that. What is back of that particular hunger? What is it that makes our mouth water? The newborn has never tasted food, good or bad: how does it know that it tastes good or bad. It must learn. It does learn; by the same process that life itself learns—by trying. Before many months the infant has tried out everything it can get its hands on. Its limit is the vigilance of parents and reachable environment. Whether maternal love is an *instinct* or not may be left to the doctors to decide, but there is no escaping the biological fact that prolonged infancy is possible only with parental oversight.

We had the benefit of mother's taster. When the pie was no good she gave it to the tramp. The mother tries it out— whether it be the four-handed mother in the forest or the two-handed mother of men. Trial and error carries the infant far; and he may prefer the blacking on father's boots to the blacking mother uses on the stove. But the food the child memorizes is the food mother makes. If the first meal tasted and smelled good, and if the pleasure of a full stomach followed the pangs of a gnawing stomach, the infant has learned a lesson.

Repeat eight times a day for months; and three times a day for years. "Like mother used to make" is good psychology because it is sound biology.

The first meal was the answer to the hunger complex. The

"set" of that meal was the conditioning factor in the next one: did it "taste like more"? If it did, the foundation was laid for an appetite for that kind of food. By and by the child is weaned: other appetites are built in by the same tastes-like-more process.

So we come to like this and that, and this and that kind of cooking, surroundings, etc. But back of appetite is always an experienced or learned process: did it look, smell, and taste good, and did it "set" well. If so, we like it; we eat it with a relish, the memories of it make our mouth water; in front of it, these memories are real stimuli to the nerves of our mouth and nose. They are keyed up to such stimuli.

We may not be hungry, yet the mere sight of caviare may touch our appetite off. The urge is not for food, it is an appetite for caviare. This appetite differs from hunger. It also has a different quality from most other pleasant sensations. As Carlson says: "the fragrance of the rose in the garden may be as pleasing as the fragrance of the roast in the kitchen, but the desire to smell the rose cannot be compared with the urge to eat the roast."

The appetite complex begins with *memories*. What is it that remembers? Cortex, yes; but the *feeling* is in the throat and mouth and nose, combined into a kinesthetic sensation in that particular region. The increased salivation and the heightened tonicity of the nerves of taste, odor, and of pressure, help to make the appetite complex.

On a hot day we may sigh for a drink of water "from the old spring," but when we have a *taste* for any particular water it is for something in the water: pure water has no taste, nor odor. Beer has both; an appetite for beer is appetite for beer. One may desire beer without being thirsty; or fudge without being hungry.

Sitting down at the table does not shut down hunger contractions; eating does. With our first mouthful, gastric juice begins to be secreted—the contractions stop. But we must be eating *food*: chewing a stick, even of tobacco, does not start

426

gastric juice any more than the sight or smell of food does. Chewing meat is good to stop a stomach gnawing. A pie or a pudding or a fruit is even better: that is why they end the meal.

We all eat our "peck of dirt." How about *dirt-eaters?* There are, especially children with abnormal appetites for clay, chalk, lead pencil, etc. Children experiment; if no harm comes and they like the taste, they keep it up. Same way with pickles, mustard, pepper, gum, licorice, tobacco. Whether an appetite is "depraved" or merely abnormal depends largely on taste, and taste depends on habit, custom, social usage. Caterpillars, snakes, dogs, overripe cheese, sharks' fins, "gamy" game, snails, frogs, toads, lizards, monkeys, grasshoppers, grubs, dogfish, brains, tripe, birds' nests, devilfish, blood: all favorite dishes—somewhere, some time. Each man to his own. Tastes are not to be disputed, nor appetites questioned.

Man must eat: it is his nature. When, where, what, depend on his nurture. Hunger is the best sauce. And the best hunger-producer is chopping wood. After that come all other forms of physical work. The body we inherit was built up by work, its functioning apparatus is arranged for work. When we do not work our body must make other arrangements. Civilization furnishes these in the form of "Institutions." They are a credit to civilization. We shall require more, for we are only at the beginning of "Progress."

4

There comes a day when the gates to the elephant house are shut—*must;* as Mr. Freud would say, he has a *libido* complex. It is also called the sex urge. The elephant is dangerous. The urge is so strong that bananas and peanuts do not inhibit it. Sometimes nothing can: he gets so mad he must be shot.

There comes a time when the farmer misses the sow's face at the trough. If he knows the livestock of his neighbors, he knows where to find her. It may be miles away and many fences in between. She will be there.

Laboratory tests have been made to determine the danger a hungry animal will face to get food. One easily measured is the crossing of an electrically stimulated plate: it must accept the shock to get at the food. No shock short of electrocution will stop the food-hungry rat. It will face the same charge for a mate.

Biologically, rape and the theft of a loaf of bread are natural behavior; celibacy and asceticism are crimes against nature.

The biologic function of sex is reproduction. In all species with sexual reproduction, the sex impulse is and must inherently be as strong as the impulse to live. The mechanism for reproduction is enormously varied, but not more so than other mechanisms useful for food and oxygen metabolism, for capturing food, for defense from enemies. The mating cycle also varies with different species, as does the period of infancy, the relationship between parents and offspring, and the methods of courtship.

In short, each species has its own *reproduction complex*. So far as the species is concerned, the individual male or female which does not play his or her part in this complex contributes nothing biologically useful to the species and might as well never have been born.

Sterility in vertebrates is not more unknown than other congenital variations which distinguish defective individuals from the normal run. In states of nature it is to be presumed that all normal individuals play their part in the reproduction complex. Why this is so is no more, no less, explicable than why a food complex impels animals to seek and ingest food.

The drive for food is backed by a sensori-motor mechanism which functions until food is secured and ingested. Food itself in the alimentary canal is stimulus or drive for further actions and reactions. But the initial drive was hunger: it was a potent impulse to reactions, thereby bringing about adjustment.

The drive for a mate, likewise, is backed by a sensori-motor mechanism which functions until the mate is secured and the sexual act completed. Subsequent changes are themselves the stimuli which impel to nest-building and other activities which will be useful for the life of the progeny.

Biologically, the chief distinction between the food-hunger and the sex-hunger impulses is that they function in different rhythms. These vary in different species, even in the same order of vertebrates. But in general the food rhythm is fairly continuous from day to day throughout life; the sex rhythm is confined to certain fairly definite years of the individual life cycle, and within these years to fairly definite seasons or periods.

A hardly less important biologic distinction between the food-impulse and the mate-impulse is that in one case the adjusting reaction is primarily individual action; in the other, two individuals of opposite sex participate—and only if they agree to such participation. Herein is an element of huge import in setting patterns of behavior, even in modifying structure.

Species vary greatly in these two respects. In some, secondary sexual differences are slight; in others, marked and highly characteristic—as in most species of birds, many species of vertebrates, and the anthropoid apes. Patterns of behavior vary, from extraordinarily complex courtship processes in some birds to next to no courtship in many vertebrates. But whether the courtship be simple or complex, short or prolonged, there must be the biologic equivalent of courtship in all species with sexual reproduction.

There are three biologically significant facts:

(1) The mate-impulse is driven by an unconscious mechanism and not by any "desire of offspring." Whole species of animals mate and never survive the mere depositing of the eggs. The primary impulse is not eggs, nests, or cradles:

it is for a mate. As in food; animals do not seek food for "processes of metabolism," they seek and ingest food because impelled by food-hunger. That hunger satisfied, the alimentary canal will do the rest and furnish the voiding stimuli. So with the mate-impulse. It knows nothing of cubs, squabs, or children. The drive is for the mate.

(2) The mere fact that this or that species reproduces through the mechanism of sex means that the two sexes must be different and must be responsive one to the other. In other words, in sexual reproduction there must be two types of bodily structure, two modes of behavior. Five tomcats in a row on a fence: the appearance of a tabby may be quite as great a stimulus for action as a dog or a rat.

(3) Sterile individuals among vertebrates are abnormal; sexually mature but unmated individuals are deficient either in inherent mate-hunger or mate-attractiveness; neither group has biologic value. The food-hunger impulse must be strong enough or the individual dies; the mate-hunger must be strong enough or the species dies. The species only lives through its individuals. The individual mate-hunger must lead to action or there is no adjustment.

In human organization sex plays its part as a determiner of certain characteristic forms of behavior. But normal inherent modes of sex behavior, no less than other inherent modes of response for adjustment useful for the species, are subject to learning: the whole sex-complex becomes conditioned. Individual sex behavior is only to be understood in the light of individual inheritance of mate-hunger mechanism and the learned modes of response for adjusting the impulse of that mechanism.

There are always: the individual; the situation. Both are complex in human society because the individual is capable of such varied responses and because society assumes the right to condition the responses. In every phase of bisexual behavior, certain unvarying biologic factors and special varying social factors combined make up the definition of the situation. But back of the sex-complex is a fact-complex which must not be mislaid:

(1) In bisexual reproduction the function of the male element is to release and set moving the energy stored in the ovum. It is the single ovum that is fertilized: thousands of male cells compete among themselves for the honor. The female is the older and more important of the two sexes.

(2) The ovum fertilized, the male is free: to roam or to die; reproduction thereafter being dependent upon the continued existence of the female until the ovum is incubated. This process requires 280 days of a woman's time. The mother is always present at delivery.

(3) After delivery, the woman also is free: to roam or to die. The offspring need never know father: many do not; nor mother: some do not. The offspring wants food. If the hand that feeds it is a black mammy's and the food is from a bottle and all agreeable, the offspring will learn to love the black mammy and the glass bottle: and, like the lamb, will follow her to school or any other place the bottle goes.

Of course, children "love" their parents; and will honor and obey them if "honor" and "obey" are conditioned into their response repertoire. The "instinct" is not confined to man. Life itself must eat, and learns to love the hand that feeds it.

Parents "wake up" to the realization that their children do not "love them any more." Exercising their "rights" as parents, they "demand" love, and call their children "unnatural" if they do not respond. A normal child learns to love anything or anybody associated with its love experience. The child does not love its parents because they are parents, but because they are lovable.

5

When a woman says: "I hate that man!" what does she hate him with? Does *hate* spring from rage impulse which drives us to anger when restrained, or is it the opposite, the *detumescence* of love? Suppose she says: "I hate lavender" —women do say such things. I heard one say: "I hate Paris." Most women "love" Paris, some "simply adore" it.

I love corned beef and cabbage. Sight or odor of corned beef and cabbage makes my mouth water. My mouth waters only when I am stimulated by something within my food-hunger repertoire. My mouth-water mechanism is made up of glands, muscles, nerves. An adequate stimulus sets it off. Call that activity *tumescence* (swelling). And note that I may leave the restaurant with a full stomach, and yet the odor of broiled mushrooms as I pass out the door sets my mouth watering again.

I sit down and order broiled mushrooms. The first one I spear has a hair on it. I try again: and encounter a dead fly. These are not pleasant things, but such make or break appetites. I have lost mine for broiled mushrooms, possibly forever. The very thought of mushrooms makes me sick: no mouth-water, no "good feeling" in the food-appetite mechanism. Call that *detumescence*.

The sex-appetite mechanism is much more complicated; has more parts, more nerves, is capable of more devastating sensations. Call it the *erogenous* (love-producing) *zone*. This zone is all in order at birth. By conditioning processes it learns to respond to widely differing stimuli by the time the mature puberty glands begin to send their impulses to satisfy what by now is a definite and specific mate-hunger.

Which means that by the time we reach the marrying age the mate we choose, if any, will be more or less already picked out for us. Romeo-and-Juliet is sound psychology and natural behavior. "That is the man I want." "I couldn't possibly love that woman." We are so certain we call it *instinct;* and say that "marriages are made in heaven."

Maybe. But it is on earth we wake up to discover that we have married a dimple, a Cupid's bow, a broad chest, a mustache, purple socks, a Roman nose, a blue dress, a trim ankle, or a head of hair. That, in short, we have married certain trimmings and accessories. And we go on through life buying magazines by their covers, cars by their colors, and coats by their buttons.

"Things and places," says Watson, "tend to become associated with organic responses, specifically those with love." Every object, by virtue of the original bent of the individual, or through conditioned reflex or habit, calls out overt or delayed response in the motor mechanism; also, "a definite and complex group of reflex activity in the erogenous zone."

Excitation in this zone arouses two fundamental kinds of impulses:

(1) Tumescence: rhythmical contraction of certain muscular tissue and increased secretions. "If functioning alone, the impulse will lead to positive seeking movements and ultimately to the unfolding of the instinctive reproductive mechanism."

(2) Detumescence: inhibition, and relaxation of other muscular tissue and inhibition of secretions. "These impulses at the motor center, if not inhibited, would release avoidance movements."

Here, then, is the sex-appetite mechanism which early in life begins to sort the little world about into loved ones and those it does not care for. Through the mechanism of habit and conditioned reflex functions, objects which at first had no emotional value "come later to arouse faintly or overtly one or other of the two impulses"—tumescence or detumescence.

To the objection that this view over-emphasizes the instinctive factor of love, Watson points out that the love and do-not-love factors are at the bottom of home, general, social, and vocational life. We work long hours to improve our position to make more money to carry on home life on a broader scale. "The activities centered about loved ones from infancy to old age are easily the most important factors in life. No wonder that our acts are connected with and evalued by the connections lying below our language level."

Here again, as always, we come back to that as yet unsolved

problem of two faces: the significance and extent of individual inheritance; the degree to which this individual inheritance can be conditioned. Do our original tendencies make us, or our parents and our teachers and our environment? Or, put the question this way, Where does nature leave off and nurture begin? Nature never leaves off—we may be certain of that. Nurture begins at once—there is no doubt about that. But, as Watson says, as long as we keep up our sentimental drivel about children instead of looking at childhood as a problem, the problem of individual bents and capacities will remain as chaotic as it is now.

As it is now, we are all tied up with sticky sentimentality about Alma Maters and hurrahing without stopping to inquire if it is worth hurrahing about. We have a huge youth-cult; enormous and costly equipment to train boys and girls in the way they want or are fitted to go? No; "in the way they *ought* to go!" As one calls the roll of the men who have rendered useful social service, one is impressed by the notion that most of them succeeded not because, but in spite, of their "training." It almost seems as if the best equipment with which to start life is a widowed mother who turns one adrift at eight.

Born with an elaborate mechanism for adjustment, we face three doctors, two nurses, several servants, father, mother, aunts, uncles, etc., all on their toes to adjust for us. Nature never gets a chance. Nurture cries when we do not smile back. To make us smile, they tickle us under the chin and trot us on their knees and bribe us with candy and ribbons and gewgaws.

And so our food-appetites, sex-appetites, fears, and rages slop over into endless things that are not to be eaten or loved, nor to be run from or killed. Indigestion—or adiposity; celibacy—or promiscuity; afraid of shadows, facts, and death; and war on our neighbors instead of against poverty, squalor, and ignorance.

Love and such move the world, move it in many ways because instinctive responses can be and must be conditioned. The conditioned response is our only mechanism for learning to behave like human beings. Love is a driving force of great dynamic power. But such grist as it does grind!

6

The newborn is a loaded stimulus for parents and community. The nature of the load it brings will vary with the sex of the child. The girl may be as welcome as the boy. But the fact of *girl* or of *boy* colors the environment for the developing child.

Suppose there are twins, a boy and a girl. Each may seem to face the same situation day after day. But, as society is constituted, each faces a different situation. The sister makes certain appeals because she is a female; the boy, because he is a male. Certain modes of behavior are expected because "You are a *boy*"; quite different responses are expected because "You are a *girl*." As a consequence, before they have a verbalized behavior they have acquired the manual and emotional habits expected of boys and girls. The girl has no inherent impulse to play dolls and mud pies, or to wear curls, ribbons, dresses, shoes, necklaces, earrings; nor has the boy for drums and other noise-making machinery, or for short hair and pants.

The girl is molded to make "womanly" responses; the boy, to behave like a "little man." Boys are conditioned to face one world; girls, to face another. The two sexes do not see alike because their eyes have not learned to look at the same things alike; for each sex, the glasses have a different color, focus, and range.

Men do not "understand women." How can they? But the reason is not because women's nature is fundamentally different from men's; rather that ten or twenty or fifty years of having to live "like a woman" go into her make-up.

Freedom of movement is soon limited for girls. Some

learn to skip the rope and play jackstones only under parental frowns. And as for climbing trees, playing marbles, going off swimming, "Who ever heard of such a thing!"

Shades of limited freedom for girls depend on families, communities, rank, class, etc. But in the background is always a general limit in movement, emotions, and language, beyond which the girl is not supposed to go. "Proper spheres," "womanly ways," "unmaidenly manners," etc.

The boy of six has a much wider field of exploration than his sister, especially if sister is "handy about the house." By ten, his freedom is greater yet. He can stamp around and shout and whistle and scrap and "talk back" in ways denied to his sister.

Because they must learn "nice ways," girls have less opportunity to learn certain specific motor habits and in general less occasion to develop their skeletal muscles. She cannot throw a ball when she is fourteen: she did not begin to throw stones at the age of three. Rules of habit formation and limits of dexterity are not inherent in each sex. How many boys of twenty could run a hundred yards in ten seconds flat if they had worn dresses and such accessories all their life?

If it is "unwomanly" for girls to throw stones and run races, it will be "unnatural" for them later to be expected to compete with men on equal terms.

A boy brought up on "Don't be a sissy" will have a behavior different from that of a sister for whom being a sissy is normal behavior.

Men and women are emotionally different; by training. Tears, pouts, whims, tantrums, grow up bisexually. A boy of ten comes into the house crying; he has been worsted in a fight. His sister enters crying: worsted in an argument. Each meets with a different situation in each parent. The girl's questions on current events generally call out special responses from parents: "Little girls are not supposed to know about business," or, "What possible interest can you have in politics?" etc.

436

Men, to "understand" women, must be brought up as women: play dolls, wear dresses, be coddled, petted, protected, favored, shielded, guarded, restricted, chucked under the chin, kissed. And thereby driven to such outlets as are open to women and have no more "expected" of them than men expect of women.

"Shades of the prison-house begin to close upon the growing child," as Wordsworth saw it. There are two: one for each sex. With different opportunities, their impulses will be conditioned along different lines. Given different tools, their pursuits will be different.

About sixteen years are required to train girls to certain "womanly" needs and desires. Thereafter it requires some one man's lifetime to satisfy these desires. If women degenerate or go in for luxury, they are only following their bent; their training "fitted" them for such paths.

Many men think such paths *natural* to women, and find themselves "adjusted" when they hang a diamond dog-collar about the neck of a woman who finds her life adjustments in luxuries from another's hands. She has given all she has for all she wants. That is adjustment. Life learns such behavior as readily as other forms.

The two sexes may "grow up together," but they travel divergent roads. By the time they mate they are likely to find themselves far apart. Even words have different values; they may not understand each other's language. But if their habits have not been abnormal, and if they retain the capacity to learn and the inherent love for knowing, a whole new world confronts them. They can begin all over again, and, as children, explore together to the ends of their days.

After all, there can be nothing in a man's world more interesting than a woman. That man is "by nature" polygamous and woman monogamous is biologic rot and has no more sanction than the Divine right of kings—and will eventually go into the same discard.

Are women as efficient as men? Efficient for what? And

if not, why not? Why am I not as efficient as Charlie Chaplin, or Arthur Somers Roche, or Jane Addams?

All normal newborns are *efficient*. After a few years, little sister can never become as efficient as little brother in many things. A woman requires a stout heart to dare to compete with a man. Her own sex says, "You should not"; the other sex says, "You cannot." If women follow the "easy" path, it is because that is the only path in which they have been trained to show efficiency.

If your water pipe bursts you do not need "efficiency": you want a competent plumber. Same way in seeking a mate. If good ones are scarce, it must be for lack of early training which fits for mateship.

Biologically, man must mate. Why men marry is a matter of individual behavior. If marriage is a "failure," as we are often assured, it must be for the same reason that any other social institution "fails." Man learns new ways to adjust to living impulses.

7

It is biologically important that the sex-complex leave nothing to chance. It must function, as must the food-complex, without having to stop to learn or acquire habits. This implies a sensori-motor mechanism with preformed reflex arcs ready to respond to adequate stimuli. The original impulse for adjustment is within the individual organism. The kind of food the organism ingests to complete the hunger reaction will be conditioned by circumstances; as will the mate by which the individual makes adjustment to the mate-hunger impulse. In either case the impulse drives the individual. There may be neither food nor mate within reach of eye, ear, or nose: the animal fares forth. The stimulus is an inherent biologic hunger of the body.

The difference between an eighteen-year-old buying flowers and a twenty-eight-year-old buying flour is ten years; both are normal situations.

It is psychologically significant that children of both sexes are born with erogenous zones which from the beginning may be excited by tactile stimuli originating outside the body. This is in keeping with the biologically important fact that the sex-mechanism is inherently perfect at birth. The *impulse* for a mate appears later: at puberty. Meanwhile the secondary sexual characters make their appearance. But the mechanism itself is so built into our structure that inaction is biologically abnormal. Yet we speak of "control"; and dose youth with endless formulæ.

One, I shall not soon forget. In a class in *Christian Ethics,* we were being lectured on the "iniquity" of certain performances. "But," protested one bold student. He got no further. The president's face flushed red, and, shaking his finger at the boy, he bellowed: "Young man, such ideas will lead you down to hell!" Perhaps. But it is yet to be demonstrated that the data of biology or the physiology of the reproduction-complex ever led anybody astray, much less "down-to-hell."

Nature is not to be swept aside by bellowings or by any "down-to-hells." If nature listened to argument and heeded threats and could be scared out of her boots by every man who claims to speak for Providence, she could shut up shop and go out of life.

Man is a marrying animal. He gets married because he is born that way. Nature spent millions of years perfecting the marriage mechanism so that it could function on its own reflex arcs and give man time to use his head to invent cattle and corn so that he could have time to educate his children. Man comes along and invents prostitution, celibacy, and other sex-psychoses, and turns his children over to celibates to be educated.

What happens to the sex-response mechanism between birth and marriageable age? Biologically, nothing: nothing is expected of it. Usually nothing does happen to it to make or mar later normal behavior. Man is born so sane that only extreme conditions, sudden changes, or habits so distorted as to make normal behavior impossible drive him insane.

The baby is rocked, petted, bathed, trotted on the knee. The erogenous zones are stimulated. "Nursing and fondling are not without sex stimulating effect," says Watson. The child loves to be rocked and trotted. It forms attachments, conditioned reflexes. The baby requires 150 days to find its feet and toes. Another 150 days to discover its own organs. This is a real discovery, but the child shows no instinctive tendency to touch. But after these zones have learned the nature of stimuli and the child has discovered them, distorted habits may be formed. Their own developing bodies may become objects of undue attention leading them into emotional attitudes. Habits and attitudes take many forms. They may become so fixed and so perverse that the child will have no adequate mode of adjustment response to normal sex stimuli later.

Sometimes normal physical development proceeds apace with weird theories of the functions of sex, driving in harmful attachments. The emotional wave which accompanies development, having no normal outlet, may be sublimated into art or any other emotional occupation; or it may be perverted and become a psychosis. Normal behavior in marriage is never experienced during some lives. No woman *naturally* hates men; nor is it in man's normal repertoire of response to hate women.

While the original impetus comes from within, the adolescent child finds itself in a world of sex stimuli. To the growing boy all girls are girls: objects of special interest. Naturally, not all make the same appeal. But throughout life we continue to react and keep eternally reacting to the fact that there are two sexes.

There are many ways of being abnormal, but no man or woman can be entirely normal for whom the bisexual world is without stimulus to normal reactions. Celibates, prudes, puritans, and old-maids-by-choice, have habits of inhibition or of restraint beyond the limits set by Nature.

A bad habit is broken when replaced by a useful one. Childhood and youth are habit-forming periods. Childish habits stay with us or are replaced by others; but an old habit is not easily shaken off. As James said of Rip Van Winkle, who excused himself for every fresh dereliction by saying, "I won't count it this time": "Well, he may not count it and a kind Heaven may not count it, but it is being counted none the less. Nothing we ever do is, in strict scientific literalness, wiped out."

It is natural for the boy to pattern his reactions toward his mother after his father, for the girl to "prefer" her father. These innocent tendencies may be *shamed* into permanent attachments, making it difficult for the boy or girl later to make perfect substitutions.

It is a boy or a girl that is born and grows up, not a food-complex or a sex-complex or a motor-mechanism for playing the piano or hurdle-racing. The boy or girl grows up all together: parts develop or rust with use or disuse. Fingers may learn to pick pockets as readily as pick berries. There are many ways by which the sex-complex may take on habits of no social value to the possessor and of no value to society. These habits are not broken by "Don'ts" or bars. They are backed by a high-strung mechanism wound up for preserving the race. When this mechanism does not function one way, it finds another. Nature backs it; training prepares the channel into which it will direct its energy.

8

There are many histories of marriage. Westermark's, in three large volumes, is a mere sketch and was out of date the day it was printed. New marriage customs have been invented.

Marriage does not stand still. It grows—backward, forward, up and down. There are as many forms of marriage behavior as there are married couples. Possibly more: some dissolve and remarry. Marriage laws vary from state to state, nation to nation, age to age. Can marriage behavior be generalized or reduced to law?

There is no biologic excuse outside structural deficiency for unmated adult human beings. Many human societies respect that law. Other communities flaunt it, disregard puberty, indefinitely postpone mating or mate casually, and make the best of children as they do of other accidents.

In other words, we get little light on human marriage behavior from the Mind of the ameba or the Social Instincts of the anthropoid apes. Human marriage behavior is as distinctly and peculiarly human as is a sewing machine or the "Wedding March" of Lohengrin. The mate instinct must be there: is there. If we are born whole, we have it: the capacity to seek a mate, the impulse to find one if it takes us overseas.

Why, then, a world of sexually unadjusted: unmarrieds, divorcés, oft-marrieds, courtesans, prostitutes, homosexuals, asexuals, dog-lovers, snake-charmers, cadets, loveless marriages, childless marriages? Endless kinds.

Two general observations: (1) Europe's population has doubled in the last hundred years despite the enormous losses from wars, disease, infantile mortality, and drains overseas. The mate-hunger is not impotent. (2) We hear only of the sexually-unadjusted. There are millions of happily mated couples in America who find no fault with nature's marriage laws or those recorded in codes.

Now for the other side: the behavior of the mate-impulse. It leads many to marry. The marriage fails: drunkenness, cruelty, infidelity, desertion, etc. The courts recognize many grounds. Why does one man become a drunkard, another beat his wife? Marriage itself is no more responsible for such misfits than is business for arson or banking for defalcation. The man who beats his wife probably beat

442

his sister or his mother. The man who drinks because or in spite of his wife would turn to drink under any other situation to which he could not adjust himself.

A larger mismated group is based on the polygamous habits of one or the other, generally the man. In sowing wild oats he scattered the energy with which he was endowed to secure a mate; and acquired the polygamous habit. After marriage he may acquire the monogamous habit; he may not—his emotional nature will not so easily find sufficient outlet in one woman. He also learned another habit: that he could get what he wanted only if he translated his wish into action. That lesson has great value, but is of no use in marriage unless he wants to be faithful to one woman. To make that want effective he has to break himself of an emotionally-reinforced habit.

The other side of that picture is the woman whose early mate-hunger was put on ice by a prudish mother. If she is brought up on kisses and kisses all her girl friends every time she sees them, she wastes a lot of emotion of biologic value. She overflows with sentimentality and has no love left for anybody. Or she grows up a "pure and innocent girl." She has no adequate response in a situation where a mate is wanted. Sheer ignorant "innocence" is no match in a situation where the man knows too much. Neither sentimentality nor ice is fit response for the facts and emotions of sex.

Between the age of fifteen and twenty-five are ten long years. During these years the mate-hunger impulse cannot be put to sleep, as one does a child; or locked in a closet, as one does—but should not—a naughty child. It is inevitable that huge amounts of energy be diverted. But where? What is to be its outlet?

"Raise the standard of men's morality!" But not by talk. Work will do it. Many a boy is so hard at work he has no further energy left. His sex-impulse is expended in life-impulse activities. Girls begin to find outlets for their energy in action, in sports and games, and in the broader affairs of life interests. All-night dances can dissipate a lot of energy for both sexes.

The boy or girl who for ten years chases pleasure as the main business of life may be "pure," but neither will be likely to acquire any socially useful habits during that time. Both men and women can become such habitual flirts that they are abnormal; they are sexual perverts.

The normal sex-complex can be broken in many ways: disappointment in love, no response on the part of the mate, etc. The sex-complex thus becomes conditioned to abnormal methods of response: tendency to avoid or be disgusted under conditions which are neither "disgusting" nor to be avoided; prudishness; sloppy sentimentality; morbid interest in the externals or accessories of sex conduct.

The sex-complex thus comes to mean for one individual one thing; for another, quite something else. It comes to be as varied as behavior itself. What it is at any one time depends on the lessons it has learned: its experience, its habits. No man or woman enters into marriage with a sex-complex slate on which something has not been written. Until recently, it was likely to be too little on the part of the woman, an ignorance so ingrained that learning was painful; too much on the part of the man, more than he could rub off.

Foundations of habits (which means *character*) are laid in homes. Nine-tenths of the girls that enter juvenile courts leave bad homes. As Thomas puts it, many a girl cannot be said to fall, because she has never risen. She is not immoral, but a-moral. The mate-hunger is turned into love for adventure, clothes, theater, attention, distinction, freedom. And some discover that the only means they have to realize these acquired appetites is their sex. They use it as they would a coin to buy advantage and pleasure. Thomas cites

Dumas as saying that girls in Paris lost their virginity as they lost their milk teeth: they could give no plausible account of the loss.

Or they marry with that same coin or buy *entrée* to the stage or a trip to Paris. Having chosen the easier road, they soon become habituated to it. Until recently, women had almost no incentive or opportunity to attempt achievement in male fields. Why should she when for every woman there was a purchaser; for some, many bidders.

Until recently, it was a woman-made world we lived in. The mere male had to go outside that world to work off his surplus energy. The wife-mother was the center of the home and it was to her interest to make it a real center. It became a hive of industry and a swarm of children. Whatever glorified it magnified her importance. Within, she was supreme. In this woman-made world men passed half their lives; the other half was spent in bringing home the bacon.

Women generally married for love, as they do now if their mate-hunger is unimpaired and they are free to marry the "man of their choice." There were three categories of women: married, old maids, and "fallen." Thousands of American communities had no "fallen" and next to no old maids.

Now women have their "rights." In obtaining "rights" she abdicated a throne: she no longer rules by divine right. The children that "bless the home" are turned over to the nurse while mother presides at bridge, over Conventions for the Proper Care of Children, over Committees to Cleanse the Slums. Result: males no longer naïvely accept matrimony or implicitly trust their wives; females turn to matrimony if they have nowhere else to turn.

All this, of course, makes for "progress." But in our social progress we have acquired special schools where boys may learn to be pimps and girls to be prostitutes, and slums which in squalor, vermin, filth, and disease, and in the number of their dope-fiends, pickpockets, paupers, degenerates, hags, and harlots, are quite as "advanced" as those of Paris or London. It is no longer necessary to go abroad to see "life"; Babylon has moved to Main Street.

Social conditions are changing, but the average American girl still approaches her majority fitted for no economically independent career. Brought up as a social parasite, it is her belief and the all-around understanding that *marriage* is her career. For that no special preparation is deemed necessary. She is a girl: what more can one ask? Few men ask more. Some do not get a whole woman. More rarely does the woman get a whole man. But sauce for the goose is not sauce for the gander in these days of holeproof socks, built-in beds, meals out, and no babies allowed; the gander may feel that as meal ticket he is entitled to a different brand of sauce.

To say that the mate-hunger is greater in one sex than in the other is nonsense. It takes different forms in the two sexes because of training and the situation. Nor are men less fond of children than are women. Having wider interests, they are bored sooner. In the divorce court the man fights as hard as the woman for the children. If there is any radical difference in sex-morality or marriage behavior—or any other kind of behavior—in the two sexes, the cause will be found in the way the two sexes become trained and organized for life and in the demands society makes on them; not in their inherent impulses.

Mamie, don't be a tomboy!

Many a mother these days nearly "dies of shame" when Mamie bobs her hair and marches off in the garb of a Girl Scout. "Girls didn't do such outlandish things in my day!" They did not. We have to learn anew what our stone-ax ancestors knew: girls can be as "outlandish" as boys! The girls themselves are just beginning to discover it. Marriage behavior is in for further conditioning. The sex-complex may become simple again.

446

A psychosis is a morbid mental state. We all have our little psychoses. That so few have big psychoses, that so few asylums are required to house the mentally unbalanced, is a tribute to our sound inheritance and our capacity to preserve our balance in increasingly complex situations and an environment which changes faster than man can change his mind.

My chief psychosis is, let us say, a morbid love for dogs. I "shudder with horror" at the sight of a dog-fight. I loathe the dog-pound and am the deadly enemy of the dog-catcher. I defy the muzzle law—openly when I dare. I endow hospitals for unadjusted dogs and cemeteries for dead ones. In short, I am "crazy" about dogs. But as I am not a menace to society, I am tolerated, even encouraged by "sympathizers."

My own darling Fido dies. Now I am crazy. I buy a satin-lined silver coffin with gold handles. I have a ceremony. Rites at the grave. Flowers. Et cetera. I spend dry-eyed stony-stared hours at the grave. I refuse to go home. I refuse to eat. My friends remonstrate: I heed them not. It rains: I pay no attention. Nothing from the outside world moves me. I am mad as a March hare. Ambulance. Psychopathic ward. What "possessed" me? The church calls it "devil" or The Devil. Freud calls it "Unconscious."

There are as many kinds and degrees of psychoses as there are of indigestion. There are few perennially sound minds in perennially sound bodies; few of us that are not off our balance or off our feed now and then. Sometimes it is serious. When we are off our balance, society suffers; when we are off our feed, we suffer. Society expects us to behave. And properly locks us up when our behavior is dangerous. But if we die of indigestion, society is not interested.

There are those who cry when they hear a dog howling, smile when it wags its tail: the wail or gurgle of an infant means nothing to them. Some children are thrown into paroxysms of fear by a dog or a fur coat. Some cower from lightning, and when the thunder roars overhead shut themselves up in a closet. I dodge an imaginary pump-handle as I go by a certain spot. Few women would touch a snake for "worlds"; some love and make pets of them. Some go miles to see a prize-fight and are disappointed if no blood flows. Whole nations go to bull-fights, knowing they will see streams of blood. Some women faint at the mere sight of blood; an English woman is insulted at the mention of it.

Psychoses? In a way. Such forms of behavior are not "natural": they are no part of our inheritance. Every peculiarity or abnormality of behavior and every psychosis can be described in terms of individual experience.

It is the emotional side that bulges in psychoses: we "adore," we "love," we are "passionately fond of," birds, cats, dogs, bull-fights, pink tights, Niagara Falls, Caruso, the night boat to Albany. Some "love" half the world of things and all the world of beings. Others are as devoted to their hates: they have dozens of ways for hating things and people. Extreme and lurid fears are the third of the three emotional Graces. A Grace in disgrace is a psychosis.

Whole nations get that way. We recently hated all Germany, even "German silver" and Dachshunds; and loved the French, down to snails and frogs' legs. We cheered at the movies when we saw a German killed, applauded when we saw a Frenchman kiss an American officer. The whole "civilized" world suffered a huge psychosis: a kill-'em-love-'em complex.

Freudian psychoses are planted in infancy and are sexual. Freud even went so far as to say that every dream is a "wish-fulfiller" and has its feet on the forbidden pleasures of childhood.

The business of the sex-impulse is mating; if the two sexes

do not pair, the sex-impulse has not attended to its business and is a biologic failure. Many do not pair, few live happily ever after; the sex-impulse has attended to everything except its own business. Being denied proper outlet, it disarranges society and long ago became the dominant force in human behavior. By the time Freud is through, life is Sex. The drive in life is love, Libido. "Thwarted libido" is responsible for all the trouble.

That sounded interesting and Freudism became a fad; then, a cult; and is now a disease and should be put out of its misery.

Here is the argument. The newborn comes into the world naked and unashamed. The world says: "That's not nice; you must not do that." That begins the Conflict: *animal instinct* versus *social Don'ts*. But instinctive "I wants" are not to be laid by "Don'ts." What then? "Substitutes." The young "mind" indulges its instinctive libido by symbols, Society's substitutes for nature's actions.

For Freud, "mind" is stuff, a product of the processes of development. Certain forces determine the trend of this development. By "psycho-analysis" this "mind" can be examined—as one examines the contents of a jug. Such examination will reveal the manner in which these determining forces have acted and reacted.

But the mind is like a jug with much sediment below the thin skim-milk on top. The sediment is the Unconscious Mind, thick with repressed instinctive impulses and "I want" memories. This stuff is a source of energy, loaded, always smoldering; it exerts influence. It is a hidden drive to action no less than the libido impulse itself.

Do the "repressions" ever rise to Consciousness? Only when disguised or distorted—as they always are in dreams. In dreams they "rise." But we do not know them, they are so distorted, so symbolized. We must have a dream-book— there are such; or we must go to a psycho-analyst—there are such. They can exorcise our big and little devils.

449

There are many physiologic and psychologic processes of ameba and man which are not well understood, but *Libido, Unconscious Mind, Symbolism,* or *Idea,* as source of energy, is devil pure and impure. It is worse than feeding unknown hormones to cure unknown diseases.

Science must formulate hypotheses—and proceed to test them. But progress is not made by assuming that spanking a child drives a libido to parts unknown which later will jump up like a Jack-in-the-box to scare the man or woman to death.

There are neuroses and psychoses: some with organic lesions; some, morbid habit systems. The personality is diseased: certain habits become so distorted that the individual's useful habits do not suffice to adjust him to his environment—home, society. These distortions usually start in childhood: the child is spoiled, petted, babied, indulged; learns to respond with lies, by cheating, by evasion; never learns to accept responsibility for misdeeds. Such an one may go through life with such habits. But let a crisis come, a change for which he has no serviceable habits of response! There are shades of unadjustment: instinctive behavior that has never been taught to "behave," emotions that have become so distorted as to be of no use to human society. With inadequate adjusting mechanism, they turn to such pursuits or practices as fall within the range of their capacity to adjust.

No child is a "born liar." But a lively youngster may become a proficient one in ten or less years, driven to learn the art because parents will be parents and boys will be boys. Every child is taught the meaning of approbation and of contempt, and learns the meaning of candy and a hickory switch. But few children learn that disguise, artifice, deception, and falsehood have no value in "getting along" with the family. The child does learn that simulation does pay. If forced, it becomes adept in such behavior. Simulation becomes an intrinsic part of its adjustment repertoire.

450

The boss, the bully, the tease, the flirt, as well as the exhibitionist, sadist, and masochist, are also specialized products of vicious home or early school training.

The instinct of self-preservation may find a perverted outlet in the impulse to be cruel to others. If continued, it makes for sadism: frightfulness, atrocities, prize-fights, cruelty for the sheer love of being cruel, including cruelty to one's own children.

The sex-complex is complex in man and in all species of animals with sexual reproduction. In human society it has become increasingly complex. It is so individualized that there are as many kinds of sex behavior as there are individuals. So many things in life are "loved" that *sentimentality* is more common than *sensuality*. The inherent emotional drive to seek and love a mate goes out to dogs and sunsets, and bathes with tears the belongings of the late beloved.

These are habits, types of behavior; they vary with age and clime. These habits function in individuals. The sex behavior of any individual is only to be understood in the light of the manner in which the individual learned to respond to the two-sex world in which he or she grew up.

To say that man is driven by sex is to say that man is a mammal, or that human reproduction is sexual. To say that a repressed libido is also a drive but hides in the Unconscious—to pop out in a bad dream or a psychosis—is the mystic's way of saying that life learns, and that reflex arcs and salivary and other glands can be and are conditioned. To say—with Freud and Jung—that the mythology and symbolism of human culture have their roots in the Unconscious, is to make a magician's cave where by psychoanalysis one can discover anything one puts into it.

"Libido" sounds more potent than love; "Unconscious" more mysterious than behavior. That is why Libido was so popular; why so many started to juggle with Unconscious.

10

This is the age of honest skepticism and the dawn of enlightenment; even as it is of credulity—spawn of ignorance and blind faith. But no age has been so capitalized and exploited by fake science as are these States to-day. Fake healers, dozens of kinds, hundreds of practitioners; thousands of suckers. A sucker is a fish that bites at any bait. The healers do not even have to bait their hook. The larger the hook, the keener they bite.

Develop your memory! Develop will-power! Learn how to be successful! Improve yourself! Learn to read character! Personality experts! Psycho-analysts! Intelligence-testers! Psychics! Even "Psychologists," on the Board Walk at Atlantic City!

Body cures. Mind cures. Pills and pamphlets. The body that runs forty years on bad fuel is not to be cured by charms—whether in sugar-coated pills, elixirs, gland extracts, massage, mud baths, mineral waters, or electric batteries. Nor can the "mind" be "developed" in ten lessons at $1 or $100 a lesson; nor by reading a "set" of books or a year's subscription to some fake "psychological" magazine.

Psychology is not magic, nor spiritualism, nor phrenology; nor the science of the soul, consciousness, unconsciousness, mind, or complexes. It is trying to be the science of human behavior. It does deal with the reactions human beings make to adjust themselves to change.

Is your own "mind," "will," "personality," or "character" a collection of facts that you can analyze and count as you can your fingers or the hairs on your hand or the buttons on your coat? Do you mean anything to yourself apart from your past experience? Every year of your life you have built something into you—taken on new experience, dropped out old ways of reacting to square with the new

452

experience. Every reaction you make is conditioned by former reactions and affected by the given situation.

We are going concerns, not hide and hair and flesh and bones and instincts and faculties. Since birth, we are playing upon and are being played upon by our environment. The sum total of our personality—or "mind" or anything you choose to call it—does not stay put. We cannot deposit it, as we do money in a bank; nor sow it, as we sow wild oats or tame wheat—and return later to gather the harvest or burn the tares. Our personality does not stay put because situations change endlessly. Personality without reference to situation is as meaningless as a horse race with the horses tied to their stalls.

Babe Ruth goes to the diamond and fans the air; Caruso gives a performance he is ashamed of. Why do "stars" and "champions" rise to heights of genius and at other times drop into mediocrity? Do they know? Do you? Can you predict what your game of tennis or golf will be to-morrow? Or whether you will sell a certain party certain bonds or insurance? You may have your selling campaign mapped out: can you predict its success? The "certain party" may have become quite a different party overnight.

In estimating both our own and others' personality, we have to reckon with emotions, instincts, memory, habits, sensations, age, experience, etc. These are variable factors. I am older to-day than I was yesterday; so much may have happened to me that I may not be the same person. Parents often suddenly realize that they do not know their own children.

Wherever our "mind" goes when we die, it certainly goes with us while we live. I can read your mind "like a book" only if I have all the pages: and for each individual there are millions. I can test your *capacity*, or your *intelligence*, or your *will*, only as I can pick a winner at the horse race. I know at the end of the race.

You can sell goods: you prove it by references. You may

fail utterly to sell my cigarettes or my talcum powder. Your *intelligence* may be A. B. with Highest Honors: you may vote like a moron, fail as husband and father, mow the flowers instead of the lawn, and prove a dead loss on a camping-out party. As for *will:* it is as "free" as air. And much more difficult to catch. I can *develop* as much will by *lessons* on will-power as I can develop water-power at Muscle Shoals by reading Couéism in a newspaper.

You and I do not, cannot, see the same things. We do not see from the same point in space or time. Our eyes are not the same. We see only what we think we see. Your experience is your experience; mine is mine. We learn by experience. Our capacity to learn is the measure of our intelligence. Intelligence as so many yards of this and so many pounds of that at so much per, may qualify a lad for clerk in a notion shop, but furnishes no measure of the lad's behavior outside that shop; or within, in case of fire, hold-up, or fainting fit of a lady customer.

Sensations. Special sense organs: eyes, ears, nose, etc. I have my nose, you have yours: Limburger cheese—same sensation? I have ears, you have ears: a baby cries—same sensation? I have eyes, you have eyes: a woman smiles—same sensation?

What is a stimulus? Cheese? Not after I have smelled it for an hour. Remove it: now it is a stimulus. A crying baby? If it cries for an hour it is a great stimulus. If it is yours I could murder it; if it is mine I telephone the doctor. We read the same column in a newspaper: as a result I buy S O S, you sell S O S. Another column may send me to sleep, send you to Europe.

Stimulus is change. Throughout life, any and every change in environment excites us if our experience—and we inherit much—teaches us that we should make response.

Our psychology is human, but our behavior is individual; for each of us, the aggregate of inherent capacities and experiences.

One can read one's own mind—in the light of past experience; predict one's own accomplishments—in the light of past achievements; and develop one's own will—by practising instead of preaching.

Psychic power? I know what power is; I know what psyche is; I also know that knowledge may be power. But I can discover only one way to get knowledge into my head: through my sense perceptions. And only one way to get any power out of that knowledge: by inference, by reason. When my inference is bad, my reasoning is faulty; I have only my pains for my trouble—my power-plant ground me no grist. When I want magic power, I go see Houdini.

11

All processes of thought function through reflex arcs which become conditioned, especially in childhood, and which tend to become habits. We learn to think *logically* just as we learn to speak *correctly* or to behave *decently*. I may think well, I may shave well—who shall say? My way of shaving and my way of thinking are my ways: the ways I have learned; they are my methods of response to certain stimuli in certain situations. I may change both to-morrow; some one is always inventing new ways of adjustment, new ways to excite human protoplasm to change its shaving soap.

New thought also. Why not? We have new foods, new scandals, new songs, new elements, new diseases, new razors, new glands, new logic. New things to think about. The new grows out of the old—as corn grew out of wild grass, or as a submarine grew out of endless discarded models, or as chemistry grew out of alchemy, or as a poem grows out of tryings-out of word combinations. Trial and error.

The point is that there is no thought without muscular or glandular activity; this is true whether the stomach thinks hunger, the dreamer thinks air-castles, the prisoner thinks freedom, or the maiden thinks of her lover. Thinking is a bodily act, as is coughing or scratching one's head. During thinking energy is consumed, mechanism is involved; and, as a rule, the whole body is interested and is listening in.

Can we listen in, can we read thought as we can test blood? Only when we can see it: as poem, as picture, on the golf links, behind the counter, at the ballot box. By works. Overt and explicit action. Money talks also.

But suppose no money is forthcoming, how can we know what he thinks about it? Overt explicit behavior is easily enough detected and is often of less consequence than the implicit response. I ask you to lend me five dollars. You hand it over. That is an *explicit* act. But your *implicit* reaction may be of far greater consequence to me: you may think me a cheap skate and decide to cut me from your list. As you give no sign of such resolve, I cannot know that my "Lend me . . ." has cost so much.

Of course, if you have *looked it* or muttered it in thought, I may be able to read your face or your lips. I may even suspect, with no overt sign on your part, that my request has moved you to more than is involved in handing over the bill. I question you; you deny that there is anything the matter with you.

As we all do at times. As the run-in suspect does. His face is a perfect mask for innocence. His self-possession is complete. He is wrongly suspected! He is innocent! The "third-degree" often breaks the mask and upsets the self-possession. More often the third-degree fails or is not available.

Many methods have been tried out to read minds that would not be read, to detect an *implicit* response where the overt side had only been suspected. All these methods go on the justifiable assumption that what the individual does registers in the individual dynamic mechanism. Apply the proper test: the mechanism will yield its secret.

An extreme case will illustrate the methods. Suppose I

return unexpectedly to my store some night, to discover my partner in some questionable act. We quarrel. And I kill him. Then cut his body up and dispose of it in the furnace— an extraordinarily difficult thing to do, but just suppose that I succeed.

The anger which prompts murder is an emotional impulse. There will be occasions and situations in which I shall have to be a man of iron to keep my emotions from betraying me. Charged with the crime, they might lead to changes in my respiration and vasomotor organization; even to increased sugar in my blood and urine.

Or in my reactions to words. Woodworth has devised an emotional questionary to serve to detect implicit behavior. There are two types of word reactions: the *free;* the *continuous.* In the free, words are fired at the subject one at a time. He is to reply with the first word that pops into his head suggested by the word used: bull—moose; rat—trap; pen—ink; teapot—dome; etc. Then comes a word which brings no response from me, or I am unusually long in reacting to it, or too quick. Or, if I am a girl suspected of being in love, I giggle, blush, or drop my eyes.

The *continuous* type throws all the work on the subject investigated. Only one word is shot at him: he is to reply to his own replies. One word will suggest another; until the subject stops—blocked, as it were. Then a new word is given to start the subject off again. And again he seems to run out of words, is blocked. Do the lines converge? Do I always stop short of "murder," or "furnace," or chopping up a human body? Is my *free* association of words shorn of its freedom wherever and whenever I approach a word which suggests the emotion or the deed I am trying to conceal?

Dreams also may yield valuable clues to the nature of personal stress and general emotional life. Also postures, attitudes, over and under reactions, poor adjustments, slips of word or pen, fumbling over names. But clues only. More often the "tests" fail completely—though they may lead to confession.

Conscience does make cowards of us all and habit keeps us straight or crooked; fear of consequences makes us cover our tracks.

"Reading the mind" is a figure of speech. The cashier of the First National may be a good reader of counterfeit money. I dump a bag of cowrie shells on his desk. Cowrie shells are money in some parts of the world. Some of my cowries are counterfeit. Can he read them?

12

The great by-product of our participation in the World War was the startling discovery that "America is a nation of morons!" *Moron* means dull or stupid, and is technically applied to children with permanently arrested mental development. Defective mentality due to congenital deficiency is "amentia"; if due to deterioration, "dementia." Congenital imbecility is generally accompanied by a thin and poorly organized brain cortex.

Nearly two million American adults were tested by the army as to their intelligence. The average was that of a normal school child of twelve. As the test sampled the nation, the cry went up, "Nation of morons!" And much bunk was and is talked and written.

What is *intelligence?* "Ability to learn or to profit by past experience?" All right. The hog is an intelligent animal; rattlesnake also; likewise hookworm and clam. "Civilization's" intelligence, measured by the amount it has profited by past experience makes a poor showing; it goes right on putting its troubles upon the Lord instead of upon itself. Voters make the poorest showing of all: they put their troubles upon the "government."

The army had to find out whether a man could react to orders and learn to use a musket; if not, he was not intelligent enough to shoot or fit to be shot at. If, on the other hand, he knew the chemistry of explosives, he was too intelligent to be shot at and was put to work in an ammunition laboratory. The army had to make tests. It used certain lists of questions.

I give you a list of questions. You may flunk completely. Have I tested your *intelligence?* Only to the extent of that particular list. Even then I have *tested* nothing of your capacity to learn or to profit by past experience.

I have a bottle of liquid before me. I ask that bottle certain questions: Are you indican, creatine, glucose, or uric acid; have you any phosphates, calcium, or iron, in you? To each the bottle replies "No." Very well, then, I cannot use you; your mother did not bring you up to be a soldier. But do I know from that test what that liquid is, or what it will do if I drop a hair or a lighted match in it? Or what it will do to me if I drink it? That bottle might be *aqua vitæ* itself, for anything I know to the contrary. I did not test it for aqua vitæ, only for urine.

There are idiots, imbeciles, morons, all degrees of feeble-minded. Grade A feeble mind passes into the low grade of a mind that is not feeble; and so on up through the grades to genius. But there may be two reasons why I *cannot* talk Chinese: never tried to learn it; could not learn it.

The deviltry of intelligence tests is the cold assumption that there is something missing in the headpiece of the boy of twelve who fails to make the grade, or that the adult of thirty with a twelve-year-old grade could not have qualified for college.

A Zulu "cannot count above four"! Awful! What a moron! He owns a hundred head of cattle. Steal one. He knows it is gone: he has a name for every beast he owns. I am "good at figures." With slate and pencil I can tell you how many minutes there are in a year. A Chinaman will reach the answer in less time and more certainly by playing with some buttons on some wires. An infant prodigy will do it in his head—right off—just like that.

We start with suppositions in judging *character, intelligence, personality*. We must, of course. But as long as we are at the mercy of our convictions, we fail to realize that the boy of twelve does not make the grade not because he cannot but usually because that grade does not appeal to him. We have our own grades. The school, on the other hand, has its own. Instead of attempting to find out what grade I can make, it throws me out for not coming up to its *standard*. The average man meekly accepts the verdict *incompetent*, and is counted with the morons.

Every individual at any given age has actual and potential assets and liabilities. He is either adjusted to his environment and has the equipment for readjustment when the environment changes, or he is not and has not. He may not be a sissy to-day; would he be a sissy under any situation? He bites his nails, spits aimlessly, fumbles his nose, flies into a rage, collects shells, is upset by a worm, shies at girls, cheats at marbles, is always tardy: will he carry these habits, bents, hobbies, and emotional attachments and antagonisms to school—and out into life?

Many a teacher's time and patience spent trying to make the boy or girl learn could be better spent trying to find out what the boy or girl has a will to learn. *Will* being a human engine that goes best with certain fuel and in certain directions. "Music lessons" have spoiled many a cook and "modern languages" many a farmer.

If America is a nation of morons, then that is the answer to the attractiveness of the intellectual feast our educational system spreads; it is not a test of the American's ability to learn.

We are cars of many makes, types, styles, gears, and motor-capacity. Some are racers and some are trucks; some are no good on dirt roads and some are tractors and can climb mountains; some are one-seaters and some are buses; some can pull only themselves, others the whole family; some use a pint a mile and some a barrel.

And as any car can be wrecked as it leaves the factory, so also by careful and scientific handling every car is good for its capacity.

But we are more than machines; we make ourselves as we go.

Is this also a measure of intelligence?

What we make ourselves into depends on many factors. But one consideration should not be overlooked: there is no *absolute* in the measure of intelligence, only *standards*—yours, mine, this community's, that society's, etc. These *standards* vary and keep varying with time and place. Christopher Columbus could not qualify for a water-tender's rating in the navy of Alfonso XIII. Of the world's hundred geniuses perhaps five could pass any of the contraptions now in vogue to *measure* intelligence. Of this same hundred few, if any, were rated "Intelligence A1" by their contemporaries. In fact, some of them were killed by their contemporaries for *lack* of intelligence. Was that a measure of the intelligence of their contemporaries?

13

During the month of August, 1914, a great nation lost its character but gained a reputation.

Character seems to be an essence, a spirit, a core, a stuff, that defies analysis: like Consciousness or Unconscious Mind. "If I could only get at his 'true character,' " we say, as though it were something quite beyond range of investigation. Or at least beyond anyone but a psycho-analyst: he might be able to "draw it out."

What do we do with a bottle that "looks like gin but may be poison"? Try it, or have a friend try it, or send it to a chemical laboratory. Are there laboratories where *character* may be analyzed? There are: palmists, phrenologists, handwriting experts, Freudists, mind-readers, clairvoyants, Swamis, mystics, and charlatans—ignorant and honest or wise and dishonest. They all "read" character.

While they are in the inner shrine with some one's "true character" or "inner self," let us not forget that human beings do not come like buttons from a mold but in individual packages. There is probably a prize in every package, if we only looked for it or knew how to find it. These packages come with a limited repertoire of habits, an unlimited amount of emotion, and an enormous capacity to learn. Further, they are keen to learn: their very bodies itch for action—they could not have peopled the earth and enslaved nature otherwise. Further, these little packages, in the natural process of becoming untied and budding like a rose or a sunflower as is their bent, become more and more tied up. With the result that by the time one is old enough to vote—whether it has learned what the ballot means or not—it belongs to mother's church and father's party, and wears the clothes, thinks the thoughts, and swears by the flag the family and the community have wished on it.

In short, its "character" may be *nil,* its reputation fine. But it is a person and is so recognized by law. It has a personality. It is a going concern. Where and how fast and how long it goes, and when it will throw a fit or jump the track or explode, depend . . . Fill in the details yourself.

We do, every day: Shall I marry her? Does he love me? Shall we invite them? Shall I accept his invitation? Shall we let her go to the dance with him? Dare I make the venture? Is he fit for our son to play with? Is his note good? Shall I employ him? Is she a good cook? Is he an honest chauffeur? Would you, if you were I?

How do we answer these questions? Call in a palmist? Some do, or there would be no palmists. But most of us answer them as we answer other questions, such as: Wonder if I dare eat that pie? Is it a real ruby? Is this a good lipstick? Shall I buy Q. E. D. or sell P. D. Q.? Shall we

send Willie to Brown or to Green? Is this road safe? Shall
we go to the movies or to church? Is the beer all gone?
Shall we quit now or play till morning? Is this suit good
enough? Shall I endow a charity now or steal another
million?

We make mistakes. With original sin loose in the world,
we must. We make mistakes in persons and things. "She
is not what I thought she was": which is correct enough, for
having met you she is to that extent different. "That is not
what I thought I bought": true again; but it is what you
were sold.

We learn by our experience. And some learn fast and
with profit, and others learn as little as possible. It all
depends.

But if we were "good" children and learned to jump at
father's orders, and to "respect" his *authoritative manner* and
commanding ways, and learned to smile and swallow "like
a good little man" the nasty medicine the doctor leaves for
poor little sick boys, we are likely later to listen with open
mouth to the man who pounds the platform or the pulpit or
fills the room with his *magnetic personality!* But if father
was a little runt without voice or influence in family affairs,
we are likely to overlook the personality in a *shrimp.*

A "pleasing," "thrilling," "absorbing" personality is one
we like to touch. Men shake their hands. Women kiss
them. When "I instinctively like that person," the *instinct*
that is talking is an unanalyzed sexual or emotional slant
based on early habits of love. A "lovable" personality
within the same sex is possible because sharp leanings toward
the other sex were not formed at the time sex matured.
Co-education is sanitary education.

We jump at our personality conclusions. We *know* he
cannot be this and she cannot be that. What we really know
is that some personalities appeal to us, others do not. We
can rarely give the real reason for our spontaneous judg-

ments. *Personalities* are rather more complex than apples or motor cars.

The most "erect carriage" may be the greatest social scoundrel unhung. The "intelligent brow" may be housed under a dunce's cap. The "squarest chin" may be a weak sister and the most henpecked man in town. The "firm mouth" may hide a flabby body and a soft head.

Some things do show through: elation, despondency, etc. But the rosiest cheeked apple may have a wormy heart. A woman with a homely face covers it with hat and veil or tresses, and sells herself on her form.

Pick fifty men at random from Fifth Avenue. Take them to the Tombs, shave their heads and photograph them. Mix the photographs in with those of fifty inmates. Call in your mind-readers and character experts. How many will they pick out? As many as the law of chance allows them. Now take the fifty *inmates,* dress them in the hair and clothes of the new arrivals, and drop them along Fifth Avenue. Call in your character experts. If they can pick these fifty "toughs" off Fifth Avenue, they should report to the Chief of Police of New York or the Attorney-General of the United States. Jobs await such men.

People who read character from hands like to hold hands; and *vice versa.* If they pay to have their hands held they do not lose their *personality,* only their money.

John Stuart Mill speaks of an event which took place on Calvary: "The man who left on the memory of those who witnessed his life and conversation such an impression of his moral grandeur that eighteen subsequent centuries have done homage to him as the Almighty in person, was ignominiously put to death. As what? As a blasphemer!"

14

Life is easily destroyed, but the matter of life is indestructible. Life easily tires, but the energy of life is not lost.

Life is dynamic. When struck—as by blow of slipper or by a chuck under the chin—a chemical reaction takes place; that reaction alters its nature. It is now something else. The change may be slight; it may be so great that its very dynamic nature is altered—the change endures for life.

Life is impelled to action because it is a reacting mechanism: certain stimuli impel it to action. What life does depends upon what life is; and that, in turn, depends upon what life does. The life that climbed up to man never ceased to recreate itself on higher levels. The oftener it reacts, the greater the ease of action; practice makes perfect. But life itself is not moved by perfection; with too much practice it grows fatigued. Had life been content with mere perfection, it would have stopped with bacteria and algæ. It essayed more difficult rôles and by greatly daring became man. It could not have built up a nature so imperious for power or so keen for experience had it been content to say: I desire nothing more; I am perfect.

A *perfect* man is as finished a product of Nature as a bacterium and may be fit for Nirvana, but not to rule or to lead men. For men are of the stock that moved up out of the slime and set no limit to their desires. They insist on action because action is the nature of their inheritance. But they must have new stimuli or they fall asleep with ennui.

We begin our life with a semifluid body of twenty-odd chemical elements which surrender their original nature in becoming welded into a compact organic system. This body builds itself up into a vastly complex machine of billions of individual bodies, each retaining something of its original nature, each surrendering something of its original nature that we may function as one individual being. The energy which drives this machine is chemical, the impulse which drives the machine to secure this energy is inherent in the living protoplasm of our body.

Chemical reactions in a chemical body. Of some reactions we are conscious, of most of them we are not conscious.

But the living mind and the living body are inseparable and together make up the individual. We never know what is in our "mind," for the mind is the living body which because of its nature must react to every vital change in its environment. We can recall to memory only a few of these reactions: those burned in. We cannot recall countless memories; we have no machinery or organs for forgetting. Nevertheless, they have left their mark; each reaction alters the protoplasm for further reactions; it is never again the same. As the universe itself is not made, but is continually being made, so with man.

This view of universe and man is repugnant to many; it disturbs the serenity of their belief in the Absolute and Eternal and the simplicity of their thought that earth and man were *created*, as a magician conjures goldfish out of nothing and rabbits out of an empty hat.

Man's chief impulse at each moment of his existence is for life: self-preservation. At certain moments food-hunger dominates the self-preservation impulse, at other moments sex-hunger dominates. But because of his capacity to supplement his motor mechanism with tools, weapons, and appliances, he was able to give his biologic impulses ever-changing outlets. He also developed language into a definite means of communication, and thereby further extended the range of possible responses to living impulses. Thus, on his repertoire of animal adjustments to vital conditions he superimposed a repertoire of human adjustments. The rise, development, spread, and decay of these purely human adjustments make up the story of the history of human culture.

The culture of any people, tribe, race, or nation at any given time is an historical problem. Memphis, Troy, and Carthage, of the Old World or the New, are riddles apart from their setting, apart from the historic factors which conditioned their development. The lives of Buddha, Confucius, Socrates, Mohammed, Tamerlane, Elizabeth, Napoleon, Washington, and Frank Smith, are also riddles without their setting.

Each age carried its loaded situation to which human beings responded in obedience to the impulse to live. Every age had its modes, norms, habits, opinions, manners, customs, taboos, and its written and unwritten codes of behavior. Mohammed born on Beacon Street would have gone to Harvard and been a Unitarian.

Every age thought itself wise and prattled of "progress"; and lagged from one to one hundred decades behind its own wisdom. Our own national habits and social, educational, legal, and governmental institutions jog along in ruts worn smooth by our forefathers. There is not a city in the United States organized as a community for the purposes of living, almost no individual that practices what he preaches or puts to useful purpose a tenth part of his brains.

A hand fitted by nature to swing from limbs and catch fleas learns in five years to drive a nail and in fifteen years to drive a car it took culture 100,000 years to make. One wonders that culture required so many years to produce the car; but one is amazed that so many children can learn to drive a car in such short time. In other words, our civilization as the "product of all the ages" loses much of its glamour when viewed against the background of what an ordinary boy or girl can learn in twoscore years.

Tokyo, Peking, Delhi, Cairo, Rome, London, New York, Main Street: random sample worlds. Into these life comes in small packages called babies, fundamentally all alike, all human, all blood-kin, all of one species. They have the same general adjustment mechanism in the same excitable protoplasm, with the same instinct for life and the same emotional-drive equipment. And all have parents to tide them over the infantile period until such time as their motor mechanism will enable them to seek their own food, water, and shelter, and in general make their own adjustments, including picking a mate.

These same babies one, five, twenty, fifty years later show differences more than skin deep, differences burned into the very protoplasm of their bodies. Which means: their habits are different, their thoughts are different. They doff their hats to different gods and play the game of life in different ways and for different stakes.

Contents of their mind? We can only answer that as we know the conditioning of their mind: what they jump at and why. Always remembering that individual variation sets a limit to our jumping mechanism; also that we know little of that limit because it is restricted by fears and hemmed in by taboos.

Into each home the baby comes as a loaded stimulus. It may be hailed as the watcher greets the dawn; or with, "Well, here it is"; or as another mouth to feed. Its arrival is a complex of stimuli. Out of these the baby is often made or broken the day it is born—a chance that must be taken these days as the price of the opportunity to become civilized.

Most of them do. Some never become adjusted. They die, as Socrates, Savonarola, Lavoisier; or they are fed to the lions by Nero, disappear on Saint Bartholomew's Day, or work in a factory. They borrow, beg, or steal. There are as many ways and degrees of unadjustment as there are of adjustment, all graduated to the ways and degrees to which adjustment is demanded.

In short, there is no knowing man without knowing men. "Everybody's doing it" and "People don't do such things" are collective reactions biologically useful in herds and early human society, but they persist in countless forms to-day and extend their influence to such unimportant biologic factors in modern life as ruffles on skirts and creases in trousers. "Everybody is" and "People don't" become potent factors in modifying the environment to which individuals are conditioned to respond.

Almost before the youngster has learned to respond to the facts of life, he is compelled to learn adjustment to the fancies of life. Human behavior as adjustment is meaningless without understanding the power of social environment to enforce its limited responses upon the newcomers. Society does not easily change its mind, because to change is to acknowledge defeat; it hates to run. Its mind being its entire body and tied up with emotion, it vents its hate on "Don'ts" and much of its energy in enforcing obedience.

But there is almost no limit to the pressure that a normal individual can stand if the pressure is applied gradually; we get calloused: to odors, sights, sounds, and bondage of trappings, and the harness by which we draw our burdens. And well for us that we can become accustomed to the burdens of things, people, and situations that we must bear. But man is not by nature a beast of burden or fitted by nature to keep his nose to a grindstone. And the man so yoked or chained is one more human being lost for activities that might be human.

As one recalls some of the monstrous situations under which human beings have lived and live their lives, one marvels at man's meekness and complacency. It can only be explained by that quality of flesh to become calloused to situations that if faced suddenly would provoke blisters and revolt.

Man's inheritance is all right and is his only inherently valuable asset. It is human behavior—individual, communal, national—that can be changed. But not by cut-and-dried programs of social reform; nor by reformers, codes, ideals, or by our present "system" of education. Life itself is not systematized or standardized: it wants to live, it wants to enjoy life. It has a pain sense; it responds to love; above all, it can learn. We start with that equipment. Herein lies the significance of the new conception of human behavior; the importance of the task that confronts the new psychology.

Organized society is—or should be—interested in socially serviceable behavior. Its problem is to control behavior for social ends and at the same time give the individual freedom to express and develop his innate capacities for normal behavior. This cannot be brought about by chance; there will be delinquents, abnormals, subnormals, as long as breeding grounds for such are regarded as normal by-products of social organization. The entire substratum of misfits will disappear only when the environment is so changed that misfits do not form part of its *normal* output.

Rational conduct is a dream. But conduct freed of sordidness, of squalor, of haunting fears, of ungoverned tempers, should be the possible fate of every normal child. We can at least make this a better world for children to be born into, and so alter their environment that they need not learn to lie, steal, murder, or commit rape or bigamy, to succeed.

The seemingly infinitely large universe is made up of the seemingly infinitely small units of electrons. The universe is what it is because of the nature of their behavior under the drive of energy. That same energy drives us. The units of our social universe are human individuals; it can be molded only as the individuals themselves are molded. Living beings are not elements, but reaction systems: their behavior can be molded. Ours is already set; but it is not necessary that we condition our children to the mold in which we hardened.

In the whole history of human thought there has been voiced only one rule of conduct of the slightest value as a standard for human behavior. It is applicable to individuals, families, communities, cities, states and nations:

"As ye would that men should do to you, do ye also to them likewise."

But note that you and I as individuals can never get a start on putting the Golden Rule into practice until we have set our own house in order. When we strip our unethical and infantile hang-overs of behavior of their veneer of rationalization we are likely to be astounded, as Watson points out, at our "susceptibility to flattery, weakness, inadequacy, or lack of knowledge, jealousy, fear of rivals, fear of being made the scapegoat," and proneness to hurl criticism upon others to escape it ourselves. The first step in setting our house in order is to remove the beam from our own eyes—perhaps the hardest task man ever set himself, certainly a task that can be achieved only by the brave.

When human society starts to practice the Golden Rule, it will lay a foundation for civilization which no flood of passion can shake. Any other conditioning of our inherent nature leaves us as we are—with an animal nature modified only by man-made devices to satisfy living impulses as old as life itself. Man is the product of evolution; humanity must be the goal of human endeavor.

15

Probably no two are of the same opinion as to what constitutes *socially useful* behavior. But there can be no doubt that many do not get out of life what life might be expected to yield, considering the length of time it has been on the job, and that many do not give to society the service society might expect to receive, considering the energy it expends on educational and social endowments. Why this is so is an enormously difficult and vastly complicated problem. Is it because society solves living with the latest mechanical contraptions and solves life with old rules? At any rate, it knows next to nothing about life, but does have a large collection of gadgets for living. As a consequence, we are at the mercy, and not in command, of the tools of living.

This is no plea for the "simple life"—or a remedy for anything. Goodness knows, we have enough prescriptions, and enough bandwagons and barkers inviting us to climb aboard. But have we a sound diagnosis of social ills and individual disabilities? Are our parents and teachers setting examples of rational and intellectual living, and are they getting into the rising generation such an outlook on life, such a conception of the possibilities of life, and such a comprehension of the unlimited capacities for life, that the next gen-eration will inevitably live a broader, saner, sounder, and more intellectual life than we are living?

And by *intellectual* I do not mean "high-brow" stuff. I mean the kind of intelligence that distinguishes men from cats and cattle—what they think about, what occupies their gray matter. There is no inherent reason why the miner, plowman, and milkmaid should not be as intellectual as the poet, auditor, or school-teacher. Coal, corn, and milk furnish us more energy than poems, balance sheets, and schools. If ignorance is bliss, all right. But this country proceeds on the theory that ignorance is a defect, that education will cure it, and that the opposite of ignorance is intelligence; and that compulsory education makes for intelligence.

But does it? What has the boy or girl of intelligent be-havior on leaving school? To say that they have a smattering of this and of that is to say what everybody knows and what has been said thousands of times: that they have added a few hundred words to their vocabulary, have memorized a few facts and formulæ, have dissected a fishworm (possibly) and a flower, and have read several hundred pages of history and polite literature. That may be education, but it is not life; nor is it hitched to human lives or human society; nor is it intelligence.

Good, honest, hard-headed *character* is a function of the home. If the proper seed is sown there and properly nour-ished for a few years, it will not be easy for that plant to be uprooted. But it is the business of the school so to engage youthful interests that youthful energies will flow into crea-tive channels. No school can really educate; but every school should nourish the enthusiasm of every normal child for learning, for exploring, for manipulating; should stimu-late the fountain of youthful curiosity and not plug it up with facts. Above all, it should not dam youth up—or down. Youth has the will, the energy, the impetus; give it raw meat and bones to chew on. Give it a place in the sun, keep it in

understanding; for such charity as will abolish the need for alms; for honesty in rulers and intelligence in legislation; for a stop-and-think-it-over week; for regard for human rights; for critical judgments; for dispassionate opinions; for hatred of shams, intolerance, falsehood, and deception; for riddance of quacks, mountebanks, impostors, charlatans, vermin, squalor, and ignorance; for a car for every family and a joy ride through life for everyone; for socially useful behavior.

Everything that man has made, done, said, and thought has been built on the impulse to live, organic hunger for food and mate, fashioned, molded, and reinforced by the emotional drive in life. Every normal human being has that equipment at birth. It is in the very marrow of the child's bones, in the protoplasm of its nerves. It is the foundation of every personality. It cannot be wiped out, crushed, or stifled; it can be warped, distorted, diseased, degraded. It can be encouraged to grow, to expand, to blossom, to bear fruit. It may produce an inspiring leader who will show the way and be the way to bring a new order into the world of human affairs. Society may kill him. Never mind. Society will build a monument to him in admiration of his having dared to be a leader. The least we can do is to keep our hands off the courage of youth.

Emotional drives are not new in man, or even in Primates. The newness, the uniqueness, are man's responses. Rage and fear once led to fight or flight; they now supply the drives which may lead to drink, to burglary, to murder, to insanity, to suicide even. As Thomas points out, the *daydreamer* may become a scientist, a swindler, or a liar; the *adventurer*, a vagabond, cowboy, missionary, geologist, or ethnologist; the *killer* may shoot big game with a rifle or with a camera; the sex-impulse may lead to a Don Juan, to a prostitute, to a love-lyric poet, or to a lover of home and family.

The problem, then, is such a reorganization of society that socially useful behavior shall be at least as profitable and interesting as unsocial or criminal behavior. Opinions may differ as to the extent to which bootlegging, prize-fighting, and prostitution are unsocial, but there is no doubt about the profitableness of these professions—as compared, let us say, with farming, preaching, and teaching school.

What is wrong with the picture? Each one, I repeat, will have his own opinion and his own remedy—and will be ready enough to express opinion and remedy, and back up both with hot argument, if necessary. But what will he *do* about it? Parents will continue to do business with unsocial or criminal professions, and teachers will probably labor in vain for a living wage; but there is one thing both parents and teachers can do: give youth the opportunity to become *conscious* of society, of human life, of humanity; encourage it to think, to speculate, to revalue, to weigh evidence, to become disgusted, to choose, to see through things, to see things and life objectively. *Critical consciousness.*

How has "progress" been made in medicine, in chemistry, in physics, in engineering, in all the respects in which progress has been made? By doubts, by questionings, by testings of hypotheses, by solutions of problems, by *critical* activity in the human cortex.

Man is a free *moral* agent and can be magnanimous and deal disinterestedly, *humanity* is a definite goal, social justice is desirable and possible, individual lives may be gloriously diversified, uniquely individualized, and yet socially useful; or, these are mere phrases, snares to catch gulls, soothing syrup for troubled souls. Here again, opinions will differ; but no one will pretend that society to-day is *organized* (as a living organism is organized) or that social relations are one whit more *intelligently* ordered than in the days of Pericles or of Julius Cæsar.

The problem, then, narrows down to this: children of

nature and creatures of circumstance as we are, can we discover what organic evolution is up to and can we help it on its way?

16

You and I and all *living beings* differ from *dead things* in one respect: we grow, and by one process; we incorporate inorganic and dead organic matter into our individual bodies. Our nature is such that we are impelled to do this. This gives us a clue to *organic* evolution.

For, note: the matter which must be incorporated within our bodies is outside us; we must get it. During organic evolution, it was not *life* that evolved; it was the *rate* and the *kind* of life that was lived; faster, freer.

The visible agencies finally evolved for the faster, freer life were: motor mechanism of bony levers worked by muscle engines; special analyzers or distance receptors; cerebral cortex; and vocal cords and voice mechanism. These agencies made for improved locomotion, more exact information, more space for storing information, and improved facilities for exchanging information. Accompanying these visible agencies or tools for a faster, freer life, there evolved special physico-chemical mechanisms for *driving* life—as though life had grown a firecracker under its tail, as it were. These agencies and the emotional-drive mechanisms man shares with other Primates and to a large extent with all mammals. Only, man's motor mechanism moves on two feet instead of four; his hands are freed from the drudgery of footwork; and his cortex is so vast that he can measure stars and electrons, but not his own capacity for intelligent action. In fact, his potentialities are as far beyond our powers of vision as we of to-day were beyond the vision of our ancestor who invented fire by rubbing two sticks together.

Are language and culture the inevitable consequences of man's nature? Are they the *goal* of the faster, freer life made possible by certain agencies and mechanisms? Is man himself the finished product of an evolution which continually created life on higher levels? The idea is worth manipulating.

Consider the *emotional* drive. Where has it not carried man? To what heights and depths has it not driven him? The fiery passion for life, the haunting fear of the unknown! The ages-long persecutions, the massacres, the burnings, the torturings, the revilings, done in the name of God to prove that God is just! The hells that have been invented to scare children into loving a merciful God! How the heavenly choir must have wept—or laughed!

Death is a common affair in nature; for millions of years man had been dying of old age or disease or killed in combat. But he suddenly becomes conscious of death! And within a few centuries he has raised a natural phenomenon to a vast and complicated rite, and expects the very stars to stand still while he breathes his last. The monuments to the dead, the worship of the dead, the prayers for the dead! Yes, and the communion with the dead! All this had to be, presumably; man had become that kind of an animal.

It was inevitable that his curiosity should impel him to explore his world, to manipulate it, to play with it and experiment with it; that with hands he should tear down and build up, that with voice he should fashion speech and with words should remold the world to his heart's desire.

It was inevitable that upon his bisexual world he should erect a family hearth; it was not inevitable that he should invent this or that kind of household gods, or that upon that hearth he rear a harem or found an order of celibacy or vestal virgins. Or that he should worship his wife, or degrade her to a parasite; or that she should make a fool or a criminal of him.

It was inevitable that his love for life and fear of death should lead him to magic rites and groveling superstitions; it was not inevitable that his religion should be used as a cloak to hide his selfishness, justify his greed, and sanctify his lust for blood and gold.

Culture, in short, was inevitable. Man was, man did. Our evidence of the causal relation of tides to moon rests on no more solid foundation. Once there were no Primates; Primates came. There was no man; man came—and with him came culture, little by little, slowly, painfully, gropingly, even reluctantly at times. But it came: words to talk with; gods to placate; rules and laws to break or obey; swirls of family life ever growing larger; tribal organization and states, torn asunder, being rebuilt, organizing and reorganizing; music, art, literature, classified knowledge, science, philosophy, moonshine; and all the countless material things made by hands, conceived by brains.

Here it is, all about us: evidence that the drive behind life has lost none of its power; proof that, impelled by that drive, man can build as well as destroy; that in his nature is more of Vishnu the Creator than of Siva the Destroyer. And this human culture that is ours by inheritance and by the efforts of the generation now living, is real. It makes up the social and much of the physical environment into which children are to-day being born. They are the same children, they bring with them the same old organic needs and hungers. How will they fare?

A.D. 2000 seems a long way off; it is no more remote than 1850. My father, now living, was a young man in 1850; my grandson, now living, may expect to be alive in 2000. How *free* will the next generation be to work out its own salvation, to guide its life in the light of wisdom? Will life be more free seventy-five years hence than it is to-day? Are we more free than were our ancestors two thousand years ago?

How free are we of to-day—from war, pestilence, earthquake, volcano, fire, sickness, idiocy, imbecility, pauperism, crime, squalor, shipwreck, stupidity, ignorance, superstition, famine, disease; from accidents of mines, factories, railroads, automobiles, and airplanes; from harsh sounds, bad air, and foul odors; from scorn, malice, and intolerance; from *vested interests* and *established opinion* in church, school, and government in home, society, and nation; from clocks, timetables, and calendars; from the decrees of fashion, the convictions of the mob, the mandates of the politicians? In short, how free are we of the ox goad and the treadmill? We know that winter will come, and provide accordingly; our expectation that there will be another harvest next year is that of the bees and the squirrels. More free to live than we were, more prepared to die; but in all respects more free? It is doubtful. It is less doubtful that we are not as free as we might be.

Fast, yes: we live at an incredible speed. Experience is disseminated and things and beings are transported across lands and seas unknown a few centuries ago, and at a speed inconceivable to the pioneers of the Pony Express. We cannot yet travel as fast as sound-waves, but it is not incredible that a future generation will travel as fast as light-waves.

In so far, then, as man has speeded living, and to the extent that he has freed human beings, he is fulfilling his destiny. But has he completed his mission? Has he made the most of his opportunities? Is he progressing, is he on the straight and shining rails, or is he in a maze, a blind alley, an appendix to a cecum which holds the threat of gangrene and destruction? There are criteria for life; is there a biologic criterion for progress?

Note again that, while culture was inevitable because man is a nervous, excitable, unarmored, defenceless, selfish, self-centered, opinionated, inquisitive, bullying, cowardly, talking, marrying animal, who requires shelter, food, and a mixed diet, and has a big head and quick wits and is handy with his hands, the particular bents culture took were no more inevitable than are the particular words I am now putting down on paper. If Buddha and Confucius, Moses and Plato,

Washington and Lincoln, were inevitable, then I can think of nothing less illuminating as a guide to human conduct than human history. If not inevitable, then they are priceless illustrations of man's capacity to transcend a nature which is generally satisfied with a few simple reactions to a stimulating world to meet a few fundamental organic needs and hungers.

Note, too, that history does not repeat itself. Why should it? Who wants it to repeat? To the best of our knowledge, nothing on this planet repeats. While the elements and the energies change not at all, or imperceptibly, the forms matter takes and the work energy performs do change. The organic needs and hungers inhere; they drive man to-day, as yester-day, as in pre-Cambrian days, they drove his ancestors.

Drove? How? By a stepping up, a raising of the potential of the power. As a result, the machine became more complicated but more highly integrated; its parts became larger but under better control; it was capable of more refined work, could vary its output, forecast the future, provide for unforeseen contingencies. *This is creative evolution.* It is real, it is tangible, its history can be read in the rock record, can be measured in the cortex of the brain, and can be seen in the fields of waving grain and in the flocks of sheep and the herds of cattle. It was in the direction of *freedom*.

What is freedom? No two dictionaries define it alike. No two generations define it alike. No one generation agrees as to who shall be free. The framers of our Magna Charta of freedom went right on killing Indians and breeding slaves. We shall get little insight into freedom from the law courts; we must look deeper. Can we find a biologic concept for freedom? Is there a *goal*, as it were, to *creative evolution?*

Our vision is so limited! We know so little of life! Who shall say?

But we shall try. All the cats, dogs, rats, and guinea-pigs martyred in the name of science have died in vain, and all the laboratories built to serve science are illusions, if the net result is but a few human lives saved and no light thrown

on what it is that is saved and whether it is worth saving.
Life can save itself if given a fair chance. What is worth
saving? What is the direction of creative evolution? What
is it that has been thrown up by ages-long stirrings of the
mud? What quality characterizes man as it does no other
animal, his Primate ancestors as it does no other order of
mammals; which distinguishes a fertilized human ovum from
all other protoplasm; which furnishes us a key to human culture, reduces our What-has-evolved to a lowest common de-
nominator, and gives us a clue to the freedom that is the
goal of creative evolution? *The capacity to modify and delay
reactions according to experience.* That kind of behavior is
called *intelligent.*

Intelligence is vague; we must give it reality. It means
to learn. But every animal learns—ameba, oyster, fish,
groundhog. The squirrel stores nuts for a wintry day. The
instinctive behavior of many animals is remarkable. But we
can speak of the evolution of *intelligent behavior.* And that
is no mere figure of speech. Nor is it without significance
that with man, and with man only, we find *human* intelligence.
Of all Primate infants, the human infant alone learns human
behavior.

Why? Because it has a larger *learning* equipment, more
ways of obeying impulses, a greater capacity to modify impulses in the light of experience.

Tap my patellar ligament, my foot kicks out; but only after
a lapse of time. The interval was short, but time was required for spinal cord to deliver the impulse after spinal
cord had received news of the tap. But tap me on the head:
I may think that over for fifty years before I thank you and
admit that you were quite justified, and thereby end my reaction in adjustment. Insult my child by just one word: I
may devote my life to the destruction of you and your family
and all that you hold dear. Some rulers have gone to war
for less. Human intelligence has taken such bents. But as

Dr. Johnson said, "God Himself, sir, does not propose to judge man until the end of his days." Why should we?

Man, as no other animal does, can delay his reactions whereby he adjusts himself to circumstances; he thereby gains a measure of control over his environment denied all other living beings. Such control is biologic freedom, the goal of creative evolution. Intelligence. What this control can lead to is just beginning to be understood. Scientific intelligence may yet be born. Freedom is as yet only a goal and a long way off, but progress toward freedom will speed up; it is of the nature of living organisms to grow by what they feed on and to climb by their own steps; the greater freedom, the faster the pace toward the goal.

That is, if man is really on the track—and that we cannot know. We do know that countless kinds of living organisms dropped from sight because they were on a by-path. But assuming that man is on the road of freedom, how can he keep going? Is there anything in his nature which conditions progress—as there are hormones which regulate growth? There is something which suggests a parallel.

Why is man not as free as he might be? Because his mind is made up; his pride of opinion outweighs his desire to know; he dismisses realities with a "God's in His Heaven— All's right with the world," and neglects the first lesson he ever learned—which is, that he can learn. Because he refuses the dare thrown to him by nature herself: Know thyself; and refuses to heed the warning written across every page of history and strewn across the face of the earth itself: the best defense is offense, versatility rather than walls or armor-plate, foresight rather than hindsight. Man alone can set man free.

The human being that can learn no more has parted with the only priceless possession in human inheritance. The men, women, or nations that harden in their mould, get set in their ways, crystallize their opinions and beliefs, and swear by and live according to their routine habits—such men, women, or nations are old; senile decay is at hand. In them creative evolution has ceased to function. And they, in their vain yearnings for immortality, forget how they learned to behave like human beings and how life itself in human beings renews its youth and speeds up the race for freedom: AS A LITTLE CHILD, WITH AN OPEN MIND.

BIBLIOGRAPHY

(The books named below do not constitute a bibliography of man, merely the more important of the recent works consulted in the preparation of this volume. Those to which I am especially indebted, and from which I have drawn freely, are indicated by an asterisk.)

*ARMSTRONG, E. F. *Enzymes.* Ch. XIV, Colloidal Behavior. New York, 1924.

BERGSON, H. *Creative Evolution.* London, 1922.

BLUMER, G. (editor) Billings-Forchheimer's *Therapeusis of Internal Diseases.* New York, 1924.

BOAS, F. *The Mind of Primitive Man.* New York, 1922.

BOGUE, R. H. (editor) *Colloidal Behavior.* New York, 1924.

BRAGG, SIR WILLIAM. *Concerning the Nature of Things.* New York, 1925.

*CANNON, W. B. *Bodily Changes in Pain, Hunger, Fear and Rage.* New York, 1922.

*CARLSON, A. J. *The Control of Hunger in Health and Disease.* Chicago, 1916.

*——"Organotherapeutics," in Billings-Forchheimer's *Therapeusis of Internal Diseases.* Blumer Edition. New York, 1924.

*CHAMBERLIN, T. C. *The Origin of the Earth.* Chicago, 1918.

*CHILD, C. M. *Senescence and Rejuvenescence.* Chicago, 1915.

——*Individuality in Organisms.* Chicago, 1915.

*——*The Origin and Development of the Nervous System.* Chicago, 1921.

——*Physiological Foundations of Behavior.* New York, 1924.

DAVENPORT, C. B. *Heredity in Relation to Eugenics.* New York, 1911.

DENIKER, J. *The Races of Man.* New York, 1900.

*DU BOIS, E. F. *Basal Metabolism in Health and Disease.* Philadelphia, 1924.

DUCKWORTH, W. L. H. *Morphology and Anthropology.* Cambridge, 1915.

EDMAN, I. *Human Traits.* Boston, 1920.

ELLIS, H. *Man and Woman.* New York, 1914.

GEDDES AND THOMSON. *Sex.* New York, 1914.

HADDON, A. C. *The Races of Man.* New York, 1925.

HARROW, B. *Glands in Health and Disease.* New York, 1922.

*HENDERSON, L. J. *The Fitness of the Environment.* New York, 1913.

*HERRICK, C. J. *An Introduction to Neurology.* Philadelphia, 1922.

*——*Neurological Foundations of Animal Behavior.* New York, 1924.

*HOWELL, W. H. *A Text-Book of Physiology.* Philadelphia, 1922.

JENNINGS, H. S. *Behavior of the Lower Organisms.* New York, 1915.

JOHNSTONE, J. *The Mechanism of Life.* London, 1921.

*JONES, F. W. *Arboreal Man.* London, 1916.

*JORDAN, E. O. *General Bacteriology.* Philadelphia, 1924.

KEANE, A. H. *Man Past and Present.* Cambridge, 1920.

*KEIBEL AND MALL. *Human Embryology.* Philadelphia, 1910-1912.

KEITH, A. *Man.* New York, 1912.

——*The Engines of the Human Body.* Philadelphia, 1920.

——*The Antiquity of Man.* London, 1920.

KENDALL, A. I. *Civilization and the Microbe.* Boston, 1923.

KROEBER, A. L. *Anthropology.* New York, 1923.

LOEB, J. *The Organism as a Whole.* New York, 1916.

——*Regeneration.* New York, 1924.

*LULL, R. S. *Organic Evolution.* New York, 1921.

——*The Ways of Life.* New York, 1925.

MACCURDY. G. G. *Human Origins.* New York, 1924.

MARSHALL, F. H. A. *Physiology of Reproduction.* London, 1922.

*McCOLLUM, E. V. *The Significance of Colloids in the Dietary.* Ch. XXIX, Colloidal Behavoir. New York, 1924.

McFARLAND, J. *Biology.* Philadelphia, 1920.

METCHNIKOFF, E. *The Nature of Man.* New York, 1906.

*MILLIKAN, R. A. *The Electron.* Chicago, 1924.

MINOT, C. S. *The Problem of Age, Growth, and Death.* New York, 1908.

BIBLIOGRAPHY

*MITCHELL, P. H. *General Physiology.* New York, 1923.

NEWMAN, H. H. *Readings in Evolution, Genetics, and Eugenics.* Chicago, 1921

OSBORN, H. F. *The Origin and Evolution of Life.* New York, 1921.

PARKER, G. H. *Smell, Taste, and Allied Senses in the Vertebrates.* Philadelphia, 1922.

*PEARL, R. *Biology of Death.* Philadelphia, 1922.

——*Studies in Human Biology.* Baltimore, 1924.

PEARSON, K. *The Chances of Death.* London, 1897.

——*The Grammar of Science.* London, 1900.

ROBERTSON, T. B. *Principles of Biochemistry.* Philadelphia, 1924.

SCHAFER, E. A. *The Endocrine Organs.* London, 1916.

THOMPSON, D. W. *Growth and Form.* Cambridge, 1917.

THOMSON, J. A. *The System of Animate Nature.* New York, 1920.

THORNDIKE, E. L. *The Original Nature of Man.* New York, 1923.

WALTER, H. E. *Genetics.* New York, 1913.

——*The Human Skeleton.* New York, 1918.

WASHBURN, M. F. *The Animal Mind.* New York, 1923.

*WATSON, J. B. *Psychology from the Standpoint of a Behaviorist.* Philadelphia, 1924.

——*Behaviorism.* New York, 1925.

*WIEDERSHEIM, R. *The Structure of Man.* London, 1895.

WILDER, H. H. *History of the Human Body.* New York, 1909.

WILSON, E. B. *The Cell in Development and Heredity.* New York, 1925.

INDEX

489

INDEX

Boas, Prof. Franz, viii, 39, 45
  grouping of man, 45
Body, change in proportions, 33
  growth processes, 201, 202
  task of, 36
Body-cells, planarian, 107
Boils, cause of, 197
Bone, sphenoid, 215
Bones, episternal, 26
  facial, 34
  frontal, 28
  growth of, 34
  nasal, 28
  skull-dome, 34
  upper arm, formation of, 27
Brain, 10, 11, 12, 32, 33, 37, 42, 58,
  65, 70, 237, 280, 295, 297, 298, 305,
  310, 316, 319, 329, 458
  cells of, 10
  correlation with hand, 70
  cortex, 280, 297, 298, 305, 319, 458
  distinguishing features of man's, 70
  formation of, 10
  Herrick on the, 329
  loss of weight with age, 37
  microcephalous, 10
    size of, 11
    weight of, 11
    use of, 11, 12
  Mitchell on the, 316
  necessity of big, 65
  sizes of, 237
  stem, 310
  structural changes, 10
  weight of, 32, 33, 42
    compared to body, 58
    in proportion to spinal cord, 58
Breathing, rate for adolescents, 172
  rate for adults, 172
  rate for children, 172
  rate for newborn, 172
Breeding, rates of productivity, 98
  variations in, 99
Bromine, 88
Bronchi, 169
Bufagin, 210, 211

Caisson, 172
Calcium metabolism, 207
Calorie, "great calorie," 127
Calories, 88, 128, 129, 156, 178
  number expended in various occu-
    pations, 128, 129
  number required for growth, 128,
    129
  potential energy, number in, 128
  produced daily by man, 88
Cambrian era, 74
Canal, alimentary, 405
Canals, semilunar, 13
Canine teeth, in apes, 71
Cannon, Prof. Walter B., viii, 136,
  213, 214, 215
  on adrenals, 215
  on adrenin, 213, 214
  time of movements, 136
Capacity, vital, 170
Capillaries, 154, 159, 161, 162, 165
Capuchin, brain of, 52
Carbohydrates, 130, 138, 139, 156, 184
  digestion of, 184
  forms of, 130
  specific, 139
  structure of, 138
Carbon, 90, 91, 94, 130
  behavior of, 91
  composition of, 94
  importance of, 91
  necessity of, 130
  relation with other elements, 91
  dioxide, 72, 79, 89, 121, 124, 130,
    171, 172, 173, 174, 175, 203, 214
    composition of, 89
    excess in blood, 124
    from glucose, 121
    functions of, 203
    in air, 130
    in blood, 72
    prevalence of, 89
Cardio-vascular apparatus, 216
Carlson, Prof. A. J., viii, 206, 207,
  227, 238
  on endocrines, 238
  on tetany, 207
  on thyroid, 206

INDEX

Carnegie Laboratory of Embryology, 5
Carotid arteries, 8
Cartilage, 7
Cartilages, of larynx, 233
  thyroid, 8
Casein, 150
Castle, Prof. W. E., viii
Catalyzer, 146, 220, 232, 268, 330, 331
Catalyzers, development of, 204
  of development, 232
Cataract of eye, 13
Cattell, Dr. McKean, viii
Caucasian race, where found, 45
Cebidae (monkeys), 49 characteristics of, 52
Cecum, 136
  in herbivorous animals, 140
Celibacy, 434, 439
Cell, characteristics of, 94, 95
  metabolism, 398
Cells, bone-forming growth of, 34
  division of, 110
  floating, 1
  Leydig, 231
  life in tissue, 122
  occurrence, 1, 2
Cellulose, 140, 153, 195
  in plants, 140
Cementum, 288
Cenozoic Age, 63
Centrosomes, behavior of, 110, 111
Cercopithecidae (baboons), 49
  characteristics of, 51
Cerebellum, 310, 311, 312, 313
Cerebral cortex, 310, 318, 321, 329, 332
Cerebri, hypophysis, 215
Cerebrum, 310, 313, 314, 315, 316, 317
  Gall on the, 315
Chamberlain, *Foundations of Nineteenth Century Civilization*, 119
Chamberlin, geologist, 80, 81
Change, continuous, 92
Character, 444, 461, 472
  foundations of, 472
Characters, acquired, 102
Charlatans, 462
Chaulmoogra oil, 200

Chemical receptors, 298
Chemotherapy, 200
Child, on excitation, 277
  on nerves, 288
  study of flatworms, 107
Children, rachitic, 143
Chimpanzee, characteristics of, 50
Chin, mental point, 28
Chlorine, 83, 137
Chlorophyl, 130
Cholelith, 152
Cholera, 231
  Asiatic, cure for, 200
  germs of, 197
Cholesterol, 151, 152
Chromatin, 77, 110
Chromogenic bacteria, 195
Chromophilic substance, 331, 332
Chromosomes, 110, 111, 112, 113,
  behavior of, 111
  inherited, 113
  number of, 110, 112
Chyle, 154
Chyme, 135
Cilia, 78, 169, 269, 270, 414
  in protoplasm, 78
Clairvoyants, 462
Cleft, embryonic bronchial, 206
Clefts, bronchial, 7,
  gill, 7, 8
Climacteric, 228
Cloaca (sewer) in human fetus, 16, 17
Clotting, of blood, 161
Cobra, venom of, 187, 198
Coccus, 195
Coccyx, tail skeleton, 27
Cod, eggs of, 98
Collip, on parathyroids, 208
Colloids, development of, 94
Color, biological significance of, 40
  in different races, 46, 47
Complex appetite, 424, 425, 426
  hunger, 425, 426
  libido, 427
  reproduction, 428
Compounds, organic, 137
  number of, 91

493

INDEX

Grape-sugar, 139
Graves' disease, 205
Grimaldi man, 48
Groins, 162
Growth, and life, 78
  forces of, 122
  power, at birth, 32
Guanidin, actions of, 207

Habit, inherited, 341, 343
Habits, 388, 389
  breaking of, 393, 394
Hair, growth of, 15
  index of type, 41
  variations in, 43
Hairy Ainu, 15
Hand, fetal, 67
  influence on civilization, 65
  utility of, 54
Hands, development of, 55
  of Primates, 66, 67
Hapalidae (marmosets), 49
Hate, 431, 432
Head, movements of, 35, 36
Heart, at branchial-cleft stage, 21, 22
  beating of, 165
  changes with age, 37, 38
  construction of, 124
  variations in structure, 22
Heat, a form of energy, 177
Heidelberg man, 48, 57
Height, 33
Hematin, 175, 176
  crystallization of, 176
Hemin, amount of, 177
Hemocyanin, copper of, 171
Hemoglobin, 173, 174, 175
  iron of, 171
Hemolytic, 176
Hemophilia, 161
Hemorrhages, use of adrenin in, 211
Henderson, fitness of environment, 86, 87
  (quoted), 89
Heredity, and energy, 93
  questions of, 112, 113
Hermaphrodite, true, 76

Hermaphrodites (Hermes-Aphrodite),
  cause of, 18
  in plants and lower animals, 18
Hernia, cause of, 17
Herrick, Prof. C. Judson, viii, 273, 318, 329, 373
  on brains, 329
  on psychology, 273
  on the cortex, 318
Hertzian waves, 296, 298, 306
Hexapoda, 188
Hirudin, 161
Homing instinct, 337
Hominidae (men), 49
Homo, from apes, 57
Homo (genus) Sapiens (species), 44, 264
Hookworm, 188
Hormone, 17, 208, 216, 220, 224
  and sex, 17
  structure acted on, 17
  pineal, 218
  production of, 227
  secretion system of, 384
  thyroid, 205
Hormones, 203, 204, 221, 225, 226, 232, 239, 240, 265, 450
  discovery of, 203
  gonad, 232
  of growth, 204
  production of, 221, 239
  sex, 226
  thyroid, 225
Hoskins, Prof. R. G., viii, 206
  on thyroid, 206
Howell, on enzymes, 149
  on heat, 182
Hrdlicka, 58
Human Anatomy, Quain, v
Human Embryology, Keibel and Mall, v
Human Embryology, Minot, v
Human morphology, 416
  physiology, 416
Humerus, at 15 years, 33
  free, 67
Hunger, 421, 422, 423, 424, 425, 426
  complex, 426, 428

INDEX

Metabolism, cell, 398
  neuron, 331
  processes of, 430
  rate of basal, 397
  sugar, 218
Metazoa, 1, 76, 106, 186, 257
  ova and sperma, 106
  (subkingdom II), 76
Metazoon, 257
Method of thinking, 382, 383, 384
Methylguanidin, 207
Micrococci, 195
Micro-organisms, assistance of, 141
  cause of higher forms of life, 80
Milk-glands (mammae), 16, 72
Millikan, composition of atoms, 84
  determination of elements, 85
  (quoted), 97
Misfits, disappearance of, 470
Mitchell, on the Brain, 316
Molars, 36
  four-cusped, 71
  third, 36
Molecule, smallest, weight of, 93
Molecules, behavior of, 93
  disaccharides, 147
  monosaccharide, 147
Molluscs, forms of, 76
Mongoloid race, 45
  type, color, 46
Monkeys (Cebidae), 49, 54, 55, 56
  babies of, 56
  hands of, 54, 55
Monosaccharides, composition of, 13?
Monotremes, 72
Monsters, artificially produced, 23
  variations of, 23, 24
Moore, Dr. C. R., viii
More, L. T., Dogma of Evolution, 101
Moron, definition, 458
Morons, 458, 459, 460
Morphology, 267
  human, 416
Morula, 5
Mosquito, Anopheles, method of production, 191

Motor areas, 316
  mechanism, characteristics of, 123
    man and oyster, 61
Mouse, heartbeats of, 166
Mouth, 6
  variations in, 22
Movements, peristaltic, 136
  rhythmic, 136
Mucin, 150
Mucus, 169
  coat of, 153
Muellerian ducts, 17
Muscle, biceps, of Gibbon, 54
  palmar, 31
  pyramidalis, 30
  quadriceps femoris, 342
  risorius, 30
  skin, 29
  sphincter, of stomach, 135
  variations, in facial, 30
  visceral, 361
Muscles, 347, 349
  calf, 35
  composition of, 123
  facial, comparison animal and
    man, 29
  flexor, 30
  groups of, 123
  jaw, 36
  mastication, 36
  number of, 29
  of alimentary canal, 133
  of stomach, 135
  rectus abdominus, 30
  serous, 134
  skeletal, 214, 361, 436
  sternalis, 30
  trained, efficiency of, 129
Mystics, 462
Myxedema, 205, 238, 239

Nails, finger and toe, 15
Nasal mucous membrane, 221
Natural Selection, 99
  effects of on race, 119
Nature, experiments of, 65
  of things, 83
Navel, 4

503

INDEX

506

INDEX

Streptococci, 195, 199
Structures, vestigial, 301
Strychnine, dose of, 198
Styloid process, 7
Sub-linguals, where found and use of, 184
Sub-maxillaries, where found and use of, 184
Succus entericus, 151
Sucrose, 146
  cane sugar, 139
Sugar
  cane, molecular weight, 141
  metabolism, 219
Sugars, three complex, 139
Sulphates, 88
Sulphur, 137
  in red blood-cells, 175
Sun, offsprings of, 80
Sunstroke, 181
Suprarenals, 208, 209
Survival, methods of, 99
  of the Fittest, 101
Suture, 28
  closing of, effect on head, 28
Swallowing center, 134
Swamis, 462
Sweat, 180
  glands, 15
    number of, 180
Symmetry, bilateral, 75
Symphysis, 236
Symptoms, of emotions, 212
Synapse, 289, 290, 332
Synapses, 307, 312
  resistance of, 207
Synaptic system, 290
Synthesis, of man, 132
  of plants, 132
Syphilis, 198, 199, 231
  cure for, 200
  germ of, 196
System, autonomic, 324, 325
  nervous, 213, 214
  glandular, 346
  lymphatic, 154

System, lymph vascular, 161
  neuromotor, 207
  neuromuscular, 182
  of hormone secretion, 384
  peripheral nervous, 323
  synaptic, 290
  urogenital, 209, 253
  vasomotor, 170, 180, 182
  visceral, 346

Tactile organ, 299
Taenia, or tapeworm, 188
Tail, signs of in man, 27
Tails, prehensile, 67
Takahashi, 143
Takamine, on Adrenin, 210
Tears, use of, 14
Teats, true, 72
Teeth, bicuspids, 19
  incisors, 19
  molars, 19
  milk, 36
  number of, in animals, 19
  number of, in man, 19
  use in Eocine time, 71
  variation in, 19, 20
  wisdom, 36
Temperature, of body, 147
Tendons, 311, 347, 349
Testes, 221
Testut, anatomist, 28
Tetanus, 207, 221
  gastric, 351
Tetany, infantile, 207
  Carlson on, 207
Tethelin, 215, 216
Theory, vasomotor, 397
Therapeusis of Internal Diseases,
  Billings-Forchheimer, viii
Thinking, 380, 381
  method of, 382, 383, 384
  Watson on, 383
Thomas, Dr. W. I., viii, 475
Thomson (quoted), 102
  experiment with bacteria, 132
  on chromosomes, 113
  on the bee, 62
Thorax, 162

509

INDEX

510

INDEX

Wiggam, *The New Decalogue of Science*, 119
Wirsung, duct of, 219
Wolffian body, cortex derived from, 209
Wolffian ducts, 17
  changes in, 17
Women, change in after fifty, 38
  heartbeats of, 166
Woodruff (quoted), 107
  study of paramecium, 98

World War, 141, 143, 144
Wrist, joint of, 67
  turtles, 67

Yaws, cure for, 200
Youth, heartbeats of, 166

Zone, erogenous, 432, 439, 440
Zymase, 147
Zymogen, activator of enzymes, 148
Zymogenic bacteria, 195